P9-CDP-254

THE THEORY
OF DECISION-MAKING

THE THEORY OF DECISION-MAKING

*An Introduction
to Operations Research*

WIESŁAW SADOWSKI

*Translated from the
Polish by*
EUGENE LEPA

Translation edited by
H. INFELD, P. KNIGHTSFIELD

PERGAMON PRESS
OXFORD · LONDON · EDINBURGH · NEW YORK ·
PARIS · FRANKFURT
PWE — POLISH ECONOMIC PUBLISHERS
WARSZAWA

PERGAMON PRESS LTD.
Headington Hill Hall, Oxford
4 and 5 Fitzroy Square, London, W.1

PERGAMON PRESS (Scotland) LTD.
2 and 3 Teviot Place, Edinburgh 1

PERGAMON PRESS INC.
122 East 55th Street, New York 22, N.Y.

GAUTHIER-VILLARS ED.
55 Quai des Grands-Augustins, Paris 6

PERGAMON PRESS G.m.b.H.
75 Kaiserstrasse, Frankfurt am Main

First English edition 1965

Library of Congress Catalog Card Number 63-22629

Printed Poland

HD
20
.5
S2
1965

Contents

Contents

Foreword

For some twenty years now a new branch of learning known as operations research has been developing. Operations research constitutes in itself a theory of planning techniques. At the hub of operations research are methods which allow us to determine an optimum decision or, in other words, to produce an optimum plan for given conditions. These methods form the subject-matter of this book.

These methods have been put to practical use in various enterprises, especially in the Soviet Union and the United States. In the near future they will unquestionably be able to render great service in planning on a national scale. This is supported by some works of Soviet scholars, chiefly Professor L. V. Kantorovich of Leningrad.

To draw up a proper plan requires the ability to carry out appropriate calculations. Operations research supplies the tools which make these calculations possible. It seems that even in those cases for which appropriate calculations are not feasible because of a lack of data, the models which we employ in operations research facilitate correct economic decisions. They facilitate a more profound analysis of the structure of the plan; they indicate the links between individual decisions; they facilitate the study of the effects of particular decisions and they compel us to be precise in our assumptions.

Of the methods used in operations research some, but not all, are new, e.g. linear programming and dynamic programming. Some of these methods, such as differential calculus, probability calculus and mathematical statistics, have been known for a long time. But they seem to be used in a new way in operations research.

When writing on operations research it is possible to approach the problem in various ways. Thus, the exposition may be intended for mathematicians, engineers psychologists, sociologists, etc. The present book is intended chiefly for economists.

The manner of presentation stems from this. The aim of the author has been to acquaint the broadest circles of economists and planners with the basic methods of operations research. The problem was not so much to teach the reader how to make practical use of these methods as to help him to understand the basis of these methods and their essence. Only by a deeper knowledge of these methods will the reader be in a position to form his own judgement of the theoretical and practical significance of operations research.

The methods of operations research draw upon various fields of mathematics, not all of which are familiar to economists. For this reason the author has tried to restrict to a minimum the knowledge of mathematics required to understand this book. In principle, it is assumed that the reader has only a knowledge of the elements of differential and integral calculus and the fundamentals of probability calculus to the extent that these subjects are taught in colleges of economics.

Therefore, wherever other fields of mathematics are used in operations research the author has confined himself to a description of the essence of the method, the presentation of examples and heuristic justification of the value of any of the procedures. In particular, none of the formal tools of linear algebra have been used in the exposition of linear programming. This manner of presentation has led to some prolixity which may bore readers having a better mathematical background. The chapter on the applications of differential calculus is very sketchy for the assumption has been that the reader knows how to use it.

The book contains many examples illustrating the various methods of operations research. The purpose of these examples is purely didactic. They are, therefore, deliberately made simple and the numbers in them are entirely conventional. Examples of practical significance are, as a rule, much more complicated and therefore much less useful in expositions of particular methods as they distract the reader's attention to detail which is not essential for an understanding of the method.

There can be two different presentations of the methods employed in operations research. Firstly, we may take as our starting point various types of questions that occur in operations research (e.g. inventory policy, optimal allocation of resources, production planning, etc). In this case, various methods applicable to a given question are discussed. It is also possible to proceed in a different way and to discuss in turn the individual methods useful for questions differing in essence. In principle, the author has followed the second manner of exposition. For he believes that in this way the exposition of operations research is more lucid.

The first six chapters constitute an exposition of the principal methods of operations research. Much space has been devoted to linear programming, first and foremost, because it is one of the most highly-developed methods today and it is of great practical importance. The final chapters discuss some special questions.

At the end of each chapter is a list of the fundamental bibliography, including books only. A bibliography embracing all the publications would by itself fill a whole volume.

The author hopes that this book will make at least a modest contribution to the improvement of planning techniques in Poland—above all, at the enterprise level

I should like to take this opportunity to fulfil a pleasant duty and to extend my heartfelt thanks to the reviewers of this book, Professor Oskar Lange and Dr. Tadeusz Czechowski. Their invaluable comments allowed me to remove from the final text many shortcomings present in the typescript.

CHAPTER 1

Introduction

1. Optimum decisions

Almost every activity by man, social groups or entire societies is connected with a specific purpose or number of purposes. We act in order to achieve our aims.

In order to conduct activities so as to achieve our ends, we must have available certain means. Generally, the means at our disposal can be employed in various ways. The conditions in which we act determine the possible ways of using these means in any given case. If the conditions in which we operate were such as to determine only one single way of using the means, the problem would be simple. However, most often or in any case very frequently, conditions allow us to utilize the means in various ways. The problem then arises of taking a decision. Namely, we have to decide how the means will be used or what set of means of those at our disposal will be chosen and utilized in the activity leading to the attainment of the goals set.

If such a decision is to be possible, we must have an appropriate criterion with which to evaluate and compare the effects of various decisions. Having such a criterion, we can determine which is the best, or optimum, decision.

With the development of culture and civilization, with technical progress, the individual's life becomes increasingly simple in the sense that he avails himself more and more of new conveniences which modern organizational forms of society make available to him; he benefits extensively from the achievements of technology. On the other hand, however, life is becoming more and more complex. To achieve specific goals by small or large groups of people, not to mention the activities of States as a whole, is a very complex matter today. This stems from the fact that, generally speaking, we aim at accomplishing many targets which can be realized in various ways, usually the fuller implementation of one implying the less complete implementation of others. In order to make the correct decision (as regards the given criterion), we can no longer rely today solely on intuition and experience. There is need of more accurate methods permitting the selection of the optimum decision. Such methods, which facilitate the choice of the optimum decision, form the subject of this book. The methods we shall discuss are quantitative, that is, they are applicable wherever the elements of our activity can be expressed in terms of quantities. The example below will explain more clearly what is understood

1

by such concepts as: activity, target, criterion, decision and optimum decision.

Example 1. A factory manufactures two articles; let us call them A and B. The volume of production, practically speaking, is limited by the manufacturing capacity of three machines (let us denote them by M_1, M_2 and M_3) required to produce the two articles. Table 1.1 gives the appropriate technical coefficients.

TABLE 1/1

Machines \ Articles	A	B	Production capacity
M_1	10	20	180
M_2	15	15	150
M_3	50	10	300

We read the table in the following manner. For the production of one unit of article A machine M_1 must be used for 10 hours, M_2 for 15 hours and M_3 for 50 hours. The next column of Table 1.1 presents the corresponding figures for article B. The last column gives the number of hours the machines can work during the period under consideration.

We have to work out a production plan that will guarantee the largest overall profit. The per unit profit on article A is 15 zlotys and on article B, 7·50 zlotys. The *activity* in this case consists of the production of commodities A and B. There are two *targets* to this activity: the production of commodity A and the production of commodity B. In the example given, the three machines or, strictly speaking, their production capacities are the means. The *conditions of the activity* are determined in our case by the data in Table 1.1. They tell how much work is required by each machine for the production of one article A or B and they determine the production capacities of the machines which must not be exceeded. We have to decide on the volume of production of articles A and B. Finally, the criterion we employ in our selection of one of the many possible decisions is profit.

In our example, the *optimum decision* is to produce 5 units of article A and 5 units of article B. This ensures a profit of 5 . 15+5 . 7·50 = 112·50 zlotys.[1] No other decision could ensure a larger profit under the given conditions.

Of course, we may use a different criterion from that used in Example 1.

Here is an example of a different criterion.

---

[1] British usage is employed here — i.e.: . to indicate multiplication and · to indicate the decimal point. The Polish zloty as monetary unit has been retained since the original examples refer to Poland.

Example 2.[1] A factory has three types of machines which can be used to manufacture two parts: *A* and *B*. Table 2.1 shows the number of *A* and *B* that can be produced per working day on the particular types of machines.

TABLE 2/1

Machine \ Parts	A	B
M_1	30	60
M_2	60	90
M_3	30	80

The interpretation of the Table is as follows. If machine M_1 is used for the entire working day to make part *A*, it could turn out 30 pieces. If, on the other hand, that machine was employed only to produce part *B*, it would make 60 pieces of that part. The entries of Table 2.1 for M_2 and M_3 are to be interpreted accordingly.

We have to plan the use of the machines so as to obtain the largest number of sets of parts *A* and *B*.

As before, the *activity* is reduced to production activity. There are two goals to this activity: production of parts *A* and *B*. The machines are the *means* which enable these goals to be realized. Table 2.1 strictly defines the *conditions* of our *activity*. The *decision* concerns the manner in which the production capacity of the machines is to be utilized. For we have to determine the proportion of the working day the individual machines will be employed to produce part *A* and the proportion to produce part *B*. The *criterion* which will allow us to evaluate the best way of using the machines will, in this case, be the number of sets of manufactured parts *A* and *B*.

The *optimum decision* proves to be to employ fully machine M_2 to make part *A* (60 units), machine M_3 for part *B* (80 units) and to use machine M_1 for 86 2/3 % of the time to produce part *A* (26 units) and 10 % of the time for part *B* (6 units). With this utilization of the machines we can produce 86 sets. No other division of work for the machines gives us a larger number of sets. Note that in the optimum solution machine M_1 is idle for 3 1/3 % of the time.

Many examples of this type can be cited from different fields. They can refer to both purely technical and purely economic questions. From the formal point of view, however, the aim will always be to find the optimum decision. It appears

[1] L. V. Kantorovich, *Matematicheskie metody organizatsiyi i planirovaniya proizvodstva (Mathematical Methods of the Organization and Planning of Production)*, Leningrad, 1939.

that there are certain methods which enable us to determine an optimum decision effectively. These methods are dealt with by the science known as *operations research*.

2. Operations research

In its present form, operations research is a relatively new branch of learning. Its development dates from the Second World War.

As the name itself indicates, operations research came into being in connection with military tactics. The term "operations" stems from military "lingo". In the military sense, operation means "the activity of a large military group (army, front or several armies or fronts) to attain a specific objective; an operation consists of a number of battles and encounters".[1] Every military operation is very complicated under present-day conditions. Its effective conduct requires appropriate preparation, an analysis of many variants for the proposed operation and an ability to select the best.

During the last war, first in Great Britain and later in the United States, groups of experts from various disciplines of science (mathematics, physics, chemistry, psychology, logic, etc.) were attached to headquarters of certain large units to analyse some of the planned operations. In a short time these groups had appreciable achievements to their credit. Some of those commonly known are: development of methods for combatting German submarines, determination of the size and type of shipping convoys, utilization of the merchant navy for military purposes, etc.

Today, in retrospect, we must say that although those groups—called operations research teams—accomplished much in solving many specific problems, their greatest service was in working out certain general methods. These methods permitted to analyse many variants of the plan for a given operation and to select the most effective. Soon these methods came to be known as operations research.

It now appears that the methods of operations research are of much wider use than in military tactics. In particular, it became evident that operations research can be used successfully to solve technical-economic problems. It marked in particular considerable progress in planning techniques.[2]

Four important, essential stages can be distinguished in operations research.[3] The first stage consists of the *construction of a model*. In other words, an accu-

---

[1] Definition as given in *Słownik wyrazów obcych (Dictionary of Foreign Expressions)*, Warsaw, 1955, PIW.

[2] At first, planning on the scale of a capitalist enterprise.

[3] Some authors mention even more stages, but it seems that they can be reduced to the four basic stages referred to here.

rate formulation of the decisions, the target of activity, the operational conditions, the methods to be used and, finally, the criterion that will enable an evaluation of the results of operations. As we know, models have played and still play an important role in science. The model reflects the fragment of reality that is of interest to us but ignores the less important elements of that reality. In building a model of the problem of interest to us, we must always bear in mind that it should take account of all the essential elements which could affect the decision.

To illustrate such a model and its principal elements, let us discuss Example 1 of Section 1.

There we had to decide upon the volume of production of two articles: A and B. Let us denote these volumes by X_A and X_B respectively. These values must be so chosen that the total profit will be the largest possible. Profit in this case is the criterion for the evaluation of the effects of the activity. The larger the profit, the better the results of the activity which consists in the manufacture of commodities A and B in the given case.

If we know the profit per unit, we can express the total profit (let us call it Z) as a function of the volume of production:

$$Z = 15X_A + 7 \cdot 5X_B. \tag{1}$$

Expression (1) defines the relationship between the profit Z, which is the criterion for the evaluation of the activity, and the variables X_A and X_B to which we have to assign appropriate values. Thus, this is a function that attaches specific values of variable Z to the various values of variables X_A and X_B. For brevity, we shall frequently refer to functions of this type simply as criterion-functions.

The pair of magnitudes X_A and X_B should be so selected that Z will have the largest possible value. However, the operational conditions do not allow us to assign completely arbitrary values to variables X_A and X_B. In our example, these conditions require that the volume of production shall not exceed the production capacity of the machines required to manufacture articles A and B. Thus, the total working time of the machine M_1 cannot exceed 180 hours. We write this simply as a relation:

$$10X_A + 20X_B \leqslant 180. \tag{2}$$

Coefficients 10 and 20 are given in Table 1.1. of Section 1.

Similar relations (3) and (4) refer to machines M_2 and M_3 respectively:

$$15X_A + 15X_B \leqslant 150 \tag{3}$$

$$50X_A + 10X_B \leqslant 300. \tag{4}$$

Since X_A and X_B denote the volume of production, they obviously must be non-negative numbers. This can be written briefly:

$$X_A \geqslant 0; \quad X_B \geqslant 0. \tag{5}$$

Relations (1), (2), (3), (4) and (5) constitute the model of the problem in question. This model, like all the models we shall deal with, consists of two parts: the first is the criterion-function, the second is made up of the conditions of the activity. In the given case, equations (2), (3), (4) and (5) describe the conditions of our activity. In other words, they stipulate the decisions to be taken as to the scale of production or, otherwise stated, the decisions that are admissible. Admissible decisions as to the volume of production of articles A and B are those which simultaneously satisfy all the relations, that is (2), (3), (4) and (5). Out of the set of admissible decisions we choose the best or optimum one. The criterion which in our case is the profit defined by formula (1) determines the decision to be regarded as optimum. We, therefore, select an admissible decision, i.e. values of X_A and X_B that satisfy conditions (2), (3), (4) and (5), for which function (1) attains the maximum value.

It should be noted that in our model there are two types of quantities: those which depend on us (X_A and X_B) and those which in the given case we treat as independent of us (here, profits per unit, technical coefficients and production capacities of the machines).

Let us adopt the convention of calling the first type of magnitudes *decision variables* and the second type of magnitudes *parameters*.

The second stage in operations research consists in the *solution of the model* or, in other words, in the determination of the optimum decision. The problem, therefore, is to determine effectively the optimum values for the decision variables. Skill in determining the optimum decision is basic if operations research is to be of any practical value.

The methods of solving various models are an essential part of operations research. This book is mainly devoted to the study of these methods. Some general remarks on methods of solving a model, i.e. on methods for the determination of the optimum decision, are presented in Section 3. At this juncture we shall say a few more words about the further stages in operations research as these will not be discussed subsequently.

The third stage is to *verify the model* and the solution obtained. If a model has already been built, i.e. if a problem has been formulated accurately and a solution arrived at, the model and the solution must be verified before the solution is applied in practice. The problem is, therefore, to confront the solution obtained with reality, as far as possible.

As mentioned earlier, in formulating accurately a problem, which means in constructing a model, we ignore a whole number of factors which we feel are inessential, i.e. which do not affect any future decision we are aiming at. But it is easy to overlook something in doing this. Many oversights can be made good relatively early, before a proposed solution is carried out. And this is exactly the purpose of the stage which we have called the verification stage.

Example 1. An enterprise is allocated a quarterly plan for the delivery of an article it produces. The problem is to draw up a quarterly production plan which, on the one hand, enables to implement the delivery plan and, on the other hand, entails the lowest possible production costs.

Of course, there can be different admissible variants of such a production plan. Suppose that the optimum production plan envisages the production of 10,000 units in the second quarter whereas the demand in that quarter is for 4,000 units. This means that 6,000 units produced in the second quarter have to be stored for delivery in subsequent quarters.

A comparison of this solution with reality may reveal that it is inacceptable since the warehouses of the enterprise can hold only 5,000 units. This means that the model of the problem to be solved was not built accurately. Namely, it did not take into account one of the important conditions under which the activity is being conducted. There should have been a clear formulation of the condition that the inventory cannot exceed 5,000 items.

Upon verification, the model is most frequently altered or slightly adjusted which, of course, affects the new final solution.

The fourth and last stage in operations research is the *elaboration of a control system.* Life is not static; it is subject to continuous, unceasing change. It might, therefore, appear that a solution which we felt was the optimum yesterday may not be so today. This stems from the fact that there may be a change in the conditions of the activity, expressed either in a change in the value of the parameters or in the altered character of the relations appearing in the model.

The control system consists in an organization which ensures quick information about any variations in the conditions. Furthermore, it consists in analysing the ways of altering a previous solution in order to obtain an optimum solution under the new, changed conditions without solving the whole problem anew.

These four stages indicate that an effective application of operations research involves cooperation of experts in many fields. Such cooperation is particularly necessary in the first, third and fourth stages. Only the second stage is chiefly the domain of mathematicians.

3. Methods of solving a model

There are many methods of solving models encountered in operations research. They can all be classified in four main groups. It appears that the method to be used in solving a model is determined in the main by the character of the parameters of that model.

The first, simplest case is that in which each parameter is treated as a known constant (which does not vary). The parameters in Examples 1 and 2 of Section 1 were of this type. In that case we said that all the parameters affecting our decision were known constants (e.g. profit per unit, production capacity of the machines, technical coefficients). *Models* containing only such parameters can be called *deterministic*. The problem is that every possible decision leads to a specific unique result. Or, stated differently, the criterion-function has one and only one value for every decision. This feature of deterministic models removes any doubt that a solution is possible, at least from the theoretical point of view. We select the values of decision variables in such a manner that the criterion-function assumes either a maximum value (e.g. profit) or a minimum value (e.g. costs).

Differential calculus forcibly suggests itself as a method of solving this type of model since it enables us to determine the maximum or minimum functions of many variables (decisive) subject to certain conditions. Indeed, differential calculus is used in the solution of deterministic models. Unfortunately, however, it has transpired that most deterministic models which appear in operations research cannot be solved by any known methods of differential calculus. Even our two extremely simple examples in Section 1 are such that the methods of differential calculus break down. Most frequently, we have to deal with deterministic models in which all the relations are linear. *Linear programming* is a method which enables to solve such linear deterministic models. It plays a special role in operations research. There are many reasons for this. First of all, in practice we often come across problems which can be presented in the form of a linear model.

Secondly, even when this is not the case, the model frequently can be transformed into a linear model.

In view of the importance of this method, we shall give particular attention to linear programming.

At times, however, there are cases in which a linear model cannot be utilized without excessive distortion of reality and yet, on the other hand, the methods of differential calculus cannot be applied to solve the model. This is quite a troublesome situation and it is doubtful whether any general method will be worked out to solve non-linear models of this type. Nevertheless, there are a number of different methods jointly called non-linear programming. In principle, we shall omit this method from our further considerations.

The parameters in the model cannot always be treated as known constants. At times they are more or less uncertain. This means that, at the moment a decision is being taken, we do not know the value of the parameter and, therefore, we cannot foresee the effect of any decision. This obviously causes considerable difficulty in the selection of what can be regarded as an optimum decision from among those that appear possible.

The lack of information on a parameter can vary in type and character. The first case is that in which the parameter is what is known as a random variable. This is the situation when we do not know the value the parameter will assume as we embark on the activity in accordance with the decision chosen, but we do know the probability of the parameter taking on any other value.

Example 1. We manufacture a perishable product (e.g. bread) and we aim at satisfying fully the demand for this product at a given time. But the demand is not known. We only know that it can be equal to:

$$1{,}500 \text{ with a probability of } 1/6$$
$$1{,}600 \text{ with a probability of } 3/6$$
$$1{,}700 \text{ with a probability of } 2/6$$

If one unit of the product is made but not sold, a loss is incurred of, say, 10 zlotys per unit. If, on the other hand, the production available is too low for the demand, then in order to satisfy the demand, we must turn out an additional amount of the product under less favourable conditions. Additional production causes an increase in cost of 8 zlotys per unit.

Production should be set at a volume that will guarantee the least possible loss whether due to surplus or inadequate output.

In this example the parameter defining the volume of demand is a random variable. The trouble is that in any decision pertaining to the magnitude of output we cannot foresee its results. For instance, in deciding on a production of 1,600 units we may run the risk that the actual demand will be 1,500 (then the loss is 1,000 zlotys), 1,600 (no loss incurred), or 1,700 (the loss is 800 zlotys). This is a case in which for each decision there are different values of the function expressing the importance of the loss in relation to the value of the actual parameter defining the volume of demand. However, at the moment when the decision is taken this information is not known. Models in which at least one of the parameters is a random variable with a known distribution, that is, with known probabilities for which the parameter assumes individual values, are called *probabilistic models*. Since the methods for the solution of this type of model are based mainly on probability calculus, we call them *probabilistic methods*.

Another case when a parameter is not known is when the parameter is not a random variable or may be a random variable having an unknown distribution. Thus, our knowledge of the parameter is even more modest than before. Frequently, however, in such cases some additional information can be obtained before a decision is taken. If this is the case, we say that we have a *statistical model*.

Example 2. A consignee receives a shipment of 10,000 electric bulbs. If there were no more than 150 bad bulbs in the lot, the consignee will regard it as good and will be prepared to accept it. However, if there were more than 150 bad bulbs in the lot, he will not regard this consignment as satisfactory and will have to reject it.

In this problem we have to decide whether to accept or to reject the lot. Without going into the problem of the basis to be adopted for the criterion we easily see that one of the parameters affecting the decision is the number of faulty items in the lot of bulbs delivered. The difficulty is that we do not know that number. We only know that it can assume (at least theoretically) any value between 0 and 10,000. If, however, it is possible to inspect a certain, appropriately selected, sample of the lot delivered (e.g. 100 bulbs), the additional information will facilitate our decision as we shall enrich our information about the parameter, which in our case is the number of faulty items in the whole lot.

This is an instance of a statistical model. Methods serving to solve this type of model are provided primarily by *mathematical statistics*.

Finally, the next case of a parameter not being known differs from the previous in that no additional information can be collected regarding the parameter (or parameters) of the model. All we know is that the parameter can assume one of many possible values, the collection of these possible values being generally known to us. This is the most difficult case. The models in which parameters of this type appear, known as strategic variables, we shall call *strategic models*. This name is explained by the fact that the problem of taking an optimum decision is in this case similar to the selection of the best strategy in a military operation. The *theory of games* is the method used to solve strategic models.

Table 1.3 gives schematically the types of models in operations research and the methods for solving them.

It should be added that the order in which we have given the four types of models encountered in operations research is not accidental. Hence, a model is deterministic when all of its parameters are known constants. If at least one of the parameters is a random variable of a known distribution, and the others are known constants, we have a probabilistic model. If at least one of the parameters is a constant of an unknown value, or a random variable of an unknown distribution (with the possibility of obtaining some partial information about these parameters), and the others are either known constants or random variables of a known distribution, we have a statistical model. Finally, if at least one of the parameters is a strategic variable and the others are of an arbitrary character, we have a strategic model.

Besides the methods mentioned in Table 1.3 there is yet another method, known as dynamic programming, which may be used to solve a certain case common to all types of models.

This is the case when we have to take a series of successive decisions and we have to determine the optimum series of these decisions.

TABLE 1/3

	Type of model			
	deterministic	probabilistic	statistical	strategic

Method of solution	differential calculus
	
	linear
	   programming
	non-linear
	   programming
		probability
		calculus
			mathematical
			statistics
				theory of games

In such cases, the use of the methods appropriate for the given models is not always the simplest way of arriving at a solution. Frequently, the application of a specific method, dynamic programming, facilitates the solution of the model.

The example in Section 2 is an instance of a *deterministic model*. It can be solved by linear programming. On the other hand, the structure of this example is such that a series of decisions (production in successive quarters) is involved. This example could, therefore, also be solved by the method of dynamic programming. Of course, in each case it is necessary to determine the simplest method.

4. On the importance and origin of operations research

From what we have said in the preceding sections it appears that the central problem of operations research is that of determining optimum decisions.

The conclusion from this is that operations research constitutes a branch of knowledge of a normative nature. The question is not of explaining why such decisions and no other decisions are taken in reality, but of elaborating methods enabling us to determine decisions which we are prepared to regard as the best.

Operations research, therefore, is nothing else than a planning technique. A planning technique is the ability to draw up an optimum plan of activity which is to lead to the fulfilment of the target.

Formally speaking, operations research came into being in the countries of the West during the Second World War. At first, as already stated, this particular planning technique was used chiefly to plan military operations. Soon, however, operations research was also applied in capitalist enterprise and in some public sectors by capitalist States.

It should be noted, however, that the history of operations research dates back to an earlier period than the Second World War. In the first place, note should be taken of the work by the Leningrad scientist, Professor L. V. Kantorovich back in 1939.[1] It presents a survey of applications of mathematical methods to planning

---

[1] Op. cit.

of an enterprise and contains an exposition of the methods of solving linear models which are a special case of deterministic models. Kantorovich, therefore, should be regarded as the creator of linear programming which a few years later was developed independently in the Western countries.

Secondly, A. E. Erlang, a Scandinavian engineer, should be mentioned as the precursor of operations research.

Back at the beginning of this century, in dealing with problems of telephony, Erlang used the methods which are specific to modern operations research, especially in regard to the solution of probabilistic models.

Some beginnings of operations research can also be found in the works of some economists of the nineteen-thirties, e.g. in the works of E. Schneider, H. Stackelberg, S. Carlsen, and others.

It is no accident that operations research did not develop fully until after the Second World War. Many of the methods which appear in operations research are extremely tedious; they involve extensive calculations. Not until the development of computer techniques and, particularly, the development of electronic mathematical machines, did these methods become of practical importance. This in turn aroused greater interest than before in the methods themselves.

Although operations research has developed particularly in capitalist countries, it appears that its importance for a socialist economy, which is entirely plannified, is incomparably greater.

On the other hand, the application of operations research in a socialist economy, whether on the scale of an enterprise or a national scale, entails some additional difficulties. These difficulties are connected to a considerable extent with the selection of the criterion for the evaluation of the activity which is to lead to the realisation of fixed targets.

In a capitalist economy, profit (or cost) is most frequently such a criterion. It is not so simple a matter in a socialist economy. Some of the difficulties involved will be dealt with in the end parts of this book. It must be added, however, that these difficulties do not appear to exclude automatically the use of operations research in a socialist economy. On the contrary, despite these difficulties, operations research can in many cases help to increase appreciably investment efficiency and thus to reduce waste and to increase labour productivity.

Frequently, exaggerated importance is ascribed to new methods. This also happens in the case of operations research. Too often it is felt that the use of these methods is a *panacea* for the many difficulties which are encountered in planning practice. Of course this is not so, primarily because in operations research we frequently artificially restrict the problem. Turning back for a moment to Example 1 of Section 1, we recall that we assumed certain quantities to be constant, independent of us. For instance, we assumed that production capacities were given in advance. In reality it may prove that these capacities could be increased substantially if the machines were operated by more highly skilled workers or if some simple technical improvements were introduced, etc. Perhaps herein lies the importance of bigger reserves than otherwise due to improper organization of production.

Nevertheless, it is perfectly clear that the methods of operations research also play a role in the detection of reserves due to inadequate organization.

Without overestimating the value of these methods, it appears that they can play no mean role in the improvement of our economy.

5. Bibliographical notes

The literature pertaining to operations research is already quite extensive. In the first place mention should be made of a text-book by three authors: C. Churchman, R. Ackoff, E. Arnoff [2] . This book deals with the main subject-matter of operations research in a fairly exhaustive manner. A collective work edited by J. McCloskey and F. Trefethen [8] is also very extensive and places great emphasis on the history of operations research.

A relatively concise exposition of operations research methods can be found in the book by M. Sasieni, A. Yaspan and L. Friedman [3].

A very good exposition of operations research is given in the book by A. Vazsonyi [14]. As for the applications of this research, the author pays particular attention to the planning of production and inventory control.

The works mentioned above deal mainly with the application of operations research to economic problems. We should note, however, that there are works containing an exposition of operations research as applied to other fields, especially to military questions. In this field mention should be made first of all of the book by P. Morse and G. Kimball [10], and also by G. Merrill, H. Goldberg and R. Helmholz [9].

J. Lesourne's book [6] goes far beyond the realm of operations research, and in addition encompasses econometric questions. Nevertheless, it is an excellent presentation of operations research, using somewhat more elaborate mathematical procedures than the aforementioned books.

An elementary exposition of operations research as applied to management in industry is presented in the book by E. Bowman and R. Fetter [1].

The book edited by V. Nemchinov [11] is a collection of papers on the theory and applications of operations research, but it deals chiefly with linear programming. A very interesting paper by L. V. Kantorovich in this collection deals with the importance and prospects for operations research in a planned economy.

Besides the books mentioned above, attention should be drawn to two works: by A. Kaufmann [3] and T. Saaty [12]. They give an exposition of mathematical methods used in operations research. Both present the material on a quite high mathematical level.

In addition to books, and we obviously have not listed all of them, there are many shorter studies published in various journals. A particularly large number of studies on operations research appear in American journals [16], [17] and [18]; and in British [19], German [21], French [20] and Italian [15] journals.

In the Soviet Union papers on operations research are not printed in special journals. The majority appear in mathematical publications. An extensive bibliography of such papers up to 1957 is to be found in Vol. I (pp. 848–850) of the joint study [7].

In Poland, too, papers on operations research (and there are not many of them) are published in various journals, chiefly mathematical, statistical and economic journals.

In conclusion, it should be noted that operations research is connected in a way with praxeology, i.e. the science of rational activity which was created by T. Kotarbiński. An exposition of praxeology which is a more theoretical discipline than operations research, is given in a book by T. Kotarbiński [4]. In chapter 5 of his book [5], O. Lange has an interesting discussion of the connections between economy, praxeology and operations research.

BIBLIOGRAPHY

[1] Bowman, E. and Fetter, R., *Analysis for Production and Management*, R. Irwin, Homewood, Ill., 1957.

[2] Churchman, C., Ackoff, R., Arnoff, E., *Introduction to Operations Research*, John Wiley, New York, 1957.

[3] Kaufmann, A., *Méthodes et modèles de la recherche opérationelle (Methods and Models of Operational Research)*, Dunod, Paris, 1959.

[4] Kotarbiński, T., *Traktat o dobrej robocie (Treatise on Good Work)*, PWN, Warsaw, 1955.

[5] Lange, O., *Ekonomia polityczna (Political Economy)*, Vol. I, PWN, Warsaw, 1959, English edition, Pergamon Press, 1963.

[6] Lesourne, J., *Technique économique et gestion industrielle (Economic Practice and Industrial Management)*, Dunod, Paris, 1958.

[7] *Matematika v SSSR za Sorok Let 1917–1957 (Mathematics in the U.S.S.R. during the Forty Years 1917–1957)*, Gosudarstvennoe Izd. Fiziko-matemat. Literatury, Moscow, 1959.

[8] McCloskey, J. and Trefethen, F. (ed.), *Operations Research for Management*, J. Hopkins Press, Baltimore, 1954.

[9] Merrill, G., Goldberg, H., Helmholz, R., *Operations Research— Armament-Launching*, D. van Nostrand, Princeton, 1956.

[10] Morse, P. and Kimball, G., *Methods of Operations Research,* J. Wiley, New York, 1950.

[11] Nemchinov, V. (ed.), *Primenenie matematiki v ekonomicheskikh issledovaniyakh (Applications of Mathematics to Economic Research),* Izdat. Sotsialno-ekonomicheskoi Literatury, Moscow, 1959.

[12] Saaty, T., *Mathematical Methods of Operations Research,* McGraw-Hill, New York, 1959.

[13] Sasieni, M., Yaspan, A. and Friedman, L., *Operations Research — Methods and Problems,* John Wiley, New York, 1959.

[14] Vazsonyi, A., *Scientific Programming in Business and Industry,* John Wiley, New York, 1958.

[15] Bolletino del Centro per la Ricerca Operativa.

[16] Journal of the Operations Research Society of America.

[17] Management Science.

[18] Naval Research Logistics Quarterly.

[19] Operational Research Quarterly.

[20] Revue de Recherche Opérationnelle.

[21] Unternehmensforschung—Operations Research.

CHAPTER 2

Applications of Differential Calculus

6. Applications of differential calculus

Differential calculus has many uses in the solution of certain deterministic models. It also plays an auxiliary role in the determination of solutions for other types of models.

Assuming that the reader has a knowledge of differential calculus as used to find the maximum or minimum value of a function of one or many variables, we shall present only two examples which apply to deterministic models. The application of differential calculus to other types of models will be dealt with later in the book.

Example 1. An enterprise is to produce quantity R of a certain article in a given time T. The demand for this article is distributed uniformly. This means that if an enterprise had a stock of this article amounting to R at the beginning of the period under consideration, the stock would decrease uniformly in time. Such a situation is illustrated in Fig. 1.6.

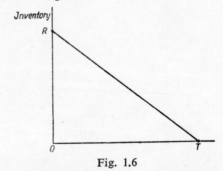

Fig. 1.6

It is necessary to determine the size of the lots in which this article should be produced so that manufacturing and storage costs will be the lowest possible. In determining the optimum lot we take into account two factors: the cost of storage and the cost of manufacture.

The cost of storage per unit article and unit time is k_1. Production costs consist of two parts. The first part does not depend on the size of the lots in which the article is produced; this comprises chiefly the cost of materials and labour. We designate by C the part of the costs which relate to the production of the article in quantity R. The second part of the costs depends on the number of lots in which the product is to be manufactured. Let k_2 stand for the fixed costs involved in starting up the production of one lot, regardless of its size.

The decision we have to take, therefore, pertains to the size of the lot in which the article shall be produced. We designate by X the size of the lot to be determined. This is a decision variable whereas the other quantities are parameters.

If we produced lots smaller than R (e.g. the size of lot $X = 1/4\ R$) then the state of the stock may be shown graphically as in Fig. 2.6. In these conditions the average stock in the warehouse would be $\dfrac{X}{2}$. We would thus have $\dfrac{R}{X}$ periods of time, the

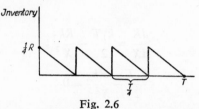

Fig. 2.6

duration of which we would designate by t and assume that in each the stock is X at the commencement of the period and 0 at the end. From the assumption of uniform distribution of demand in time, it follows that in each period t the average stock is indeed $\dfrac{X}{2}$.

In this connection storage costs K_m for the period T would be:

$$K_m = \frac{X}{2} \cdot k_1 \cdot t \cdot \frac{R}{X} = \frac{k_1 tR}{2}. \tag{1}$$

Of course, the magnitude of t depends on the selected lot size X, namely:

$$t = \frac{T}{\dfrac{R}{X}} = \frac{TX}{R}. \tag{2}$$

Substituting (2) to (1), we finally obtain:

$$K_m = \frac{k_1 TX}{2}. \tag{3}$$

Similarly, we calculate the production costs K_p, which amount to:

$$K_p = C + \frac{R}{X} \cdot k_2 \tag{4}$$

The combined storage and production costs (K) will be the sum of the storage costs (3) and the production costs (4):

$$K = K_m + K_p = \frac{k_1 TX}{2} + C + \frac{R}{X} \cdot k_2. \tag{5}$$

In this example costs K are the criterion.

Thus, expression (5) is a criterion-function which enables us to select the magnitude of X. That is, we select an X for which expression (5) will assume the smallest possible value; this must be a non-negative number ($X > 0$), because of the meaning we have given this variable (lot size). This is the only condition in the problem. The model in this case, therefore, consists of two parts: the condition $X > 0$ and criterion (5).

In order to find the value X_0 of variable X for which expression (5) is a minimum, we must differentiate function K in relation to variable X and make the derivative equal 0.

$$\frac{dK}{dX} = \frac{k_1 T}{2} - \frac{Rk_2}{X^2},$$
$$\frac{k_1 T}{2} - \frac{Rk_2}{X^2} = 0. \tag{6}$$

Rewriting equation (6), we obtain

$$X^2 = \frac{2Rk_2}{k_1 T},$$

and, therefrom

$$X_0 = \sqrt{\frac{2Rk_2}{k_1 T}}. \tag{7}$$

In view of the assumption that $X > 0$, the square root must be positive ($+$).

For accuracy we should still verify whether the solution obtained, (7), is really a solution, that is, whether for X_0 defined by formula (7) the expression (5) does really reach a minimum. This can be verified from the sign of the second derivative of expression (5) at the point $X = X_0$:

$$\frac{d^2 K}{dX^2} = \frac{2Rk_2}{X^3}. \tag{8}$$

The second derivative given by formula (8) at the point $X = X_0$ is positive since

$$\frac{2Rk_2}{X_0^3} = \frac{k_1 T}{\sqrt{\frac{2Rk_2}{k_1 T}}} > 0.$$

From this it appears that both R, k_1, k_2 and T are positive numbers.

In this way we are certain that for X_0 defined by formula (7) the production and storage costs are really a minimum.

Let the demand be $R = 40,000$ articles for a period $T = 12$ months. The cost of storing a single article for a month is $k_1 = 2$ zlotys, whereas the fixed cost of starting production of one lot is $k_2 = 1,200$ zlotys. Then, in accordance with formula (7), the optimum lot size is

$$X_0 = \sqrt{\frac{2 . 40,000 . 1,200}{2 . 12}} = 2,000.$$

This means that the article should be manufactured in lots of 2,000 units each. Formula (2) indicates the frequency of the production cycle of the individual lots

$$t = \frac{12 . 2,000}{40,000} = 0 \cdot 6.$$

Since we used a month as the unit of time, lots should be produced every 18 days (assuming the average length of a month to be 30 days).

The example we have solved is the simplest version of the subject known in literature as "the economic lot size". We shall return to this problem further on.

The model considered above was extremely simple. It had only one decision variable. More often, however, we encounter cases in which there are more such variables and they must satisfy more complicated conditions. The next example pertains to such a situation.

Example 2. An enterprise is to produce in a given time T a quantity R_1 of article A and a quantity R_2 of article B. The demand for both articles is uniform in time. We have to find in what lot size article A, and article B are to be manufactured if the storage cost per unit of article A per unit time is $k_1^{(A)}$ and of article B, $k_1^{(B)}$; the fixed costs involved in commencing production of one lot[1] of article A are $k_2^{(A)}$ and of article B $k_2^{(B)}$. We have to find a lot size X_1 for article A and a lot size X_2 for article B for which the total storage and manufacturing costs will be a minimum. However, in determining the optimum lot size, we must take into account the capacity of the warehouse. That capacity is $P\,m^3$ and a unit of article A occupies $p_1\,m^3$, whereas article B takes up $p_2\,m^3$.

Reasoning as in the solution of Example 1, we can easily write the form of the function of total cost connected with the production and storage of the two articles:

$$K = \frac{k_1^{(A)}TX_1}{2} + \frac{R_1 k_2^{(A)}}{X_1} + \frac{k_1^{(B)}TX_2}{2} + \frac{R_2 k_2^{(B)}}{X_2}. \tag{9}$$

---

[1] In our further considerations we shall neglect the part of production cost which is independent of the size of the lots in which the articles are manufactured (raw materials, labour, etc.), as they do not affect the solution, the volume of output being set in advance.

It is necessary to choose a pair of values $X_1 > 0$ and $X_2 > 0$ for which costs K will be the lowest. However, we must bear in mind that we are interested only in those pairs of values of variables X_1 and X_2 which satisfy the condition pertaining to warehouse capacity. This condition can be written as an inequality

$$p_1 X_1 + p_2 X_2 \leqslant P. \tag{10}$$

Condition (10) means that the solution obtained must lie within the hatched area of Fig. 3.6.

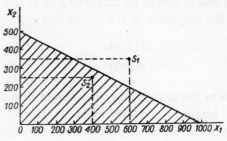

Fig. 3.6

In this drawing we have assumed that $p_1 = 0 \cdot 1 \ m^3$, $p_2 = 0 \cdot 2 \ m^3$ and $P = 100 \ m^3$. If function K reaches a minimum at point S_1 for these values, the solution would be inadmissible because of warehouse capacity. The solution must therefore be so changed that condition (10) is satisfied. If, however, function K reaches a minimum at point S_2, the solution is final.

Therefore, to solve the problem set it is necessary to proceed as outlined below:

1. Fix the minimum of function K (determined by formula (9)), bearing in mind that $X_1 > 0$ and $X_2 > 0$. For this purpose we find the derivative of function K for variable X_1, and then for variable X_2.

We set both derivatives equal to zero and obtain the set of equations:

$$\frac{k_1^{(A)}T}{2} - \frac{R_1 k_2^{(A)}}{X_1^2} = 0,$$

$$\frac{k_1^{(B)}T}{2} - \frac{R_2 k_2^{(B)}}{X_2^2} = 0. \tag{11}$$

Solving equations (11), we obtain:

$$X_1 = \sqrt{\frac{2R_1 k_2^{(A)}}{k_1^{(A)}T}}, \tag{12}$$

$$X_2 = \sqrt{\frac{2R_2 k_2^{(B)}}{k_1^{(B)}T}}.$$

Note that the expressions obtained (12) are analogous to formula (7).

2. Verify whether solution (12) satisfies condition (10). If it does, the solution obtained is final.

3. If solution (12) does not satisfy condition (10), it means that the warehouse capacity is too small. In this connection, the solution should be so determined that expression (9) reaches a minimum on the assumption that the condition

$$p_1 X_1 + p_2 X_2 = P \tag{13}$$

is satisfied.

We obtain this condition from condition (10) by replacing the $\leqslant$ sign by an equality sign. When, however, expression (9) attains a minimum outside area (10), it follows that the best feasible solution will lie on the boundary of area (10), namely on the straight line described by equation (13).

Formally speaking, the minimum of function (9) should be found by fulfilling condition (13). Such a conditional minimum can be found by employing the Lagrangian multiplier technique. For this purpose we set up the expression

$$\Phi(X_1, X_2) = K + \lambda(p_1 X_1 + p_2 X_2 - P) \tag{14}$$

where K is defined by formula (9) and λ is the Lagrangian multiplier. The expression next to λ is obtained from equation (10) by transposing P to the left-hand side. Differentiating function (14) successively in respect to unknowns X_1 and X_2 and setting the resultant derivatives equal to zero, we arrive at a system of two equations

$$
\begin{aligned}
\frac{k_1^{(A)} T}{2} - \frac{R_1 k_1^{(A)}}{X_1^2} + \lambda p_1 &= 0, \\
\frac{k_1^{(B)} T}{2} - \frac{R_2 k_2^{(B)}}{X_2^2} + \lambda p_2 &= 0.
\end{aligned}
\tag{15}
$$

These two equations, together with equation (13), constitute a system of three equations with three unknowns X_1, X_2 and λ, wherein the unknown λ is not given any real meaning. The values obtained for X_1 and X_2 from the solution of the above system of equations are the final solutions.[1]

7. Bibliographical notes

On the assumption that the reader has a knowledge of the fundamentals of differential calculus, we confined ourselves in Section 6 to two examples illustrating the application of calculus to operational research. We did not enter into any discussion

---

[1] Of course, we must check to see whether the solution obtained is really the minimum of function K.

of the conditions in which differential calculus can be used; we passed'over the question of the conditions that would be necessary and adequate for the existence of a maximum or minimum, etc.

We shall repeatedly make use of differential calculus in other sections of the book, mainly to determine maximum or minimum values of functions.

An exposition of differential calculus can be found in many textbooks. The book by F. Leja [2] is particularly recommended. In it the reader will also find an exposition of integral calculus. We shall also make use of integral calculus to some extent in further analyses. A more elementary presentation of differential and integral calculus is given in a book by Z. Galas [1], although it omits the question of boundary maxima and minima, which are important from our point of view.

The reader who wishes to find a complete solution to Example 2 of Section 6 will encounter some difficulty in calculation. The problem amounts to the solution of an equation of the fourth degree. Methods of solving equations beyond the second degree can be found in algebra textbooks, e.g. by W. Sierpiński [4].

It is worth adding that in practice it frequently becomes necessary to use approximate calculations, i.e. calculations which permit to determine effectively a solution to a certain degree of approximation. These methods are extremely important since they allow solutions to be obtained in a relatively simple manner when accurate calculations would be tedious. The reader can learn the most important methods of this type and the subject matter of approximate calculations from a book by J. Lukaszewicz and M. Warmus [3].

Differential calculus is a fairly old branch of mathematics. It is by no means a method as, for instance, linear programming, which came into being in conjunction with operations research. For this reason, there are no books especially devoted to the use of differential calculus in operational research. Such applications can, on the other hand, be found in every textbook on operational research and in many articles.

BIBLIOGRAPHY

[1] Galas, Z., *Matematyka, Kurs podstawowy dla wyższych szkół ekonomicznych (Manual for Advanced Schools of Economics)* Łódź–Warsaw, 1959, PWN.

[2] Leja, F., *Rachunek różniczkowy i całkowy (Differential and Integral Calculus)* Warsaw, 1954, PWN. (also earlier and later editions).

[3] Łukaszewicz, J. and Warmus, M., *Metody numeryczne i graficzne (Numerical and Graphic Methods)* Warsaw, 1956, PWN.

[4] Sierpiński, W., *Zasady algebry wyższej (Principles of Higher Algebra)*, Warsaw–Wrocław, 1946, Monografie matematyczne, Vol. XI.

CHAPTER 3

Linear Programming

8. Introductory notes on linear programming

Linear programming is a method of solving a certain specific type of model. The essential feature of this method, as the name suggests, is that it can be used only for linear models, i.e. those involving linear relations only.

In some simple cases, a linear programme may be solved by means of the graphic method. Let us now consider several examples of this type. This will give us an idea what the solution of a linear programme involves.

Example 1. An industrial enterprise makes two products A and B. Their manufacture calls for the use of three machines which we shall label M_1, M_2 and M_3. These machines can be employed to manufacture products A and B during some fixed part of the day. Machine M_1 can be utilized for 24,000 seconds, machine M_2 for 40,000 seconds and machine M_3 for 27,000 seconds. We also know the working times of the individual machines required to obtain a unit of product A and the analogous times needed to produce a unit of product B. These data are given in Table 1.8.

TABLE 1/8

Machines	Amount of work by machine (sec.) per unit product		Max. total working time of machine (sec.)
	A	B	
M_1	3	6	24,000
M_2	8	4	40,000
M_3	9	3	27,000

In addition, we have data on profits per unit of products A and B. The per unit profit on A is 9 groszy and on B, 6 groszy.

Our task is to ascertain the quantities in which products A and B should be manufactured so as to obtain the largest total profit. In order to solve this problem, we have to formulate it with great precision, i.e state it in the mathematical language. First of all we must determine, therefore, the decision variables for our particular

23

case. The volume of output of A will be one decision variable and we denote it by X_A; the volume of output of B will be the second, and we denote it by X_B. All the other quantities which appear in our model are parameters (numerical values of Table 1.8 and unit profits).

It should be pointed out that when constructing a model, this must take into account certain technical conditions. In the example under consideration they may be reduced to two problems:

a) we cannot exceed the maximum working time of the individual machines,

b) we must take into account the fact that the working time of the individual machines required to manufacture a unit of product A and a unit of product B is as given by the figures of Table 1.8.

It is, therefore, readily seen that the total working time of machine M_1 required to turn out X_A units of product A and X_B units of product B is $3X_A + 6X_B$. On the other hand, this time must not exceed the maximum working time of that machine, i.e. 24,000 seconds. We can, therefore, easily write the condition

$$3X_A + 6X_B \leqslant 24{,}000. \tag{1}$$

Similarly, for machine M_2:

$$8X_A + 4X_B \leqslant 40{,}000. \tag{1'}$$

And, finally, for machine M_3:

$$9X_A + 3X_B \leqslant 27{,}000. \tag{1''}$$

For accuracy, we further assume that our decision variables satisfy a certain physical condition. This condition is the result of the values we have given to variables X_A and X_B. These magnitudes represent the volume of output of products A and B; in this respect, the positive values of these variables alone are of any real significance. We write this in the following manner:

$$X_A \geqslant 0; \quad X_B \geqslant 0. \tag{2}$$

Thus, conditions (1), (1'), (1'') and (2) determine the pairs of values of variables X_A and X_B to be taken into account in the selection of the best pair, i.e. that pair which would ensure maximum total profit. So, for instance, it is possible to ascertain that for the pair $X_A = 1{,}000$ and $X_B = 1{,}000$, all the conditions mentioned above are satisfied, since

$$3 . 1{,}000 + 6 . 1{,}000 = \ 9{,}000 < 24{,}000$$

$$8 . 1{,}000 + 4 . 1{,}000 = 12{,}000 < 40{,}000$$

$$9 . 1{,}000 + 3 . 1{,}000 = 12{,}000 < 27{,}000$$

and $1{,}000 > 0$ and $1{,}000 > 0$.

It is quite evident that there are very many such pairs of values of X_A and X_B which satisfy conditions (1), (1'), (1'') and (2). For the purpose of the solution that pair should be chosen for which the total profit is the highest.

Designating the total profit by Z, it may be written as below:

$$Z = 9X_A + 6X_B. \tag{3}$$

Therefore, we now have a complete model of our problem. The point is to select from all the pairs of values of X_A and X_B satisfying the conditions of the model, i.e. conditions (1), (1'), (1'') and (2), the pair for which function (3) assumes the maximum value. The profit, as determined by formula (3), acts here as the criterion.

Since there are only two decision variables in the given example, it can be solved graphically, without calculations.

In Fig. 1.8 we have a system of coordinates in which we measure the volume of output of product A (we designate it as before by X_A) along the horizontal axis, and the output of product B by X_B, along the vertical axis.[1]

Condition (2) means that only the points which are on the positive coordinates can be considered as possible solutions. In other words, this solution can lie only in the first quadrant of the coordinates system, shown in Fig. 1.8.

Condition (1) of our model has a straightforward graphical interpretation. If we were to assume for a moment that we manufacture only product A on machine M_1 and use up its total production capacity for the purpose (24,000 seconds), we could obtain $24,000 \div 3 = 8,000$ units of product A. Similarly, by using machine M_1 exclusively to manufacture product B, we could obtain $24,000 \div 6 = 4,000$ units of product B. It is obvious that by joining the point at 8,000 on the X_A axis, we obtain a segment which contains all possible combinations of pairs X_A and X_B that could be obtained by utilizing fully machine M_1. We marked this segment by I in Fig. 1.8. However, since condition (1) does not stipulate that we have to utilize the entire production capacity of machine M_1 (the left-hand side of relation (1) can be equal to, or less than, the right-hand side), the set of feasible pairs of X_A and X_B for machine M_1 is represented by the set of points that lies not only on but also below segment I. An analogous interpretation can be given to condition (1'). Thus, similar reasoning leads us to the conclusion that for machine M_2 the set of feasible pairs of values of X_A and X_B is represented by the sets of points lying on and below segment II.

Finally, from condition (1'') it follows that for machine M_3 the feasible pairs of values of X_A and X_B are represented by the set of points lying on and below segment III.

---

[1] For simplification, 1,000 products are adopted as a unit in Fig. 1.8

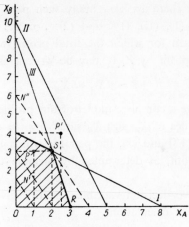

Fig. 1.8

In other words, it can be said that the production capacity of machine M_1 enables to realize any combination of the volume of production of A and B represented by any point within the set of points lying on or below segment I. Analogous sets are determined by the production capacities of machines M_2 and M_3.

Conditions (1), (1'), and (1'') must be satisfied simultaneously. This means that for our solution we can take into account only the points which are part at the same time of the three sets mentioned above. The set of these points, known as the set of feasible solutions, is shown hatched in Fig. 1.8. This set does not exceed the limit below axis X_A or to the left of axis X_B because it satisfies conditions (2) which stipulate that the X_A and X_B values must be positive. Thus, for example, point P, i.e. the pair of values $X_A = 1,000$ and $X_B = 3,000$, belongs to the set of feasible solutions, whereas point P', i.e. the pair of values $X_A = 2,500$ and $X_B = 4,000$, does not.

The point to be taken as the final solution from the set of feasible solutions will be determined by the criterion which in our case is the profit defined by formula (3). It is apparent that using the graphic method, it is easy to indicate the point which affords the final solution. Let us assume for the moment that, aside from the technical conditions (i.e. conditions (1), (1') and (1'')), we want to determine a production that will yield a profit of 90 zlotys, or in other words 9,000 groszy. This profit can be achieved by producing 1,000 units of product A (9,000 $\div$ 9 = 1,000) or 1,500 units of product B (9,000 $\div$ 6 = 1,500). An identical profit can be obtained by turning out any combination of products A and B represented by a point on segment N' joining the point at 1,000 on axis X_A and the point at 1,500 on axis X_B. This segment can be called the line of constant profit (in this case, 90 zlotys). Any number of such lines of constant profit could be drawn for various sizes of the profit. All of them will have the same slope (therefore, they will be parallel to each other), which is determined by the profit per unit product. The higher we go to the right of the origin of the coordinates system, the higher will be the profits represented by the intersection lines. For instance, the line of constant profit for a profit of 180 zlotys will pass through the point at 2,000 on axis X_A and the point at 3,000 on axis X_B.

Our task is to determine a point which ensures the highest profit from the points within the set of feasible solutions. This can be done in the following simple manner. We apply a ruler to one of the possible lines of identical profit (e.g. N') and move it, without changing direction, upwards to the right. This signifies a shift to lines that ensure increasing profits. The solution will be a point which lies in the area of feasible solutions and at the same time is on the line of constant profit furthest from the origin. In our case this solution will be point S lying on the line of constant profit N''. This point is still within the set of feasible solutions. It is readily seen that all the other feasible solutions yield a smaller total profit than does point S. From Fig. 1.8 we read for point S: $X_A = 2,000$ and $X_B = 3,000$. The total profit will be $2,000 \times 9 + 3,000 \times 6 = 36,000$ groszy, i.e. 360 zlotys.

In Example 1 we saw the graphic method of solving linear models. It was apparent that this method can only be used when there are two decision variables in the model, and any number of conditions. We shall give below several typical situations which may be encountered illustrating these with examples, and we shall operate for the time being with models having two decision variables.

Example 2. A farm is engaged in breeding pigs. The pigs are fed on various products grown on the farm. In view of the need to ensure certain nutrient constituents, it is necessary to buy additionally one or two products, which we shall call A and B.

The content of the various products (per unit) in nutrient constituent (e.g. vitamins, proteins, etc.) is given in Table 2.8.

TABLE 2/8

Nutrient	Nutrient content in product		Minimum amount of nutrient
	A	B	
M_1	36	6	108
M_2	3	12	36
M_3	20	10	100

The last column of Table 2.8 also gives the minimum nutrient constituents M_1, M_2 and M_3 which must be given to the pigs within a given unit of time. The question we ask ourselves is: How much do we have to buy of product A and B

(within the given unit of time) to furnish the pigs the nutrient constituents M_1, M_2 and M_3 in quantities not less than the minimum specified in Table 2.8 at the lowest possible cost of buying products A and B?

In order to answer this question, we must know the prices of the individual products. Let us assume that product A costs 20 zlotys per unit and product B, 40 zlotys.

Proceeding to solve the problem, we first introduce the decision variables. These will be X_A for the purchased quantity of product A and X_B for the purchased quantity of product B.

The model of our problem will be:

$$36X_A + 6X_B \geqslant 108 \tag{4}$$

$$3X_A + 12X_B \geqslant 36 \tag{4'}$$

$$20X_A + 10X_B \geqslant 100 \tag{4''}$$

$$X_A \geqslant 0; \quad X_B \geqslant 0 \tag{5}$$

$$K = 20X_A + 40X_B \quad \text{(minimum)}. \tag{6}$$

The group of conditions (4), (4') and (4'') refers to constituents M_1, M_2 and M_3 respectively. These conditions indicate that the quantity of products A and B purchased must at least provide the minimum amounts of nutrient constituents given in Table 2.8. Condition (5) means that the solution, i.e. the amount of products A and B purchased, can only be expressed in positive numbers. Finally, expression (6) is the function of costs which acts as the criterion. In other words, of the feasible solutions, i.e. those which satisfy conditions (4), (4'), (4'') and (5) we shall select one for which the function of costs assumes the smallest value. Hence the word "minimum" next to relation (6). In Fig. 2.8 is given the set of feasible solutions (hatched) and the solution given by point S. For point S we have $X_A = 4$ and $X_B = 2$. The construction of the set of feasible solutions is analogous to that in Example 1.8. Let us discuss it briefly at this point.

First, let us consider condition (4). Let us assume for the moment that we want to find for X_A and X_B such values that constituent M_1 will be given in the minimum amount of 108 precisely. If we were to present this ingredient in the form of product A, then X_A would have to be $108 \div 36 = 3$. If, on the other hand, we wanted to supply the 108 units of ingredient M_1 in the form of product B, then X_B would be $108 \div 6 = 18$. By joining the point at 3 on the X_A axis with the point at 18 on the X_B axis, we obtain segment I which contains the quantitative combinations of products A and B that ensure a supply of exactly 108 units of ingredient M_1. Since 108 or more units of this ingredient are to be supplied, because of condition (4), it is necessary to consider the values of X_A and X_B which are determined by the points on segment I, or by points to the right upwards of that segment. Similarly, because of condition (4') it is necessary to take into consideration all points in segment II or to the right above it and, finally because of condition (4″) the points in segment III or above to the right of it must be accounted for. Conditions (5) mean that the set of feasible solutions cannot contain points lying to the left of axis X_A (since $X_B \geqslant 0$) nor can it contain points lying below axis X_A (since $X_B \geqslant 0$). Thus, to find the optimum point for the set of feasible solutions, i.e. the point for which the costs expressed by formula (6) are the lowest, we first have to plot a line of constant cost for any value of K. Let us assume, for instance, that the costs are 320 zlotys. For this sum we can buy $320 \div 20 = 16$ units of product A or $320 \div 40 = 8$ units of product B, or alternatively some combination of products A and B represented by some point lying on the line of identical cost K'. The lines parallel to K', lying below to the left of it, will represent the lines of constant costs, below 320 zlotys only. In the set of feasible solutions we look, therefore, for a point that lies on the lowest line of constant cost.

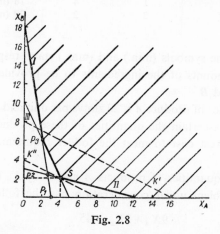

Fig. 2.8

Applying a ruler to line K', we move it down to the left, (always at the same angle of inclination to the axes of coordinates) until we reach a point in the area of feasible solutions, lying on the lowest line of constant cost. As we can see from Fig. 2.8, this will be point S which lies on line K''. As mentioned above, the decision variables for points S will have the values $X_A = 4$ and $X_B = 2$. This means that four units of product A and two units of product B bought will ensure that the contents of the ingredients M_1, M_2 and M_3 will be at least equal to the minimum requirements stipulated in Table 2.8, and the total purchasing cost will be the lowest. This means that by reducing expenditure on products A and B the content in one or all the ingredients of the fodder purchased would fall below the required amounts (given in Table 2.8).

In Example 3 below, we shall consider a similar problem to that of Example 2, involving, however, some essential modifications.

Example 3. Products A and B, which serve as fodder for pigs, contain different amounts of two nutritive ingredients M_1 and M_2 which we are to provide to the animals in certain fixed quantities. These products, moreover, contain certain amounts of ingredient M_3, which can be harmful if present in the fodder in excessive amounts. Table 3.8 shows the data relating thereto.

TABLE 3/8

Nutrient	Nutrient content in product		Minimum or maximum amount of nutrient
	A	B	
M_1	9	3	45 (min.)
M_2	1	4	16 (min.)
M_3	2	2	20 (max.)

In the last column the symbols (min.) and (max.) stand respectively for the minimum or maximum amounts of the ingredients to be provided in the fodder containing products A and B.

Knowing that the price of product A is 20 zlotys per unit and the price of product B 40 zlotys, we have to ascertain the quantities of these products to be supplied for the animals at the lowest cost to meet the fodder requirements given in the last column of Table 3.8.

If we designate the quantities of products A and B by X_A and X_B as previously, the model of the problem under consideration has the following form:

$$9X_A + 3X_B \geqslant 45 \tag{7}$$

$$X_A + 4X_B \geqslant 16 \tag{7'}$$

$$2X_A + 2X_B \leqslant 20 \tag{7''}$$

$$X_A \geqslant 0; \quad X_B \geqslant 0 \tag{8}$$

$$K = 20X_A + 40X_B \quad \text{(minimum)}. \tag{9}$$

It should be borne in mind that, as in the previous example, the word "minimum" next to expression (9) means that the values of the decision variables X_A and X_B must be chosen so that, satisfying all the conditions of the model, they render expression (9) minimum.

The graphic solution of this model is presented in Fig. 3.8.

It is of interest to note the manner in which the area of feasible solutions has been constructed.

From conditions (7), (7') and (7'') it follows that this set embraces points in segments I and II and points above to their right as well as points in segment III together with points below to the left of it. The set of points which satisfy these relations simultaneously is shown as a hatched area in Fig. 3.8. Using the line of constant costs, as in Example 2, we can readily find the solution which is represented by point S. This means that the quantity of product A is 4 units and of product B 3 units.

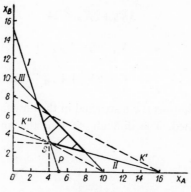

Fig. 3.8

It should be noted that at times we may encounter linear programmes which offer many solutions (each of our previous examples comprised only one) or alternatively offer no solution at all. We shall discuss in turn these two situations in two further examples.

Example 4. We use three raw materials: M_1, M_2 and M_3 in the manufacture of products A and B. The consumption of these materials per unit of products A and B is given in Table 4.8. The total consumption of the various raw materials for the production of A and B must not exceed certain limits, as given in the last column of Table 4.8.

TABLE 4/8

Raw material	Consumption of raw material per unit product		Limits on consumption of material
	A	B	
M_1	3	1	18
M_2	2	4	40
M_3	2	2	24

Knowing that the profit per unit product A is 6 zlotys and per unit product B, 4 zlotys, the volume of production for A and B should be so fixed as to obtain the largest total profit, without exceeding the allocation of raw materials. We construct the model of this problem on the basis of the above information designating the output of product A by X_A and the output of product B by X_B:

$$3X_A + X_B \leqslant 18 \tag{10}$$

$$2X_A + 4X_B \leqslant 40 \tag{10'}$$

$$3X_A + 2X_B \leqslant 24 \tag{10''}$$

$$X_A \geqslant 0; \; X_B \geqslant 0 \tag{11}$$

$$Z = 6X_A + 4X_B \quad \text{(maximum)}. \tag{12}$$

The area of feasible solutions is constructed in the now familiar pattern. In Fig. 4.8 this area is shown hatched. The difficulty is that the lines of constant profit are

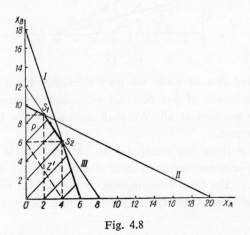

Fig. 4.8

parallel to one of the segments (in our case, to segment III). In the present case, therefore, there is no single point in the set of feasible solutions which lies on the line of maximum constant profit. As may be seen from the drawing, there may be many such points. They are the points of the segment $S_1\ S_2$ which is part of segment III. This means that we shall obtain an identical maximum profit whatever the point selected on segment $S_1\ S_2$.

Example 5. Two raw materials M_1 and M_2 are used in the manufacture of products A and B. Table 5.8 gives the consumption of these raw materials per unit product. Total consumption of materials must not exceed the fixed allocations given in Table 5.8.

Raw material	Consumption of raw material per unit product		Limits on consumption of material
	A	B	
M_1	1	5	20
M_2	3	5	30

The profit per unit of product A is 4 zlotys and per unit of product B, 8 zlotys. We have to determine the output of products A and B (these outputs are designated by X_A and X_B respectively) which will guarantee the maximum profit provided that the output of B is not less than 8 units.

The model of our problem is

$$X_A + 5X_B \leqslant 20 \tag{13}$$

$$3X_A + 5X_B \leqslant 30 \tag{13'}$$

$$X_B \geqslant 8 \tag{14}$$

$$X_A \geqslant 0 \tag{15}$$

$$Z = 4X_A + 8X_B \quad \text{(maximum)}. \tag{16}$$

This model, as is evident from Fig. 5.8, offers no solution whatever. This is due to the fact that the set of feasible solutions is empty or, in other words, that there is no set of feasible solutions. The set of points which satisfy conditions (13) and (13') are marked in Fig. 5.8 by the symbol Z_1. The set of points satisfying condi-

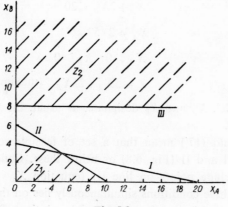

Fig 5.8

tions (14) and (15) is marked by Z_2. It is quite obvious that there is not one single point that would be part of both Z_1 and Z_2. In other words, no point satisfies all the conditions of the model at the same time.

Models of this type are frequently said to be inconsistent. The reason for this name is that to satisfy one group of conditions is inconsistent with the satisfaction of another group of conditions.

Let us look at another example. It will be characteristic of the type in which one of the conditions appearing in the model is an equality.

Example 6. We manufacture two products A and B. Machines of the type M_1 and M_2, which are necessary for the manufacture of these products, form a bottleneck. Table 6.8 gives the production capacities of both machines for both products.

TABLE 6/8

Machines	No. of machine hours per unit product		Max. time machine works per 24 hrs.
	A	B	
M_1	2	1	12
M_2	2	2	20

A production plan is to be drawn up ensuring a maximum total profit (the profit per unit product A is 5 zlotys and per unit product B, 25 zlotys), and it is assumed that the proportion in which goods A and B are to be produced is fixed in advance: the output of product A must be two and a half times that of product B.

The model of our problem will, therefore, have the following form:

$$2X_A + X_B \leqslant 12 \tag{17}$$

$$2X_A + 2X_B \leqslant 20 \tag{17'}$$

$$X_A = 2 \cdot 5 X_B \tag{18}$$

$$X_A \geqslant 0; \ X_B \geqslant 0 \tag{19}$$

$$Z = 5X_A + 25X_B \quad (\text{maximum}). \tag{20}$$

In the above model, X_A and X_B designate, as usual, the volume of production of articles A and B.

Conditions (17) and (17') mean that a set of feasible solutions may embrace points on segments I and II (Fig. 6.8) or below these. Condition (18) states that this set can also include points on line III (equation $X_A = 2 \cdot 5 \ X_B$). The set of points satisfying all three conditions simultaneously lies on the segment OS. In our case, therefore, segment OS gives the set of feasible solutions. Point S on this segment lies on the line of constant profit ensuring the maximum profit. This is the solution and it means that $X_A = 5$ and $X_B = 2$.

The examples considered above have illustrated different types of models which can be solved by linear programming. An essential feature of these models is that they contain only linear relations. In all cases, we confined ourselves to models

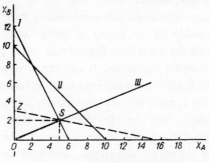

Fig. 6.8

with two decision variables only. We did so in order to present these models graphically. This enabled us to understand the fundamentals of solving such models. It may be easily guessed that in the presence of a larger number of decision variables the graphic method must fail and in such conditions there remains only the analytical method, i.e. the computational method.

The theory of linear programming provides various algorithms, i.e. procedures affording a solution by appropriate calculations. Some of these algorithms are general, which means that they can be used to solve any linear model; others are applicable only to certain special cases. All these algorithms are based fundamentally on the concept of solving linear models, which we have shown on examples in Section 8. In some of the subsequent Sections we shall deal with some algorithms which the theory of linear programming provides.

9. The simplex algorithm

The general form of a linear model with n decision variables is

$$K = p_1 X_1 + p_2 X_2 + \ldots \ldots + p_n X_n \text{ (maximum or minimum) (1)}$$

$$a_{11} X_1 + a_{12} X_2 + \ldots \ldots + a_{1n} X_n \leqslant b_1$$

$$a_{21} X_1 + a_{22} X_2 + \ldots \ldots + a_{2n} X_n \geqslant b_2$$

$$\cdot \; \cdot \; \cdot \; \cdot \; \cdot \; \cdot \; \cdot \; \cdot \; \cdot \; \cdot \; \cdot \; \cdot \; \cdot \; \cdot \; \cdot \; \cdot \; \cdot \tag{2}$$

$$\cdot \; \cdot \; \cdot \; \cdot \; \cdot \; \cdot \; \cdot \; \cdot \; \cdot \; \cdot \; \cdot \; \cdot \; \cdot \; \cdot \; \cdot \; \cdot$$

$$a_{m1} X_1 + a_{m2} X_2 + \ldots \ldots + a_{mn} X_n = b_m.$$

3*

The value of function (1) constitutes the criterion here. This should be under-stood to mean that from the set of values of decision variables, $X_1, X_2, \ldots, X_n$ which satisfy the group of conditions (2) as a solution should be adopted these values of the individual variables for which function (1) becomes a maximum or minimum, according to the nature of the problem.

Conditions (2) can be inequalities of the type "$\leqslant$" or "$\geqslant$", or alternatively they may be equalities. We have expressed this symbolically by placing each of the three possible types of relationship in the group of conditions (2).

We shall now deal with the algorithm for solving linear programmes. This algorithm is known as the simplex algorithm. It has the advantage of being universal, i.e. any linear model which affords a solution can be solved by it. Unfortunately, as we shall see, this algorithm is quite tedious, as it entails a great deal of computational work. In certain individual cases, i.e. for certain special forms of linear models, the algorithm from which the solution is determined can be appreciably simplified. We shall consider some simplified algorithms, although of limited application, in subsequent Sections.

The principle of the simplex algorithm consists in adopting as a starting point a certain solution for a model of which all we know is that it is feasible, i.e. that it satisfies the group of conditions (2). We subsequently improve this solution at consecutive stages until, after a certain finite number of stages, we arrive at the optimum solution.

In order to explain what a simplex algorithm is, let us solve a number of examples. We shall begin with the examples which we previously solved graphically in the preceding Section.

Example 1. The problem is as in Example 1, Section 8.

The model of our problem, as we may recall, is as follows:

$$3X_A + 6X_B \leqslant 24{,}000 \tag{3}$$

$$8X_A + 4X_B \leqslant 40{,}000 \tag{4}$$

$$9X_A + 3X_B \leqslant 27{,}000 \tag{5}$$

$$Z = 9X_A + 6X_B \text{ (maximum).} \tag{6}$$

Further on, when discussing linear programmes, we shall not repeat the conditions stipulating that the decision variables must assume non-negative values. We shall bear in mind that these conditions must always be satisfied.

The technique of computing the simplex algorithm requires that all relations of the model be transformed into equations with the unknowns (decision variables) on their left-hand sides, and the free terms (non-negative) on the right-hand sides.

Inequalities are transformed into equations by introducing some new variables.

As for relation (3), on the left-hand side we have the total time necessary for machine M_1 to produce quantity X_A of article A and X_B of article B. This time must not exceed 24,000 sec. Therefore, if we designate by S_1 any unutilized working time of machine M_1 (the difference between the time the machine can work and the time it actually does work), then relation (3) may be written as equation:

$$3X_A + 6X_B + S_1 = 24,000. \qquad (3')$$

Similarly, designating by S_2 any unutilized working time of machine M_2, and by S_3 any unutilized working time of machine M_3, we can write relations (4) and (5)

$$8X_A + 4X_B + S_2 = 40,000 \qquad (4')$$

$$9X_A + 3X_B + S_3 = 27,000 \qquad (5')$$

We have now introduced three new variables: S_1, S_2, S_3. These variables, unlike X_A and X_B, will be called slack variables (also known as pseudo-variables).

TABLE 1/9

	S_1	S_2	S_3	X_A	X_B		
S_1	1	0	0	3	6	24,000	$\div 3 = 8,000$
S_2	0	1	0	8	4	40,000	$\div 8 = 5,000$
S_3	0	0	1	9	3	27,000	$\div 9 = 3,000$

Having the system of equalities (3'), (4') and (5'), we proceed to compile a simplex table (Table 1.9). The table consists of a certain number of columns corresponding to the total number of slack and decision variables. Each column is headed by a variable. The number of rows in the Table corresponds to the number of slack variables; for each row there is one slack variable shown at the side of the Table. The order in which the variables appear in the rows and columns of the Table is basically of no importance. However, once an order has been determined, it must be adhered to in all further transformations of the initial Table.

Table 1.9 can be read in two ways: by rows or by columns. The first row gives the coefficient of equation (3'), i.e. the equation in which the first slack variable S_1 appears. The coefficients next to the individual variables in equation (3') are written in the column corresponding to the given variable. Thus, for instance, the coefficient next to X_B is 6; it is, therefore, written in column X_B. In the first rows of columns, S_2 and S_3, the coefficients are zero since these variables do not appear in equation (3').

We fill similarly the second row; it contains the coefficients of equation (4') in which variable S_2 appears. The coefficients of equation (5') are entered in the third row.

Table 1.9 can also be read by columns. Bearing in mind that S_1, S_2 and S_3 stand for the unused production capacities of machines M_1, M_2 and M_3, we can read column "X_B" for instance, as follows: to obtain one unit of X_B it is necessary to "use up" 6 units of unutilized production capacity of machine M_1, 4 units of unutilized production capacity of machine M_2, and 3 units of unutilized production capacity of machine M_3. In other words, column X_B can be interpreted as the relation

$$X_B = 6S_1 + 4S_2 + 3S_3.$$

A similar interpretation can be given the other columns. For instance, column S_1 expresses the identity relation

$$S_1 = S_1.$$

Generally speaking, the coefficients in Table 1.9 can be interpreted as a rate of transformation of one "commodity" into another of its kind. These coefficients state how many units of the "commodity" in the row have to be utilized to obtain a unit of the commodity in the column. For instance, coefficient 8 at the intersection of row S_2 and column X_A means that 8 units of S_2 are needed for one unit of X_A.

As a rule, we adopt as an initial solution in the simplex algorithm such a solution for which all the decision variables are zero. This means that in the initial decision it is assumed that $X_A = 0$ and $X_B = 0$. This is, of course, an admissible solution. From equations (3′), (4′) and (5′) it follows that the values of slack variables given below correspond to such a solution:

$$S_1 = 24,000$$
$$S_2 = 40,000$$
$$S_3 = 27,000.$$

These values are entered in the last column (without heading) of Table 1.

Having the initial solution, we improve it stepwise by considering various possibilities. The initial solution can be changed by introducing X_A (that is, by assuming for X_A a value greater than zero) or X_B. Next, we make computations which will show us which of these two possibilities is more profitable.

From formula (6) (the value of function (6) being the criterion) it follows that by introducing one unit of X_A in the new solution the value of Z is increased by 9. The introduction of one unit of X_A also causes S_1 to decrease by 3, S_2 by 8 and S_3 by 9. But this will not have any effect on the value of function (6) since variables S_1, S_2 and S_3 do not appear in it (this can be interpreted to mean that these variables appear in function (6) as components having zero coefficients).

On the other hand, the introduction of one unit of X_B in the solution would cause the function which is to be brought to a maximum to rise by 6. It is, therefore, better to introduce commodity A in the solution in as large a quantity as possible.

For each unit of X_A we have to use 3 units of S_1 of which we have 24,000. Therefore, the "reserve" of S_1 (i.e. the unutilized manufacturing capacity of machine M_1) allows us to introduce commodity A in the quantity:

$$24,000 \div 3 = 8,000.$$

We show this computation at the right-hand side of Table 1.9. The "reserve" of 40,000 units of S_2 enables us to introduce the following quantity of commodity A:

$$40,000 \div 8 = 5,000.$$

Finally, the "reserve" of S_3 allows 3,000 units of commodity A to be introduced. Therefore, ultimately only 3,000 units of commodity A (this is the smallest number obtained in the divisions carried out) will be introduced in the new improved solution. We cannot introduce a larger quantity of A in the solution since the production capacity of machine M_3 does not allow us to do so.

It is readily seen that by introducing a quantity $X_A = 3,000$ units of commodity A, we exhaust fully the production capacity of machine M_3. Thus, row S_3 in our table will disappear and a new one, X_A, will appear in its place. The new situation is shown in Table 2.9. It will have the same columns as before, except that in the third row X_A will replace S_3.

TABLE 2/9

	S_1	S_2	S_3	X_A	X_B		
S_1	1	0	$-\dfrac{1}{3}$	0	5	15,000	$\div\, 5 = 3,000$
S_2	0	1	$-\dfrac{8}{9}$	0	$\dfrac{4}{3}$	16,000	$\div\, \dfrac{4}{3} = 12,000$
X_A	0	0	$\dfrac{1}{9}$	1	$\dfrac{1}{3}$	3,000	$\div\, \dfrac{1}{3} = 9,000$

We first fill the last column (without heading). Since we have introduced 3,000 units of commodity A into the new solution we write that number in row X_A. As may be seen from Table 1.9, for each unit of X_A, we had to use up 3 units of S_1, and so the total used was $3 \times 3,000 = 9,000$ units of S_1. Previously we had available a quantity of 24,000 units of S_1, this number now decreases and amounts to $24,000 - 9,000 = 15,000$.

Similarly, the consumption of S_2 was $8 \times 3,000 = 24,000$ units, therefore the remaining quantity of S_2 will be $40,000 - 24,000 = 16,000$.

Since the rows in Table 2.9 have been changed, the coefficients which we interpret as rates of transformation must also be changed. We begin by filling the "simplest" columns — the columns having the same headings as the rows. In our case, these will be columns S_1, S_2 and X_A. In column S_1 only in row S_1 will there figure number 1; the remaining rows will have 0. Similarly, in column S_2 only in row S_2 will there be number 1 and in column X_A only in row X_A. As for the two other columns, we proceed as follows. Table 1.9 shows that the variable which we introduced in the new solution could be expressed (interpretation of the column) as

$$X_A = 3S_1 + 8S_2 + 9S_3. \tag{7}$$

In the new table, row S_3 has disappeared. Let us therefore express S_3 in terms of S_1, S_2 and X_A, i.e. of the variables entered in the rows of the new Table 2.9.

Dividing both terms of equation (7) by 9, we obtain

$$\frac{1}{9}X_A = \frac{1}{3}S_1 + \frac{8}{9}S_2 + S_3 \tag{7$'$}$$

or

$$S_3 = -\frac{1}{3}S_1 - \frac{8}{9}S_2 + \frac{1}{9}X_A. \tag{8}$$

Relation (8) determines the coefficients for column S_3 of the new table.

In order to fill the coefficients of column X_B, we proceed from the data of Table 1.9. We express X_B in terms of variables S_1, S_2 and S_3 as follows:

$$X_B = 6S_1 + 4S_2 + 3S_3. \tag{9}$$

In this equation we substitute to S_3 the expressions given by formula (8):

$$X_B = 6S_1 + 4S_2 + 3\left(-\frac{1}{3}S_1 - \frac{8}{9}S_2 + \frac{1}{9}X_A\right).$$

After carrying out the necessary calculations, we finally obtain

$$X_B = 5S_1 + \frac{4}{3}S_2 + \frac{1}{3}X_A.$$

The coefficients obtained are entered in column X_B of Table 2.9. Before proceeding with further calculations, it should be noted that negative coefficients have appeared in the new table. How should these negative coefficients be interpreted?

We know that the coefficient at the intersection of a given row with a given column gives the rate of transformation of "goods" in the row into "goods" in the column. In other words, this is the quantity of goods from a given row required to obtain one unit of goods from the appropriate column. Therefore, if this coefficient is negative, an increase of one unit in the quantity of goods from the given column in the solution not only will not lead to consumption of goods from the given row, but will even cause an increase.

For instance, in Table 2.9 there are negative coefficients in column S_3 which may be read as follows:

$$S_3 = -\frac{1}{3}S_1 - \frac{8}{9}S_2 + \frac{1}{9}X_A$$

The negative coefficients for S_1 and S_2 are not surprising. From the solution given in the last column of Table 2.9 it follows that $S_3 = 0$, i.e. that the entire production capacity of machine M_3 is engaged in the manufacture of goods A. If we wanted to have one second of free working time for machine M_3, i.e. if we wanted $S_3 = 1$, this could be achieved by reducing the output of commodity A by 1/9th of a unit. Therefore, by reducing the production of goods A by 1/9th, we obtain one free second of working time for machine M_3. The problem, however, is that in reducing the output of A by 1/9th, we free machines M_1 and M_2 for a number of seconds. As we recall (cf. equation (7'))

$$\frac{1}{9}X_A = \frac{1}{3}S_1 + \frac{8}{9}S_2 + S_3,$$

therefore, we free machine M_1 for 1/3 of a second and machine M_2 for 8/9 of a second. No wonder, therefore, that in the column S_3 in row S_1 of Table 2.9 we obtain a negative number — 1/3 and in row S_2 a negative number too of — 8/9.

Having explained this let us proceed to the example. Let us now consider a new commodity which was not accounted for in this solution, and which it would be most profitable to introduce in the new solution. Theoretically, S_3 and X_B are possible. The others, i.e. S_1, S_2 and X_A, are already accounted for in the solution. It may be easily seen that by introducing S_3 in the solution we do not exercise any direct influence on the value of the function which is to be a maximum, i.e. function (6). However, by introducing one unit of S_3 causes S_1 to increase by 1/3 and S_2 by 8/9 in the new solution. And this, too, will have no influence on function (6). On the other hand, the fact that we have to reduce X_A by 1/9th has a negative effect. For, each unit of X_A yields 9 groszy and, therefore, reducing X_A by 1/9th causes Z to drop by 1 grosz.

This is an unfavourable result and it is therefore necessary to investigate additionally whether by introducing X_B in the solution, this will contribute to increase the value of function (6).

Increasing X_B by one unit causes the profit to rise by 6 grosz. The resultant need to reduce S_1 by 5 units and S_2 by 4/3 of a unit has no direct effect on Z. A one-third reduction in X_A, however, causes the value of Z to drop by $\frac{1}{3} \cdot 9 = 3$. Finally, increasing X_B by one unit leads to a rise in the value of Z by 6 grosz — 3 grosz = 3 grosz. It is therefore profitable to introduce the maximum possible amount of X_B in the solution. The available quantity of S_1 would allow to introduce 15,000 ÷ 5 = 3,000 units of X_B in the solution. The available quantity of S_2 makes it possible to introduce 16,000 ÷ 4/3 = 12,000 units of X_B. And, finally, the available quantity of X_B makes it possible to introduce 3,000 ÷ 1/3 = 9,000 units of X_B.

It is apparent, therefore, that S_1 is one of the factors which limit most the possibility of introducing X_B in the solution. Finally, we can introduce 3,000 units of X_B in the solution, thus completely exhausting the available reserve of S_1.

In Table 3.9, row X_B appears in place of row S_1 ($X_B = 3,000$).

The introduction of 3,000 units of X_B causes S_2 to be reduced by $\frac{4}{3} \cdot 3,000$ = 4,000. Hence, the quantity S_2 in the new solution will be

$$S_2 = 16,000 - 4,000 = 12,000.$$

TABLE 3/9

	S_1	S_2	S_3	X_A	X_B	
X_B	$\frac{1}{5}$	0	$-\frac{1}{15}$	0	1	3,000
S_2	$-\frac{4}{15}$	1	$-\frac{4}{5}$	0	0	12,000
X_A	$-\frac{1}{15}$	0	$\frac{2}{15}$	1	0	2,000

Similarly, the quantity of X_A in the new solution can be calculated to be $3,000 - \frac{1}{3} \cdot 3,000 = 2,000$.

In order to ascertain whether the solution obtained can be improved, we would have to calculate new coefficients for Table 3.9; with the aid of these, each variable in a column would be expressed in terms of the variables in the rows, i.e. X_B, S_2 and X_A.

As usual, the columns of variables which appear in the rows are easiest to fill. Thus, in the column S_2 there will be 1 in row S_2 and all the other entries will be zero. We fill columns X_A and X_B in a similar fashion.

In order to fill the remaining columns, we take as a starting point from Table 2.9 the column of goods which appear in the new solution

$$X_B = 5S_1 + \frac{4}{3}S_2 + \frac{1}{3}X_A. \tag{10}$$

From this equation we determine S_1 (i.e. the goods which have disappeared in the new solution) as a function of X_B, S_2 and X_A (i.e. goods which appear in the rows of the new Table 3.9).

After dividing the terms by 5, equation (10) assumes the form

$$\frac{1}{5}X_B = S_1 + \frac{4}{15}S_2 + \frac{1}{15}X_A$$

or,

$$S_1 = \frac{1}{5}X_B - \frac{4}{15}S_2 - \frac{1}{15}X_A.$$

The coefficients obtained are entered in column S_1 of Table 3.9. In order to compute the coefficients of column S_3 we again start from Table 2.9:

$$S_3 = -\frac{1}{3}S_1 - \frac{8}{9}S_2 + \frac{1}{9}X_A.$$

Substituting the above expression for S_1, we obtain

$$S_3 = -\frac{1}{3}\left(\frac{1}{5}X_B - \frac{4}{15}S_2 - \frac{1}{15}X_A\right) - \frac{8}{9}S_2 + \frac{1}{9}X_A$$

or, after simple calculations, we arrive at:

$$S_3 = -\frac{1}{15}X_B - \frac{4}{5}S_2 + \frac{2}{15}X_A.$$

We can now introduce S_1 or S_3 in the new solution. If we introduce one unit of S_1 in the solution, function (6) will be affected as follows:

$$0 - \frac{1}{5} \cdot 6 - \left(-\frac{4}{15}\right) \cdot 0 - \left(-\frac{1}{15}\right) \cdot 9 = -\frac{6}{5} + \frac{3}{5} = -\frac{3}{5}.$$

The explanation of the calculation is simple. The first zero represents the direct effect on the value of Z of introducing one unit of S_1 in the solution. The next term, $\frac{1}{5} \times 6$ gives the reduction in the value of Z due to the need to reduce X_B by 1/5. The third term $\left(-\frac{4}{15} \times 0\right)$ denotes a decrease in the value of Z

caused by the need to increase S_2 by $\dfrac{4}{15}$. The last term concerns the influence of variations in X_A on the value of Z.

Our result is that the introduction of one unit of S_1 in the solution causes a "rise" in the value of Z by $-3/5$. Of course, the negative "rise" simply means a decrease in the value of the function for which we are trying to find a maximum. Hence, the possibility considered is not profitable.

Let us now study the effects of introducing one unit of S_3 in the solution. The analogous calculations will be:

$$0-\left(-\frac{1}{15}\right).6-\left(-\frac{4}{5}\right).0-\frac{2}{15}.9=\frac{2}{5}-\frac{6}{5}=-\frac{4}{5}.$$

Therefore, this possibility too is unprofitable.

The conclusion from this is that no change in the solution obtained in Table 3.9 will lead to any improvement. The final solution, therefore, is $X_A = 2,000$ and $X_B = 3,000$. The solution obtained contains some additional information which is implicit in the values of X_A and X_B, namely, that the manufacturing capacity of machine M_2 will not be fully utilized in the optimum solution. The quantity S_2 determines the extent of non use.

It should be noted, as may have been anticipated, that our solution agrees with the solution previously obtained by the graphical method.

It is perhaps worth while checking briefly what our consecutive solutions looked like and their corresponding values of function Z. The appropriate data taken from the above calculations are given in Table 4.9.

TABLE 4/9

Solution	X_A	X_B	Z
I	0	0	0
II	3,000	0	27,000
(optimum) III	2,000	3,000	36,000

This table shows that each solution is better than the preceding as indicated by the increasing values of Z.

Attention should also be drawn to the geometric interpretation of our consecutive solutions. Turning back for a moment to Fig. 1.8, we note that point 0 (the origin of the system) corresponds to the first solution, point R to solution II and point S to the final solution. Consequently, our search, aiming at determining an optimal point for the points belonging to the set of feasible solutions was relatively short. It was along the edge of that area. We shall come back to this observation later.

Let us in turn solve the next example of Section 8 by means of the simplex algorithm. This example, however, will involve slightly greater difficulties than Example 1.

Example 2. The problem is as in Example 2, Section 8. In accordance with the reasoning in Section 8, the model of our problem is:

$$36X_A + 6X_B \geqslant 108$$
$$3X_A + 12X_B \geqslant 36 \tag{11}$$
$$20X_A + 10X_B \geqslant 100$$

$$K = 20X_A + 40X_B \text{ (minimum).} \tag{12}$$

In keeping with the observation made when solving the previous example, we shall convert condition (11) into equations by introducing appropriate slack variables.

$$36X_A + 6X_B - S_1 = 108$$
$$3X_A + 12X_B - S_2 = 36 \tag{11'}$$
$$20X_A + 10X_B - S_3 = 100$$

The slack variables are introduced here in a slightly different manner than in Example 1. The first of the conditions (11) stipulates that the content of the nutritive constituent M_1 shall be greater than or equal 108. To obtain an equation from an inequality we must subtract a certain magnitude (non-negative) from the left-hand term. Hence, a minus sign in front of S_1, which denotes a possible surplus of constituent M_1 supplied in the fodder. The position is similar when variables S_2 and S_3 are being introduced and interpreted.

But here some difficulty is experienced from the outset.

Zero values are usually given to decision variables in the initial solution using the simplex algorithm. From conditions (11), however, it is evident that this solution is outside the area of feasible solutions since, if zero values are substituted to X_A and X_B, conditions (11) are not satisfied. This is also apparent from Fig. 2.8; point 0, corresponding to the origin of the coordinates system, does not lie within the area of feasible solutions (that area has been hatched in Fig. 2.8). A certain conflict arises here. Using the simplex algorithm it is more convenient to begin the entire procedure from the zero solution, but this is not feasible in the present case. We resort, therefore, to an expedient. Let us imagine that we have a certain quantity of constituent M_1 from some other source, i.e. not in the form of products A and B which we designate by s_1. In this case, the first condition of group (11') is satisfied by a certain value of s_1 (this of course is the value $s_1 = 108$), even at values for which X_A and X_B are zero. This condition can be written

$$36X_A + 6X_B - S_1 + s_1 = 108. \tag{13}$$

Similarly, if we have a certain quantity of constituent M_2, for instance, s_2 from some other source (not in the form of products A and B), then even if $X_A = 0$ and $X_B = 0$, the second condition of (11') can be satisfied (for $s_2 = 36$)

$$3X_A + 12X_B - S_2 + s_2 = 36. \tag{14}$$

In a similar manner, the third condition will assume the form

$$20X_A + 10X_B - S_3 + s_3 = 100. \tag{15}$$

Therefore, our present model, expressed by relations (13), (14) and (15), enables us to adopt as an initial solution $X_A = 0$ and $X_B = 0$. However, our assumption that we have nutritive constituents from some other source, not in the form of products A and B, is actually inconsistent with our problem. In our problem we aimed at using only products A and B to satisfy the conditions necessary for supplying the appropriate quantity of constituents. In other words, none of the magnitudes s_1, s_2 and s_3 may come in the final solution; we call these *artificial variables* (as they are introduced into the problem artificially). The question arises how to safeguard against this.

As we recall, cost K, defined by formula (12), is our criterion which enables us to evaluate the individual solutions. We shall regard as better the solution which guarantees the lowest possible costs while satisfying the conditions postulated. Thus, in order to ensure that variables s_1, s_2 and s_3 do not enter in the final solution, it is enough to introduce these magnitudes in the costs function with very high coefficients. This means that it is very costly to procure constituents M_1, M_2 and M_3 otherwise than as products A and B. Of course, it may be anticipated that, under such conditions only a certain amount of products A and B will enter in the optimum solution, and we shall not avail ourselves of other sources of supply for these constituents because of the costs, i.e. in the final solution s_1, s_2 and s_3 will assume zero values.

Therefore, the function of costs (12) now takes the form

$$K = 20X_A + 40X_B + Ms_1 + Ms_2 + Ms_3 \tag{16}$$

where M denotes a very large (or infinite) number. In assuming $X_A = 0$ and $X_B = 0$ for our initial solution, we also assume that $S_1 = 0$, $S_2 = 0$ and $S_3 = 0$, since these are surpluses of constituents M_1, M_2 and M_3 supplied in the form of products A and B. Hence, so that conditions (13), (14) and (15) may be satisfied, we have $s_1 = 108$, $s_2 = 36$ and $s_3 = 100$.

We enter these in Table 5.9 which will also contain corresponding coefficients for the above three equations. The interpretation of this Table, as of each simplex table, is the same as before. The Table can be read by rows and columns, and the coefficients can be interpreted as rates of transformation of one type of goods into another.

TABLE 5/9

	s_1	s_2	s_3	S_1	S_2	S_3	X_A	X_B		
s_1	1	0	0	−1	0	0	36	6	108	÷ 36 = 3
s_2	0	1	0	0	−1	0	3	12	36	÷ 3 = 12
s_3	0	0	1	0	0	−1	20	10	100	÷ 20 = 5

Now, computations must be carried out in order to determine which of the variables S_1, S_2, S_3, X_A and X_B is to enter in the solution. These computations are given in Table 6.9.

TABLE 6/9

Rise in costs caused by introduction of one unit into the solution				
S_1	S_2	S_3	X_A	X_B
0	0	0	20	40
$-(-1).M=M$	$-0.M=0$	$-0.M=0$	$-36.M=-36M$	$-6.M=-6M$
$-0.M=0$	$-(-1).M=M$	$-0.M=0$	$-3.M=-3M$	$-12.M=-12M$
$-0.M=0$	$-0.M=0$	$-(-1).M=M$	$-20.M=-20M$	$-10.M=-10M$
M	M	M	$20-59M$	$40-28M$

In order to explain how these calculations were carried out and the conclusions derived from them, let us consider by way of example variable X_A. The cost function (16) shows that by introducing one unit of A in the solution, this leads to an increase in cost by 20 units. On the other hand, introducing one unit of X_A in the solution causes s_1 to decrease in value by 36 units. We have assumed that the per unit cost of s_1 is M. A reduction of 36 units in s_1, therefore, causes the costs to drop by $36M$ and this number has to be subtracted from 20. Similarly, bringing in one unit of X_A in the solution causes s_2 to decrease by 3 units, which means a fall in costs by $3M$. And this number also has to be subtracted from 20. For analogous reasons, the number 20 has to be reduced once more by $20M$, since s_3 decreased by 20 units. Finally, therefore, the increase in costs amounts to $20-59M$. Since M is a very large number, in actual fact $20-59M$ will be less than zero (negative). A negative rise in costs means a drop in costs.

Let us consider another column of Table 6.9, e.g. column S_1. The introduction in the solution of one unit of S_1 (surplus of nutrient M_1 over the required minimum of 108) does not directly involve a rise in costs, but it does require the variable s_1 to be reduced in value by -1, (or actually an increase by 1). This "reduction" of s_1 by -1 leads to a "reduction" of costs by $-1M$; this figure must be subtracted from 0. There are no further changes since the insertion of s_1 does not require changing s_2 or s_3, as may be seen from Table 5.9.

On the basis of Table 6.9, we introduce in the new solution the variable which yields the biggest reduction in costs or, in other words, the smallest rise in costs. This will be variable X_A. At the side of Table 5.9 calculations are made to permit a decision as to the maximum amount of X_A which can be brought in to the solution. It appears that we can put 3 units of X_A in the new solution. We write this in Table 7.9 where row X_A replaces row s_1 of Table 5.9.

Three units of X_A in the solution lead to a decrease in s_2 by $3 . 3 = 9$ units, and to a reduction of s_3 by $20 . 3 = 60$ units. In this manner, we obtain a new solution: $X_A = 3$, $s_2 = 27$, $s_3 = 40$.

TABLE 7/9

	s_1	s_2	s_3	S_1	S_2	S_3	X_A	X_B	
X_A	$\dfrac{1}{36}$	0	0	$-\dfrac{1}{36}$	0	0	1	$\dfrac{1}{6}$	3	$\div \dfrac{1}{6} = 18$
s_2	$-\dfrac{1}{12}$	1	0	$\dfrac{1}{12}$	-1	0	0	$\dfrac{23}{2}$	27	$\div \dfrac{23}{2} = 2\dfrac{8}{23}$
s_3	$-\dfrac{5}{9}$	0	1	$\dfrac{5}{9}$	0	-1	0	$\dfrac{20}{3}$	40	$\div \dfrac{20}{3} = 6$

The new coefficients for Table 7.9 must now be computed. The starting point, as usual, is the column (from Table 5.9) of the variable entering the new solution

$$X_A = 36s_1 + 3s_2 + 20s_3.$$

From this solution we determine variable s_1 (i.e. the variable which disappears from the new solution) as a function of X_A, s_2 and s_3. Dividing both terms by 36, we obtain

$$\frac{1}{36}X_A = s_1 + \frac{1}{12}s_2 + \frac{5}{9}s_3$$

or, after rearrangement,

$$s_1 = \frac{1}{36}X_A - \frac{1}{12}s_2 - \frac{5}{9}s_3$$

Having entered these coefficients in column s_1 of Table 7.9, we then calculate the coefficients for the remaining columns.

$$S_1 = -s_1 = -\frac{1}{36}X_A + \frac{1}{12}s_2 + \frac{5}{9}s_3$$

$$S_2 = -s_2$$

$$S_3 = -s_3$$

$$X_B = 6s_1 + 12s_2 + 10s_3 = 6\left(\frac{1}{36}X_A - \frac{1}{12}s_2 - \frac{5}{9}s_3\right) + 12s_2 + 10s_3$$

$$= \frac{1}{6}X_A + \frac{23}{2}s_2 + \frac{20}{3}s_3.$$

Table 8.9 gives the calculations which enable to determine which of the variables s_1, S_1, S_2, S_3 or X_B will enter in the new solution. These calculations are analogous to those of Table 6.9, except that we are now proceeding from the coefficients of Table 7.9.

TABLE 8/9

Increase in costs caused by introduction of one unit into the solution				
s_1	S_1	S_2	S_3	X_B
M	0	0	0	40
$-\frac{1}{36}.20 = -\frac{5}{9}$	$-\left(-\frac{1}{36}\right).20 = \frac{5}{9}$	$-0.20 = 0$	$-0.20 = 0$	$-\frac{1}{6}.20 = -\frac{10}{3}$
$-\left(-\frac{1}{12}\right).M = \frac{1}{12}M$	$-\frac{1}{12}.M = -\frac{1}{12}M$	$-(-1).M = M$	$-0.M = 0$	$-\frac{23}{2}.M = -\frac{23}{2}M$
$-\left(-\frac{5}{9}\right).M = \frac{5}{9}M$	$-\frac{5}{9}.M = -\frac{5}{9}M$	$-0.M = 0$	$-(-1).M = M$	$-\frac{20}{3}.M = -\frac{20}{3}M$
$-\frac{5}{9} + 1\frac{23}{36}M$	$\frac{5}{9} - \frac{23}{36}M$	M	M	$36\frac{2}{3} - 18\frac{1}{6}M$

Table 8.9 shows that it is now most profitable to bring in variable X_B in the solution since an additional unit of X_B gives the smallest rise in costs (negative, which means a decrease in costs). As can be seen from Table 7.9, $2\frac{8}{23}$ units of X_B can be introduced in the new solution. The variable s_2 will disappear from the new solution and its place will be taken by X_B. The new solution is presented in Table 9.9.

4

The starting point for the calculations of the new coefficients will be column X_B of Table 7.9.

$$X_B = \frac{1}{6}X_A + \frac{23}{2}s_2 + \frac{20}{3}s_3.$$

In the new Table 9.9 row s_2 has disappeared; we therefore determine this variable from the above equation as a function of X_A, X_B and s_3. Dividing both terms of our equation by 23/2, we obtain

$$\frac{2}{23}X_B = \frac{1}{69}X_A + s_2 + \frac{40}{69}s_3$$

TABLE 9/9

	s_1	s_2	s_3	S_1	S_2	S_3	X_A	X_B		
X_A			0	$-\dfrac{2}{69}$	$\dfrac{1}{69}$	0	1	0	$2\dfrac{14}{23}$	$\div \dfrac{1}{69} = 180$
X_B			0	$\dfrac{1}{138}$	$-\dfrac{2}{23}$	0	0	1	$2\dfrac{8}{23}$	
s_3			1	$\dfrac{35}{69}$	$\dfrac{40}{69}$	-1	0	0	$24\dfrac{8}{23}$	$\div \dfrac{40}{69} = 42$

or, after rewriting

$$s_2 = -\frac{1}{69}X_A + \frac{2}{23}X_B - \frac{40}{69}s_3.$$

Having the above expression, we can proceed to calculate the coefficients of columns S_1, S_2, S_3, X_A and X_B.

Thus, from Table 7.9 we have

$$S_1 = -\frac{1}{36}X_A + \frac{1}{12}s_2 + \frac{5}{9}s_3.$$

Substituting for s_2 the expression just computed, we obtain

$$S_1 = -\frac{1}{36}X_A + \frac{1}{12}\left(-\frac{1}{69}X_A + \frac{2}{23}X_B - \frac{40}{69}s_3\right) + \frac{5}{9}s_3 = -\frac{2}{69}X_A + \frac{1}{138}X_B + \frac{35}{69}s_3.$$

We enter these coefficients in Table 9.9. We calculate in a similar fashion the remaining coefficients:

$$S_2 = -s_2 = \frac{1}{69}X_A - \frac{2}{23}X_B + \frac{40}{69}s_3$$

$$S_3 = -s_3.$$

Columns s_1 and s_2 i.e. columns of those artificial variables which no longer appear in the solution, are not recorded since, because of their very high coefficients in the costs function, we may be sure that these variables will no longer be accounted for in further solutions. Now, therefore, only S_1 or S_2 or S_3 can appear in the new solution. Which of these variables should appear in the solution is determined by the calculations in Table 10.9.

TABLE 10/9

Increase in costs caused by introduction of one unit into the solution		
S_1	S_2	S_3
0	0	0
$-\left(-\dfrac{2}{69}\right).\,20 = \dfrac{40}{69}$	$-\dfrac{1}{69}.\,20 = -\dfrac{20}{69}$	$-0\,.\,20 = 0$
$-\dfrac{1}{138}.\,40 = -\dfrac{20}{69}$	$-\left(-\dfrac{2}{23}\right).\,40 = \dfrac{80}{23}$	$-0\,.\,40 = 0$
$-\dfrac{35}{69}.\,M = -\dfrac{35}{69}\,M$	$-\dfrac{40}{69}.\,M = -\dfrac{40}{69}\,M$	$-(-1)\,.\,M = M$
$\dfrac{20}{69} - \dfrac{35}{69}\,M$	$\dfrac{220}{69} - \dfrac{40}{69}\,M$	M

The smallest (negative) rise in costs corresponds to variable S_2; therefore, this variable will be brought into the new solution. It should be noted that in assessing the magnitude of variable S_2 in the solution, we take into account only variables X_A and s_3. The rate of transformation of X_B into S_2 is negative (cf. Table 9.9) which means that by introducing variable S_2 in the solution, not only do we not cause quantity X_B to decrease but even the value of X_B will increase. For every unit increase in S_2, X_B increases by 2/23.

The new solution is given in Table 11.9.

TABLE 11/9

	s_1	s_2	s_3	S_1	S_2	S_3	X_A	X_B		
X_A				$-\dfrac{1}{24}$	0	$\dfrac{1}{40}$	1	0	2	
X_B				$\dfrac{1}{12}$	0	$-\dfrac{6}{40}$	0	1	6	$\div \dfrac{1}{12} = 72$
S_2				$\dfrac{7}{8}$	1	$-\dfrac{69}{40}$	0	0	42	$\div \dfrac{7}{8} = 48$

It is obtained in a simple manner from Table 9.9. In the new solution the quantity of X_A is

$$2\frac{14}{23} - \frac{1}{69} \cdot 42 = 2.$$

The value of X_B in the new solution is

$$2\frac{8}{23} + \frac{2}{23} \cdot 42 = 6.$$

Finally, S_2 assumes the value of 42.

Below we compute the coefficients of columns S_1 and S_3

$$S_2 = \frac{1}{69}X_A - \frac{2}{23}X_B + \frac{40}{69}s_3.$$

Therefore,

$$\frac{69}{40}S_2 = \frac{1}{40}X_A - \frac{6}{40}X_B + s_3$$

or,

$$s_3 = -\frac{1}{40}X_A + \frac{6}{40}X_B + \frac{69}{40}S_2.$$

From this we obtain directly the coefficients of columns S_1 and S_3

$$S_1 = -\frac{2}{69}X_A + \frac{1}{138}X_B + \frac{35}{69}\left(-\frac{1}{40}X_A + \frac{6}{40}X_B + \frac{69}{40}S_2\right) = -\frac{1}{24}X_A + \frac{1}{12}X_B + \frac{7}{8}S_2$$

$$S_3 = -s_3 = \frac{1}{40}X_A - \frac{6}{40}X_B - \frac{69}{40}S_2.$$

S_1 or S_3 may be accounted for in the succesive solution. The other variables, i.e. X_A, X_B and S_2 appear already in the solution. We do not consider the possibility of bringing in artificial variables in the solution since they will not appear in the final solution.

From Table 12.9 it follows that we shall bring in variable S_1 in the solution. This will entail a negative increase, i.e. a drop in the costs.

TABLE 12/9

Increase in costs caused by introduction of one unit into the solution	
S_1	S_3
0	0
$-\left(-\dfrac{1}{24}\right) \cdot 20 = \dfrac{10}{12}$	$-\dfrac{1}{40} \cdot 20 = -\dfrac{1}{2}$
$-\dfrac{1}{12} \cdot 40 = -\dfrac{40}{12}$	$-\left(-\dfrac{6}{40}\right) \cdot 40 = 6$
$-\dfrac{7}{8} \cdot 0 = 0$	$-\left(-\dfrac{69}{40}\right) \cdot 0 = 0$
$-2\dfrac{6}{12}$	$5\dfrac{1}{2}$

In the new solution variable S_1 amounting to 48 units will replace S_2. The new solution is given in Table 13.9. The new coefficients in Table 13.9 are calculated by the known method as below:

$$S_1 = -\frac{1}{24} X_A + \frac{1}{12} X_B + \frac{7}{8} S_2.$$

Therefore,

$$\frac{8}{7} S_1 = -\frac{1}{21} X_A + \frac{2}{21} X_B + S_2.$$

TABLE 13/9

	S_1	S_2	S_3	S_1	S_2	S_3	X_A	X_B	
X_A				0	$\dfrac{1}{21}$	$-\dfrac{2}{35}$	1	0	4
X_B				0	$-\dfrac{2}{21}$	$\dfrac{1}{70}$	0	1	2
S_1				1	$\dfrac{8}{7}$	$-\dfrac{69}{35}$	0	0	48

or

$$S_2 = \frac{1}{21}X_A - \frac{2}{21}X_B + \frac{8}{7}S_1$$

$$S_3 = \frac{1}{40}X_A - \frac{6}{40}X_B - \frac{69}{40}\left(\frac{1}{21}X_A - \frac{2}{21}X_B + \frac{8}{7}S_1\right)$$

$$= -\frac{2}{35}X_A + \frac{1}{70}X_B - \frac{69}{35}S_1.$$

Table 14.9 indicates that the solution obtained is final since neither S_2 nor S_3 brought into the solution reduce the costs. On the contrary, in both cases we would have a rise in costs. This proves that we have already arrived at the best solution.

Turning back to Fig. 2.8, we see that our analytical solution agrees with the graphical solution.

TABLE 14/9

Increase in costs caused by introduction of one unit into the solution	
S_2	S_3
0	0
$-\frac{1}{21} \cdot 20 = -\frac{20}{21}$	$-\left(-\frac{2}{35}\right) \cdot 20 = \frac{8}{7}$
$-\left(-\frac{2}{21}\right) \cdot 40 = \frac{80}{21}$	$-\frac{1}{70} \cdot 40 = -\frac{4}{7}$
$-\frac{8}{7} \cdot 0 = 0$	$-\frac{69}{35} \cdot 0 = 0$
$\frac{60}{21}$	$\frac{4}{7}$

In conclusion, let us compile a table of consecutive solutions and give the values of corresponding costs. This table will have five columns as we must bring in variables X_A, X_B, s_1, s_2 and s_3. Artificial variables must be accounted for in the solutions as, otherwise, the initial solution which we adopted for X_A and X_B ($X_A = 0, X_B = 0$) would be inadmissible, i.e. would not satisfy the conditions of the problem.

TABLE 15/9

Solution	X_A	X_B	s_1	s_2	s_3	K
I	0	0	108	36	100	$244\,M$
II	3	0	0	27	40	$60 + 67\,M$
III	$2\frac{14}{23}$	$2\frac{8}{23}$	0	0	$24\frac{8}{23}$	$146\frac{2}{23} + 24\frac{8}{23}\,M$
IV	2	6	0	0	0	280
V	4	2	0	0	0	160

Table 15.9, shows that the consecutive solutions produce decreasing costs (we recall that M is very large) until finally the end solution cannot be improved any further, i.e. ensures the lowest possible costs.

Table 15.9 also shows which points of Fig. 2.8, viz., O, P_1, P_2, P_3 and S, correspond to the successive solutions. As can be seen, the first three solutions lie outside the area of feasible solutions. However, thanks to the introduction of artificial variables s_1, s_2 and s_3, these solutions have satisfied the conditions of the problem, although at prohibitive costs.

Let us now proceed to solve analytically the next example of Section 8.

Example 3. Problem as in Example 3, Section 8.

We recall at this point that the model in this problem had the form

$$9X_A + 3X_B \geqslant 45$$

$$X_A + 4X_B \geqslant 16 \tag{17}$$

$$2X_A + 2X_B \leqslant 20$$

$$K = 20X_A + 40X_B \text{ (minimum).} \tag{18}$$

This model contains two first conditions similar in type to those of Example 2, and a third condition which is analogous (in form) to the conditions of Example 1. Introducing slack and artificial variables, which we designate by S and s, respectively, we have our model in the form:

$$9X_A + 3X_B - S_1 + s_1 = 45$$

$$X_A + 4X_B - S_2 + s_2 = 16 \tag{17'}$$

$$2X_A + 2X_B + S_3 \quad = 20$$

$$K = 20X_A + 40X_B + Ms_1 + Ms_2 \text{ (minimum).} \tag{18'}$$

Here, as before, M stands for a very large number. Below are given the tables and calculations involved in obtaining the consecutive solutions.

First stage:

TABLE 16/9

	s_1	s_2	S_1	S_2	S_3	X_A	X_B		
s_1	1	0	−1	0	0	9	3	45	$\div 9 = 5$
s_2	0	1	0	−1	0	1	4	16	$\div 1 = 16$
S_3	0	0	0	0	1	2	2	20	$\div 2 = 10$

TABLE 17/9

Increase in costs caused by introduction of one unit into the solution			
S_1	S_2	X_A	X_B
0	0	20	40
$-(-1).M = M$	$-0.M = 0$	$-9.M = -9M$	$-3.M = -3M$
$-0.M = 0$	$-(-1).M = M$	$-1.M = -1M$	$-4.M = -4M$
$-0.0 = 0$	$-0.0 = 0$	$-2.0 = 0$	$-2.0 = 0$
M	M	$20 - 10M$	$40 - 7M$

In the next solution X_A appears to be the best alternative.

Second stage:

TABLE 18/9

	s_1	s_2	S_1	S_2	S_3	X_A	X_B		
X_A			$-\dfrac{1}{9}$	0	0	1	$\dfrac{1}{3}$	5	$\div \dfrac{1}{3} = 15$
s_2			$\dfrac{1}{9}$	−1	0	0	$\dfrac{11}{3}$	11	$\div \dfrac{11}{3} = 3$
S_3			$\dfrac{2}{9}$	0	1	0	$\dfrac{4}{3}$	10	$\div \dfrac{4}{3} = 7\dfrac{1}{2}$

$$X_A = 9s_1 + s_2 + 2S_3 \quad \text{or} \quad \frac{1}{9}X_A = s_1 + \frac{1}{9}s_2 + \frac{2}{9}S_3.$$

Therefore,

$$s_1 = \frac{1}{9}X_A - \frac{1}{9}s_2 - \frac{2}{9}S_3$$

$$S_1 = -s_1 = -\frac{1}{9}X_A + \frac{1}{9}s_2 + \frac{2}{9}S_3$$

$$S_2 = -s_2$$

$$X_B = 3\left(\frac{1}{9}X_A - \frac{1}{9}s_2 - \frac{2}{9}S_3\right) + 4s_2 + 2S_3 = \frac{1}{3}X_A + \frac{11}{3}s_2 + \frac{4}{3}S_3.$$

TABLE 19/9

Increase in costs caused by introduction of one unit into the solution		
S_1	S_2	X_B
0	0	40
$-\left(-\frac{1}{9}\right).20 = \frac{20}{9}$	$-0.20 = 0$	$-\frac{1}{3}.20 = -\frac{20}{3}$
$-\frac{1}{9}.M = -\frac{1}{9}M$	$-(-1).M = M$	$-\frac{11}{3}.M = -\frac{11}{3}M$
$-\frac{2}{9}.0 = 0$	$-0.0 = 0$	$-\frac{4}{3}.0 = 0$
$\frac{20}{9} - \frac{1}{9}M$	M	$\frac{100}{3} - \frac{11}{3}M$

The best alternative is X_B.

Third stage:

TABLE 20/9

	s_1	s_2	S_1	S_2	S_3	X_A	X_B	
X_A			$-\frac{12}{99}$	$\frac{1}{11}$	0	1	0	4
X_B			$\frac{1}{33}$	$-\frac{3}{11}$	0	0	1	3
S_3			$\frac{18}{99}$	$\frac{4}{11}$	1	0	0	6

$$X_B = \frac{1}{3}X_A + \frac{11}{3}s_2 + \frac{4}{3}S_3 \quad \text{or} \quad \frac{3}{11}X_B = \frac{1}{11}X_A + s_2 + \frac{4}{11}S_3.$$

In other words,

$$s_2 = -\frac{1}{11}X_A + \frac{3}{11}X_B - \frac{4}{11}S_3$$

$$S_1 = -\frac{1}{9}X_A + \frac{1}{9}\left(-\frac{1}{11}X_A + \frac{3}{11}X_B - \frac{4}{11}S_3\right) + \frac{2}{9}S_3$$

$$= -\frac{12}{99}X_A + \frac{1}{33}X_B + \frac{18}{99}S_3$$

$$S_2 = -s_2 = \frac{1}{11}X_A - \frac{3}{11}X_B + \frac{4}{11}S_3.$$

TABLE 21/9

Increase in costs caused by introduction of one unit into the solution	
S_1	S_2
$\quad\quad\quad\quad 0$	$\quad\quad\quad\quad 0$
$-\left(-\dfrac{12}{99}\right).20 = \dfrac{240}{99}$	$-\dfrac{1}{11}.20 = -\dfrac{20}{11}$
$-\dfrac{1}{33}.40 = -\dfrac{120}{99}$	$-\left(-\dfrac{3}{11}\right).40 = \dfrac{120}{11}$
$-\dfrac{18}{99}.0 = 0$	$-\dfrac{4}{11}.0 = 0$
$\dfrac{120}{99}$	$\dfrac{100}{11}$

It is evident from Table 21.9 that both alternative changes to the solutions are unprofitable as both lead to increased costs. The solution arrived at in Table 20.9 is therefore final.

The consecutive solutions and their corresponding costs are given in Table 22.9.

TABLE 22/9

Solution	X_A	X_B	s_1	s_2	K
I	0	0	45	16	$61M$
II	5	0	0	11	$100+11M$
III	4	3	0	0	200

Points O, P and S in Fig. 3.8 correspond to the consecutive solutions.
Example 4. Problem as in Example 4, Section 8.
The model of this problem had the following appearance:

$$3X_A + X_B \leqslant 18$$
$$2X_A + 4X_B \leqslant 40 \tag{19}$$
$$3X_A + 2X_B \leqslant 24$$
$$Z = 6X_A + 4X_B \quad \text{(maximum)}. \tag{20}$$

After introducing slack variables the above model can be rewritten as below:

$$3X_A + X_B + S_1 = 18$$
$$2X_A + 4X_B + S_2 = 40 \tag{19'}$$
$$3X_A + 2X_B + S_3 = 24$$
$$Z = 6X_A + 4X_B. \tag{20'}$$

We shall solve this example by the now known method. The example differs from previous ones in that it affords many solutions as we recall from Section 8. It is of interest to see the effect of the simplex algorithm in such cases.

First stage:

TABLE 23/9

	S_1	S_2	S_3	X_A	X_B		
S_1	1	0	0	3	1	18	$\div 3 = 6$
S_2	0	1	0	2	4	40	$\div 2 = 20$
S_3	0	0	1	3	2	24	$\div 3 = 8$

TABLE 24/9

Increase in profit caused by introduction of one unit into the solution	
X_A	X_B
6	4
$-3.0 = 0$	$-1.0 = 0$
$-2.0 = 0$	$-4.0 = 0$
$-3.0 = 0$	$-2.0 = 0$
6	4

More profitable is the alternative of introducing variable X_A. In the new solution X_A assumes the value 6.

Second stage:

	S_1	S_2	S_3	X_A	X_B		
X_A	$\frac{1}{3}$	0	0	1	$\frac{1}{3}$	6	$\div \frac{1}{3} = 18$
S_2	$-\frac{2}{3}$	1	0	0	$\frac{10}{3}$	28	$\div \frac{10}{3} = \frac{42}{5} = 8\frac{2}{5}$
S_3	-1	0	1	0	1	6	$\div 1 = 6$

$$X_A = 3S_1 + 2S_2 + 3S_3 \text{ or } \frac{1}{3}X_A = S_1 + \frac{2}{3}S_2 + S_3 .$$

Or.

$$S_1 = \frac{1}{3}X_A - \frac{2}{3}S_2 - S_3$$

$$X_B = \frac{1}{3}X_A - \frac{2}{3}S_2 - S_3 + 4S_2 + 2S_3$$

$$= -\frac{1}{3}X_A + \frac{10}{3}S_2 + S_3 .$$

Increase in profit caused by introduction of one unit into the solution	
S_1	X_B
0	4
$-\frac{1}{3} . 6 = -2$	$-\frac{1}{3} . 6 = -2$
$-\left(-\frac{2}{3}\right) . 0 = 0$	$-\frac{10}{3} . 0 = 0$
$-(-1) . 0 = 0$	$-1 . 0 = 0$
-2	2

Table 26.9 shows that variable X_B is now accounted for in the solution. In the new solution its value will be 6.

Third stage:

TABLE 27/9

	S_1	S_2	S_3	X_A	X_B		
X_A	$\dfrac{2}{3}$	0	$-\dfrac{1}{3}$	1	0	4	$\div \dfrac{2}{3} = 6$
S_2	$\dfrac{8}{3}$	1	$-\dfrac{10}{3}$	0	0	8	$\div \dfrac{8}{3} = 3$
X_B	-1	0	1	0	1	6	

$$X_B = \frac{1}{3}X_A + \frac{10}{3}S_2 + S_3.$$

Or.

$$S_3 = -\frac{1}{3}X_A - \frac{10}{3}S_2 + X_B$$

$$S_1 = \frac{1}{3}X_A - \frac{2}{3}S_2 + \frac{1}{3}X_A + \frac{10}{3}S_2 - X_B$$

$$= \frac{2}{3}X_A + \frac{8}{3}S_2 - X_B.$$

TABLE 28/9

Increase in profit caused by introduction of one unit into the solution	
S_1	S_3
0	0
$-\dfrac{2}{3} \cdot 6 = -4$	$-\left(-\dfrac{1}{3}\right) \cdot 6 = \quad 2$
$-\dfrac{8}{3} \cdot 0 = 0$	$-\left(-\dfrac{10}{3}\right) \cdot 0 = \quad 0$
$-(-1) \cdot 4 = \quad 4$	$-1 \cdot 4 = -4$
0	-2

The results of Table 28.9 lead to the following conclusions. It is definitely unprofitable to bring in variable S_3 in the solution. Each increase of S_3 by one unit leads to a decrease in profit by 2 units. On the other hand, the introduction of variable S_1 in the solution does not worsen or improve the situation. From the calculations made to the right of Table 27.9 it appears that 3 units of variable S_1 could be brought

The theory of decision-making

into the solution. The total profit, however, would then be the same as in the previous solution. Below are given the calculations which correspond to the next stage of the simplex algorithm.

Fourth stage:

TABLE 29/9

	S_1	S_2	S_3	X_A	X_B		
X_A	0	$-\dfrac{1}{4}$	$\dfrac{1}{2}$	1	0	2	
S_1	1	$\dfrac{3}{8}$	$-\dfrac{5}{4}$	0	0	3	$\div \dfrac{3}{8} = 8$
X_B	0	$\dfrac{3}{8}$	$-\dfrac{1}{4}$	0	1	9	$\div \dfrac{3}{8} = 24$

$$S_1 = \frac{2}{3}X_A + \frac{8}{3}S_2 - X_B \quad \text{or} \quad \frac{3}{8}S_1 = \frac{1}{4}X_A + S_2 - \frac{3}{8}X_B.$$

Therefore,

$$S_2 = -\frac{1}{4}X_A + \frac{3}{8}S_1 + \frac{3}{8}X_B$$

$$S_3 = -\frac{1}{3}X_A - \frac{10}{3}\left(-\frac{1}{4}X_A + \frac{3}{8}S_1 + \frac{3}{8}X_B\right) + X_B$$

or

$$S_3 = \frac{1}{2}X_A - \frac{5}{4}S_1 - \frac{1}{4}X_B.$$

TABLE 30/9

Increase in profit caused by introduction of one unit into the solution			
S_2		S_3	
	0		0
$-\left(-\dfrac{1}{4}\right) \cdot 6 =$	$\dfrac{3}{2}$	$-\dfrac{1}{2} \cdot 6 = -3$	
$-\dfrac{3}{8} \cdot 0 =$	0	$-\left(-\dfrac{5}{4}\right) \cdot 0 =$	0
$-\dfrac{3}{8} \cdot 4 =$	$-\dfrac{3}{2}$	$-\left(-\dfrac{1}{4}\right) \cdot 4 =$	1
	0		-2

As may have been easily assumed, Table 30.9 indicates that S_2 can be brought in again in the solution.

Table 29.9 shows that 8 units of S_2 can be brought in. As a result, we obtain exactly the same solution as in Table 27.9.

Tables 27.9 and 29.9 afford two possible solutions (with the same maximum profit). However, in the present case, a whole number of solutions also offering the same maximum profit may easily be found.

According to Tables 28.9 and 27.9, at most 3 units of S_1 can be brought into the new solution without any change in the total profit. Any number of S_1 not exceeding three units could, therefore, be brought into the new solution. For instance, if two units of S_1 were brought into the new solution then:

$$X_A \text{ would decrease by } \frac{2}{3}.2 = \frac{4}{3}$$

$$S_2 \text{ would decrease by } \frac{8}{3}.2 = \frac{16}{3}$$

$$X_B \text{ would decrease by } -1.2 = -2$$

Therefore, in our new solution, we would arrive at

$$X_A = 4 - \frac{4}{3} = 2\frac{2}{3}$$

$$S_2 = 8 - \frac{16}{3} = 2\frac{2}{3}$$

$$X_B = 6 - (-2) = 8$$

$$S_1 = 2.$$

Point P in Fig. 4.8 would correspond to this solution. The conclusion derived from the solution of our present example is simple. If we came across a case in which one alternative change to the solution does not affect the value of the criterion-function and the other alternatives are unprofitable, this would mean that the problem offers many equivalent solutions.

Let us compile a table of the solutions obtained.

TABLE 31/9

Solution	X_A	X_B	Profit
I	0	0	0
II	6	0	36
III	4	6	48
IV	2	9	48
V	$2\frac{2}{3}$	8	48

As we recall from Section 8, the next example, No.5, did not have any solution since the set of conditions was inconsistent. When there are more variables, it is not always easy to verify whether or not the conditions of the model are inconsistent. It is interesting to ascertain how the simplex algorithm operates when applied to a case which offers no solution.

Example 5. Problem as in Example 5, Section 8.

The model of the problem is

$$X_A + 5X_B \leqslant 20$$
$$3X_A + 5X_B \leqslant 30 \tag{21}$$
$$X_B \geqslant 8$$
$$Z = 4X_A + 8X_B \quad \text{(maximum)}. \tag{22}$$

After introducing the slack variables, and an artificial variable in the third condition, we have the model

$$X_A + 5X_B + S_1 = 20$$
$$3X_A + 5X_B + S_2 = 30 \tag{21'}$$
$$X_B - S_3 + s_1 = 8$$
$$Z = 4X_A + 8X_B - Ms_1 \quad \text{(maximum)}. \tag{22'}$$

Artificial variable s_1 with coefficient M (a very large number) having a minus sign was brought into function Z which is to be maximised in order that this variable shall appear in the final solution. This reasoning is analogous to that followed in solving Example 2.

First stage:

TABLE 32/9

	s_1	S_1	S_2	S_3	X_A	X_B		
S_1	0	1	0	0	1	5	20	$\div 5 = 4$
S_2	0	0	1	0	3	5	30	$\div 5 = 6$
s_1	1	0	0	-1	0	1	8	$\div 1 = 8$

TABLE 33/9

Increase in profit caused by introduction of one unit into the solution		
S_3	X_A	X_B
0	4	8
$-0.0 = 0$	$-1.0 = 0$	$-5.0 = 0$
$-0.0 = 0$	$-3.0 = 0$	$-5.0 = 0$
$-(-1).(-M) = -M$	$-0.(-M) = 0$	$-1.(-M) = M$
$-M$	4	$8 + M$

According to Table 33.9 the most profitable choice is to bring in variable X_B in the new solution.

Second stage:

TABLE 34/9

	s_1	S_1	S_2	S_3	X_A	X_B	
X_B	0	$\frac{1}{5}$	0	0	$\frac{1}{5}$	1	4
S_2	0	-1	1	0	2	0	10
s_1	1	$-\frac{1}{5}$	0	-1	$-\frac{1}{5}$	0	4

$$X_B = 5S_1 + 5S_2 + s_1 \quad \text{or} \quad \frac{1}{5}X_B = S_1 + S_2 + \frac{1}{5}s_1.$$

That is,

$$S_1 = \frac{1}{5}X_B - S_2 - \frac{1}{5}s_1$$

$$S_3 = -s_1$$

$$X_A = \frac{1}{5}X_B - S_2 - \frac{1}{5}s_1 + 3S_2 = \frac{1}{5}X_B + 2S_2 - \frac{1}{5}s_1.$$

TABLE 35/9

Increase in profit caused by introduction of one unit into the solution		
S_1	S_3	X_A
0	0	4
$-\frac{1}{5}.8 = -\frac{8}{5}$	$-0.8 = 0$	$-\frac{1}{5}.8 = -\frac{8}{5}$
$-(-1).0 = 0$	$-0.0 = 0$	$-2.0 = 0$
$-\left(-\frac{1}{5}\right).\left(-M\right) = -\frac{1}{5}M$	$-(-1).(-M) = -M$	$-\left(-\frac{1}{5}\right).\left(-M\right) = -\frac{1}{5}M$
$-\frac{8}{5} - \frac{1}{5}M$	$-M$	$2\frac{2}{5} - \frac{1}{5}M$

The data of Table 35.9 indicate that any change in the solution given in Table 34.9 worsens the situation; in our case, it leads to a reduction in profit. However, our solution contains positive values both for the decision and slack variables, and the artificial variable ($s_1 = 4$). The fact that the final solution contains an artificial variable shows that the conditions of the problem were inconsistent. In other words, the conditions of the problem cannot be satisfied by the assignment of appropriate values to the decision variables.

Thus, in our case, it was found that:

$$X_B = 4; \quad S_2 = 10; \quad s_1 = 4.$$

To produce 4 units of product B involves the consumption of $4 \times 5 = 20$ units of raw material M_1 (this is the limit of consumption) and the consumption of $4 \times 5 = 20$ units of raw material M_2. The limit for material M_2 is 30 and therefore we have the remaining surplus of $S_2 = 10$. Raw material M_1 does not allow any further increase in the output of commodity B, whereas one of the conditions stipulates that X_B should have a value of at least 8. Hence, in our solution the value of the artificial variable s_1 is 4. Therefore, if we could procure from some other source four units of product B and add them to the output of commodity B, fixed by the allocation of materials, only then would the targets set be realized.

To sum up, therefore, we can say that the presence of an artificial variable in the final solution is evidence that the conditions of the problem are inconsistent. In our case, this stemmed from the fact that the production targets for product B were too high in relation to the raw materials available for its manufacture.

Example 6. The problem is as that of Example 6, Section 8.

The model of the problem under consideration is:

$$2X_A + X_B \leqslant 12$$
$$2X_A + 2X_B \leqslant 20 \tag{23}$$
$$X_A = 2 \cdot 5 X_B$$
$$Z = 5X_A + 25X_B \text{ (maximum)}. \tag{24}$$

There is no difficulty in introducing slack variables in the first two conditions of the model. But we have to consider how the third condition should be modified, which from the outset has the appearance of an equation.

After introducing slack variables, the first two conditions assume the form:

$$2X_A + X_B + S_1 = 12$$
$$2X_A + 2X_B + S_2 = 20.$$

Had we not brought in any additional variable in the third condition, we would have had only two rows in the simplex table. In the first table, these would be rows S_1 and S_2. This would, in fact, mean ignoring the third condition. For this reason, a variable must be brought into the condition which has the form of an equation. This must be an artificial variable since its value in the final solution must be zero to ensure that in actual fact equation $X_A = 2 \cdot 5 X_B$. This variable with coefficient $-M$ must also be brought into function Z in which, as usual, M is a very large number.

Finally, our model takes the form

$$2X_A + X_B + S_1 = 12$$

$$2X_A + 2X_B + S_2 = 20 \qquad (23')$$

$$X_A - \frac{5}{2}X_B + s_1 = 0$$

$$Z = 5X_A + 25X_B - Ms_1 \qquad (24')$$

From this model it is evident that in the initial solution, where we assume $X_A = 0$ and $X_B = 0$, also $s_1 = 0$. But we should not conclude from this that row s_1 need not be entered in the simplex table.

Below is the solution of the example given.

First stage:

TABLE 36/9

	s_1	S_1	S_2	X_A	X_B		
S_1	0	1	0	2	1	12	$\div 2 = 6$
S_2	0	0	1	2	2	20	$\div 2 = 10$
s_1	1	0	0	1	$-\dfrac{5}{2}$	0	$\div 1 = 0$

The only profitable choice is to introduce variable X_A in the solution. It appears, however, (cf. Table 36.9) that zero units of X_A can be brought into the new solution. In fact, therefore, the new solution will not differ from the initial one. In the new Table (38.9), however, there will be an X_A row instead of row s_1. In this Table there is consequently a change in the rate of transformation which is the starting point in our search for better solutions.

TABLE 37/9

Increase in profit caused by introduction of one unit into the solution	
X_A	X_B
5	25
$-2.0 = 0$	$-1.0 = 0$
$-2.0 = 0$	$-2.0 = 0$
$-1.(-M) = M$	$-\left(-\dfrac{5}{2}\right).(-M) = -\dfrac{5}{2}M$
$5 + M$	$25 - \dfrac{5}{2}M$

Second stage:

TABLE 38/9

	s_1	S_1	S_2	X_A	X_B	
S_1		1	0	0	6	12	$\div 6 = 2$
S_2		0	1	0	7	20	$\div 7 = 2\frac{6}{7}$
X_A		0	0	1	$-\frac{5}{2}$	0

$$X_A = 2S_1 + 2S_2 + s_1.$$

Therefore,

$$s_1 = -2S_1 - 2S_2 + X_A$$

$$X_B = S_1 + 2S_2 - \frac{5}{2}(-2S_1 - 2S_2 + X_A) = 6S_1 + 7S_2 - \frac{5}{2}X_A.$$

Now only variable X_B can possibly be introduced in the solution (because of its high negative coefficient in the profit function, s_1 will not appear in the solution any more). One unit of X_B will produce the following increase in profit:

$$25 - 6.0 - 7.0 - \left(-\frac{5}{2}\right).5 = 25 + 12\frac{1}{2} = 37\frac{1}{2}.$$

Therefore, it is of advantage to introduce as much of X_B in the solution as possible. The limiting factors for X_B are variables S_1 and S_2 alone. On the other hand, the negative rate of transformation of X_A into X_B means that in our case an increase in X_B leads to a rise in the value of X_A.

Third stage:

TABLE 39/9

	s_1	S_1	S_2	X_A	X_B	
X_B		$\frac{1}{6}$	0	0	1	2
S_2		$-\frac{7}{6}$	1	0	0	6
X_A		$\frac{5}{12}$	0	1	0	5

$$X_B = 6S_1 + 7S_2 - \frac{5}{2}X_A \quad \text{or} \quad \frac{1}{6}X_B = S_1 + \frac{7}{6}S_2 - \frac{5}{12}X_A$$

therefore,

$$S_1 = \frac{1}{6}X_B - \frac{7}{6}S_2 + \frac{5}{12}X_A.$$

Now the only variable we can bring into the solution is S_1. But, as can be seen, even one unit of S_1 brought in produces a fall in profit. This is evident from the following calculation:

$$0 - \frac{1}{6}.25 - \left(-\frac{7}{6}\right).0 - \frac{5}{12}.5 = -6\frac{1}{4}.$$

Therefore, the solution of Table 39.9 is final; it agrees, naturally, with the graphical solution obtained in Section 8 (cf. Fig. 6.8).

TABLE 40/9

Solution	X_A	X_B	s_1	Profit
I	0	0	0	0
II	0	0	0	0
III	5	2	0	75

It should be noted that linear models in which one or more relations are equations can be solved in a somewhat different, simpler manner than described above. Let us return to the model of the example just considered. This model expressed relations (23) and (24). For relations in the form of an equation one variable can always be expressed in terms of another. In our case, variable X_A can be expressed in terms of X_B:

$$X_A = 2 \cdot 5 X_B.$$

In the inequalities we can substitute $2 \cdot 5 X_B$ for X_A and we obtain

$$2 . 2 \cdot 5 X_B + X_B \leqslant 12$$

$$2 . 2 \cdot 5 X_B + 2 X_B \leqslant 20$$

$$Z = 5 . 2 \cdot 5 X_B + 25 X_B \quad \text{(maximum)}$$

or, by simplifying:

$$6 X_B \leqslant 12$$

$$7 X_B \leqslant 20$$

$$Z = 37 \cdot 5 X_B \quad \text{(maximum)}.$$

The resultant model is extremely simple, and the solution can be obtained immediately; it will be $X_B = 2$. If the model were not so simple, the normal procedure of the simplex algorithm would have to be employed. In the present case, we would have to introduce slack variables S_1 and S_2, obtaining

$$6X_B + S_1 = 12$$

$$7X_B + S_2 = 20$$

$$Z = 37 \cdot 5 X_B \quad \text{(maximum)}.$$

TABLE 41/9

	S_1	S_2	X_B		
S_1	1	0	6	12	$\div 6 = 2$
S_2	0	1	7	20	$\div 7 = 2\frac{6}{7}$

The only choice for the first solution, and it is a profitable one, is to introduce variable X_B. In the new solution, it will assume the value $X_B = 2$.

TABLE 42/9

	S_1	S_2	X_B	
X_B	$\dfrac{1}{6}$	0	1	2
S_2	$-\dfrac{7}{6}$	1	0	6

It can easily be seen that this is the final solution. We thus obtained $X_B = 2$ and hence, $X_A = 2 \cdot 5 \cdot 2 = 5$, i.e. exactly the same solution as before. Thus, in the case of models containing equations, the same procedure as described here may be followed.

Let us give an example of the application of a simplex algorithm in which the number of decision variables is greater than 2. In such a case we can obtain a solution only by calculation, since the graphical method can, obviously, no longer be used.

Example 7. A certain firm manufactures three products: A, B and C. The minimum production plan gives the minimum output for each of the three articles: a minimum of 100 units of article A, 200 units of article B and 150 units of article C must be produced.

The manufacture of all three articles requires, among other things, two raw materials P_1 and P_2. The firm can procure no more than 500 and 400 units of these raw materials respectively. The problem is to select a volume of output which, on the one hand, ensures the fulfilment of the production plan as to range of products and, on the other hand, guarantees a maximum total profit. The per unit profit from the individual products will be: $A = 2$ zlotys, $B = 5$ zlotys and $C = 4$ zlotys.

The consumption of raw materials P_1 and P_2 per unit product A, B and C is given in Table 43.9.

TABLE 43/9

Raw material	Consumption of raw material per unit product		
	A	B	C
P_1	$\dfrac{1}{2}$	1	1
P_2	2	$\dfrac{1}{2}$	$\dfrac{1}{5}$

We begin our solution of the above problem by determining the decision variables. In our case, these will be the volume of output of the individual products. We designate them by X_A, X_B and X_C respectively. The model of our problem will be:

$$Z = 2X_A + 5X_B + 4X_C \quad \text{(maximum)} \tag{25}$$

$$\frac{1}{2}X_A + X_B + X_C \leqslant 500 \tag{26}$$

$$2X_A + \frac{1}{2}X_B + \frac{1}{5}X_C \leqslant 400 \tag{27}$$

$$X_A \geqslant 100 \tag{28}$$

$$X_B \geqslant 200 \tag{29}$$

$$X_C \geqslant 150. \tag{30}$$

The total profit Z defined by formula (25) is the criterion in our model. Condition (26) stipulates that the total consumption of raw material P_1 cannot exceed 500 units; similarly, relation (27) states that the total consumption of raw material P cannot be more than 400 units. Conditions (28), (29) and (30) are the result of the minimum production plan allocated to the enterprise for each of the three products.

The next step is to introduce slack variables into the model, and artificial variables if necessary. Relations (26) and (27) can easily be changed into equations by the addition of slack variables S_1 and S_2 to their left-hand sides (these variables may denote unused quantities of raw materials P_1 and P_2 in relation to the raw materials allocated).

$$\frac{1}{2}X_A+X_B+X_C+S_1 = 500 \tag{26'}$$

$$2X_A+\frac{1}{2}X_B+\frac{1}{5}X_C+S_2 = 400. \tag{27'}$$

In order to change relations (28), (29) and (30) into equations, slack variables S_3, S_4 and S_5 must be introduced (with minus signs since the left-hand side of each of these relations is greater than the right-hand side).[1] However, as we recall, this is not enough. For, if we were to take zero values for all decision variables in our initial solution, we would have $X_A = X_B = X_C = 0$, and this would be inconsistent with the given conditions; we would be outside the area of feasible solutions. Therefore, let us introduce artificial variables. Then, s_1 will denote the volume of product A not manufactured in the establishment but purchased elsewhere. The situation will be similar in respect to the other artificial variables, s_2 and s_3, relating to products B and C. Therefore, relations (28), (29) and (30) will assume the form:

$$X_A-S_3+s_1 = 100 \tag{28'}$$

$$X_B-S_4+s_2 = 200 \tag{29'}$$

$$X_C-S_5+s_3 = 150. \tag{30'}$$

However, since we do not want the artificial variables s_1, s_2, s_3 to appear in the final solutions, we assume that the purchase price of products A, B and C is prohibitive, e.g. M zlotys. As a result, the profit function (25) which is to be a maximum becomes:

$$Z = 2X_A+5X_B+4X_C-Ms_1-Ms_2-Ms_3. \tag{25'}$$

Now we can proceed to compile a simplex table, assuming that in the first solution we have

$$X_A = 0,\ X_B = 0,\ X_C = 0,\ S_3 = 0,\ S_4 = 0,\ S_5 = 0,$$

---

[1] Here, S_3, S_4 and S_5 stand for outputs of products A, B and C over and above the planned target.

and, therefore,

$$S_1 = 500, \ S_2 = 400, \ s_1 = 100, \ s_2 = 200, \ s_3 = 150.$$

TABLE 44/9

	s_1	s_2	s_3	S_1	S_2	S_3	S_4	S_5	X_A	X_B	X_C	
S_1				1					$\frac{1}{2}$	1	1	500
S_2					1				2	$\frac{1}{2}$	$\frac{1}{5}$	400
s_1	1					-1			1			100
s_2		1					-1			1		200
s_3			1					-1			1	150

For the sake of simplicity, we have not entered zeros in Table 44.9. Thus the empty squares should be taken to mean that the values are 0.

It is obvious that X_B will be the most profitable choice. According to Table 44.9, X_B takes on the value of 200 and s_2 disappears from the new solution (i.e. $s_2 = 0$ in the new solution). We obtain this result by reasoning in a similar manner as in the previous examples. As a result of the available amount of S_1 (500), 500 units ($500 \div 1 = 500$) of X_B can be introduced in the solution; 800 units ($400 \div 1/2 = 800$) because of S_2; and 200 units ($200 \div 1 = 200$) on account of s_2. We do not need s_1 and s_3 to obtain X_B, and thus finally 200 units of X_B will enter in the new solution.

Below we give a number of consecutive tables, leaving it to the reader to verify the accuracy of the calculations.

TABLE 45/9

	s_1	s_2	s_3	S_1	S_2	S_3	S_4	S_5	X_A	X_B	X_C	
S_1		-1		1		1			$\frac{1}{2}$		1	300
S_2		$-\frac{1}{2}$			1		$\frac{1}{2}$		2		$\frac{1}{5}$	300
s_1	1					-1			1			100
X_B		1					-1			1		200
s_3			1					-1			1	150

TABLE 46/9

	s_1	s_2	s_3	S_1	S_2	S_3	S_4	S_5	X_A	X_B	X_C	
S_1		-1	-1	1			1	1	$\frac{1}{2}$			150
S_2		$-\frac{1}{2}$	$-\frac{1}{5}$		1		$\frac{1}{2}$	$\frac{1}{5}$	2			270
s_1	1					-1			1			100
X_B		1					-1			1		200
X_C			1					-1			1	150

TABLE 47/9

	s_1	s_2	s_3	S_1	S_2	S_3	S_4	S_5	X_A	X_B	X_C	
S_1	$-\frac{1}{2}$	-1	-1	1		$\frac{1}{2}$	1	1				100
S_2	-2	$-\frac{1}{2}$	$-\frac{1}{5}$		1	2	$\frac{1}{2}$	$\frac{1}{5}$				70
X_A	1					-1			1			100
X_B		1					-1			1		200
X_C			1					-1			1	150

TABLE 48/9

	s_1	s_2	s_3	S_1	S_2	S_3	S_4	S_5	X_A	X_B	X_C	
S_4				1		$\frac{1}{2}$	1	1				100
S_2				$-\frac{1}{2}$	1	$\frac{7}{4}$		$-\frac{3}{10}$				20
X_A						-1			1			100
X_B				1		$\frac{1}{2}$		1		1		300
X_C								-1			1	150

We have not filled columns s_1, s_2 and s_3 in Table 48.9 since the artificial variables will certainly not appear again in the solution and, therefore, the coefficients in these columns are of no interest to us. At the same time, it can be ascertained that the last column of Table 48.9 gives the final solution of the problem. We obtain proof of this upon considering three possible alternatives: S_1, S_3 and S_5.

By introducing one unit of S_1 in the solution, we cause function Z to decrease in value by 5 zlotys (cf. column s_1). One unit of S_3 brought into the solution causes a reduction of 1/2 zlotys in the value of function Z, and finally one unit of S_5 reduces the value of function Z by 1 zlotys.

The final solution, therefore, is

$$X_A = 100, \quad X_B = 300 \text{ and } X_C = 150.$$

Moreover, Table 48.9 indicates that in this solution there are 20 units of unused raw material P_2 ($S_2 = 20$). In addition, we produce a certain amount of product B exceeding the plan ($S_4 = 100$).

Recapitulating our considerations of the simplex algorithm for various types of examples, we come to the following conclusions.

A simplex algorithm is universal and enables to solve all types of linear programmes. Its point of departure is the appropriate introduction of slack and artificial variables. Having built a model of the problem we are to solve, we arrange all the relations of this model so that each relation contains variables on the left-hand side and a free (non-negative) term on the right-hand side. If the free expression is negative, we multiply both sides of the relation by —1, remembering to change the direction of the inequality. Once we have the model in this form, we proceed to introduce slack and artificial variables. The rules for this are:

1) When the left-hand side is less than the free expression, we add a slack variable to the left-hand side, and change the sign of inequality to equality. The slack variable brought into the relation will appear in the first simplex table as a row.
2) When the left-hand side is greater than the free expression, we subtract a slack variable from the left-hand side and add an artificial variable, changing the inequality sign to an equality sign. Only the artificial variable will be entered as a row in the first simplex table.
3) When the left-hand side is equal to a free expression, we add an artificial variable to the left-hand side, leaving the equal sign. The artificial variable thus introduced will appear as a row in the first simplex table. We can also determine k variables in terms of the remaining variables from all k equations, provided this is not too involved. The resultant values for the k variables should be substituted to all the inequalities.
4) If our criterion is a certain function which is to be a maximum, we bring into this function all the artificial variables of the model having coefficient $-M$, where M is a very large number (this value need not be specified). If the criterion-function has to be minimized, all the artificial variables of the model are introduced into it with a coefficient $+ M$, where M is again a very large number.

It follows from the above rules that the number of rows in a simplex table is equal to the number of conditions in the model (for each condition we introduce a slack or artificial variable as a row). A further conclusion is that the number of variables which can assume non-zero values in the final solution is equal at most to the number of conditions in the model. For instance, if we have a model with five decision variables, but with only two conditions, then no more than two decision variables can have non-zero values in the solution, whereas all the other decision variables will have to be zero.

As we recall, the value of the simplex algorithm is that it enables us to pass from one solution to other improved solutions. The method of passing from one solution to the next improved one was discussed in detail on the basis of examples. It is interesting to know through how many consecutive stages a problem will have to pass from the initial solution (in which we assume that all the decision variables are equal to zero) to the optimum solution. Without dwelling on this subject, we should simply like to state that the number of consecutive stages to be completed is generally equal to the number of conditions in the model (or, no more than double the number of conditions).

Although this assertion is not entirely correct it does allow us to foresee with some approximation the number of stages to be completed in order to arrive at an optimum solution.

10. Degeneracy in the simplex algorithm

In Section 9, we discussed the application of the simplex algorithm to the solution of linear programmes. At this point attention should be drawn to a difficulty which may arise in some cases when the simplex algorithm is used. We may run into this difficulty when passing from one solution to the next improved solution.

As we recall, the way to proceed from one solution to the next is as follows.

The variables in the present solution correspond to the rows of the simplex table. If we want to find the next solution, we compare the changes which could be made in the present solution. In other words, we compute the values of the criterion-function to show how they will be affected by introducing a variable which does not appear in the present solution. Naturally, we make the most advantageous choice.[1] Appropriate calculations determine the value which the new variable will assume in the new solution. The coefficients of the column for the new variable are, we recall, the rates of transformation of the goods in the given row into the goods in the column. These coefficients, therefore, tell us how many units of the goods from a given row have to be used to yield one unit of the goods in a column. The rates corresponding to the new variable and the current solution enable us to find the value the new variable will assume in the new conditions and which of the old variables will be eliminated. However, it does happen at times, that it is difficult

---

[1] If there are two or more equally advantageous choices, we obviously select any one of them.

to determine which variable to eliminate. The difficulty is that in certain situations more than one variable has to be eliminated. In such conditions we speak of degeneracy. When degeneracy appears, the simplex algorithm requires some slight modification. We shall discuss this question on the basis of a formal example.

Example 1.[1] We have the following model of a certain problem in which there are four decision variables:

$$\frac{1}{4}X_1+9X_4 \leqslant 60X_2+\frac{1}{25}X_3$$

$$\frac{1}{2}X_1+3X_4 \leqslant 90X_2+\frac{1}{50}X_3$$

$$X_3 \leqslant 1$$

$$K = -\frac{3}{4}X_1+150X_2-\frac{1}{50}X_3+6X_4 \text{ (minimum)}.$$

In order to solve the above model, we rearrange all the relations in the model so that those on the left-hand side contain all the decision variables and those on the right-hand side contain the free expressions alone. We then have

$$\frac{1}{4}X_1-60X_2-\frac{1}{25}X_3+9X_4 \leqslant 0$$

$$\frac{1}{2}X_1-90X_2-\frac{1}{50}X_3+3X_4 \leqslant 0$$

$$X_3 \leqslant 1.$$

The next step is to introduce slack variables (because of the direction of the inequality we do not bring in artificial variables):

$$\frac{1}{4}X_1-60X_2-\frac{1}{25}X_3+9X_4+S_1 = 0$$

$$\frac{1}{2}X_1-90X_2-\frac{1}{50}X_3+3X_4+S_2 = 0$$

$$X_3+S_3 = 1$$

$$K = -\frac{3}{4}X_1+150X_2-\frac{1}{50}X_3+6X_4 \text{ (minimum)}.$$

[1] This is Beale's example which I cite from a book by S. I. Glass: *Linear Programming*, New York, 1958, McGraw-Hill.

The theory of decision-making

And the first simplex table is:

Table 1/10

	S_1	S_2	S_3	X_1	X_2	X_3	X_4		
S_1	1			$\frac{1}{4}$	-60	$-\frac{1}{25}$	9	0	$\div \frac{1}{4} = 0$
S_2		1		$\frac{1}{2}$	-90	$-\frac{1}{50}$	3	0	$\div \frac{1}{2} = 0$
S_3			1			1		1	

As before, the empty squares mean that the coefficients are zero.

From a consideration of function K (criterion) which we are to minimize, we easily see that X_1 is the most advantageous choice. If we bring in one unit of X_1 in the solution, the value of function K increases by -3.4, which actually means a decrease.

From Table 1.10 it is evident that we immediately meet with the difficulty mentioned at the outset. By introducing variable X_1 in the new solution (the "amount" being zero), we can eliminate either S_1 or S_3. But it appears that we cannot make this choice arbitrarily. An arbitrary selection of the variable we are eliminating may lead to a vicious circle of the simplex algorithm. When this happens, we arrive at the initial solution after a certain number of stages without having obtained an optimum solution. This means that we are back where we started. In order to verify this, let us decide arbitrarily that in our example we shall eliminate variable S_1. We obtain the following table:

Table 2/10

	S_1	S_2	S_3	X_1	X_2	X_3	X_4		
X_1	4			1	-240	$-\frac{4}{25}$	36	0	
S_2	-2	1			30	$\frac{3}{50}$	-15	0	$\div 30 = 0$
S_3			1			1		1	

The next most advantageous choice is X_2. By bringing in $X_2 = 1$ in the new solution, the following increase is obtained for K:

$$150 - (-240) \cdot \left(-\frac{3}{4}\right) = 150 - 180 = -30.$$

All other choices are less advantageous, as can easily be verified. Now X replaces S_2 in the new solution. At the present stage, there is no doubt at all that in introducing X_2, we are limited only by the value of S_2 in regard to the solution from Table 2.10. The value of X_2 in the new solution is zero.

TABLE 3/10

	S_1	S_2	S_3	X_1	X_2	X_3	X_4		
X_1	-12	8		1		$\dfrac{8}{25}$	-84	0	$\div \dfrac{8}{25}=0$
X_2	$-\dfrac{1}{15}$	$\dfrac{1}{30}$			1	$\dfrac{1}{500}$	$-\dfrac{1}{2}$	0	$\div \dfrac{1}{500}=0$
S_3			1			1		1	$\div 1=1$

At this stage, it is most advantageous to introduce X_3 in the next solution. By bringing in $X_3 = 1$ in the new solution, the value of K is increased by

$$-\frac{1}{50}-\frac{8}{25}\cdot\left(-\frac{3}{4}\right)-\frac{1}{500}\cdot 150 = -\frac{1}{50}+\frac{6}{25}-\frac{15}{50} = -\frac{4}{50}.$$

From Table 3.10 it appears that once again two variables, X_1 and X_2, can be selected to be eliminated. Assuming that we can freely select the variable to be eliminated, we remove variable X_1.

Here, then, is the next table:

TABLE 4/10

	S_1	S_2	S_3	X_1	X_2	X_3	X_4		
X_3	$-\dfrac{75}{2}$	25		$\dfrac{25}{8}$		1	$-\dfrac{525}{2}$	0	
X_2	$\dfrac{1}{120}$	$-\dfrac{1}{60}$		$-\dfrac{1}{160}$	1		$\dfrac{1}{40}$	0	$\div \dfrac{1}{40}=0$
S_3	$\dfrac{75}{2}$	-25	1	$-\dfrac{25}{8}$			$\dfrac{525}{2}$	1	$\div \dfrac{525}{2}=\dfrac{2}{525}$

At this point the best choice will be X_4. If in our new solution $X_4 = 1$, the increase in the value of K will be

$$6-\left(-\frac{525}{2}\right)\cdot\left(-\frac{1}{50}\right)-\frac{1}{40}\cdot 150 = 6-\frac{21}{4}-\frac{15}{4} = -3.$$

The theory of decision-making

Variable X_4 will assume a zero value in the new solution and will replace X_2.

TABLE 5/10

	S_1	S_2	S_3	X_1	X_2	X_3	X_4		
X_3	50	-150		$-\dfrac{125}{2}$	10,500	1		0	$\div 50 = 0$
X_4	$\dfrac{1}{3}$	$-\dfrac{2}{3}$		$-\dfrac{1}{4}$	40		1	0	$\div \dfrac{1}{3} = 0$
S_3	-50	150	1	$\dfrac{125}{2}$	$-10,500$			1	

S_1 will be the next most profitable choice. By introducing $S_1 = 1$ into the solution, we increase the value of K by

$$-50 \cdot \left(-\frac{1}{50}\right) - \frac{1}{3} \cdot 6 = 1 - 2 = -1.$$

Variable S_1 can again enter in place of X_3 or X_4. Let us eliminate X_3.

TABLE 6/10

	S_1	S_2	S_3	X_1	X_2	X_3	X_4		
S_1	1	-3		$-\dfrac{5}{4}$	210	$\dfrac{1}{50}$		0	
X_4		$\dfrac{1}{3}$		$\dfrac{1}{6}$	-30	$-\dfrac{1}{150}$	1	0	$\div \dfrac{1}{3} = 0$
S_3			1			1		1	

Our most profitable choice now will be S_2 and one unit of S_2 introduced in the solution will increase the value of K by:

$$-\frac{1}{3} \cdot 6 = -2.$$

In the new solution S_2 will assume the value zero.

It may be noted that Table 7.10 is identical to Table 1.10. From this point, the entire cycle is repeated. Once again X_1 will be the best choice, etc.

TABLE 7/10

	S_1	S_2	S_3	X_1	X_2	X_3	X_4	
S_1	1			$\frac{1}{4}$	-60	$-\frac{1}{25}$	9	0
S_2		1		$\frac{1}{2}$	-90	$-\frac{1}{50}$	3	0
S_3			1			1		1

This example proved that a simplex algorithm, when not supplemented by an additional rule defining which variable is to be eliminated (if more than one variable can be selected to be eliminated), does not offer a solution. But it should be added that by some fortunate coincidence we could so select the variables for elimination that we would ultimately obtain an optimum solution. However, we can scarcely rely on some fortunate coincidence, and an elimination rule should be provided which will ensure an optimum solution for a case of degeneracy. There is such a rule. Unfortunately, it is not simple to justify, so we shall merely formulate it and illustrate it on the basis of the above example.

The starting point for our reasoning was Table 1.10 to which we refer here again.

TABLE 8/10

	S_1	S_2	S_3	X_1	X_2	X_3	X_4		
S_1	1			$\frac{1}{4}$	-60	$-\frac{1}{25}$	9	0	$\div \frac{1}{4} = 0$
S_2		1		$\frac{1}{2}$	-90	$-\frac{1}{50}$	3	0	$\div \frac{1}{2} = 0$
S_3			1			1		1	

As we recall, the best choice was X_1. The difficulty was that two variables S_1 and S_2 could be eliminated. The rule determining which of the two should be eliminated is given below.

In our discussions we shall confine ourselves to the rows of variables which can be removed. In our case these will be rows S_1 and S_2. We analyse then the columns of the simplex table, starting from the left-hand side of the table and taking into account only rows S_1 and S_2 as mentioned above. The coefficients in the first column are divided by the corresponding coefficients of the variable column which appears in the new solution (in our case X_1). Therefore, in our example we first consider column S_1 for which we take into account only two rows:

TABLE 9/10

	S_1
S_1	$1 \div \dfrac{1}{4} = 4$
S_2	$0 \div \dfrac{1}{2} = 0$

We eliminate the variable corresponding to the lowest coefficient obtained in this way. In our case, we have to eliminate S_2. It must be added here that if we obtained the same numbers from the division, we would then have to go on to the next column and, after carrying out the necessary divisions, select again the smallest number, etc.

The new simplex table, after S_2 has been eliminated and X_1 brought in, is presented in Table 10.10.

TABLE 10/10

	S_1	S_2	S_3	X_1	X_2	X_3	X_4		
S_1	1	$-\dfrac{1}{2}$			-15	$-\dfrac{3}{100}$	$\dfrac{15}{2}$	0	
X_1		2		1	-180	$-\dfrac{2}{50}$	6	0	
S_3			1			1		1	$\div 1$

The next best choice is X_3 (it leads to the most marked decrease in the value of function K). The only "candidate" for elimination is S_3. In its place, therefore, we put X_3 which assumes a value of 1 in the new solution.

TABLE 11/10

	S_1	S_2	S_3	X_1	X_2	X_3	X_4	
S_1	1	$-\dfrac{1}{2}$	$\dfrac{3}{100}$		-15		$\dfrac{15}{2}$	$\dfrac{3}{100}$
X_1		2	$\dfrac{2}{50}$	1	-180		6	$\dfrac{2}{50}$
X_3			1		1			1

It is easily verified that no change in the solution obtained will reduce the value of function K. Therefore, the solution in Table 11.10 must be regarded as final.

In this way, modifying slightly the simplex algorithm — this should always be done in a case of degeneracy — we obtained the final solution in a simple manner.

11. The transportation algorithm

As stated in the preceding Sections, the simplex algorithm makes it possible to solve any linear model. But this algorithm is laborious. For this reason, wherever possible, we try to simplify the calculations. One such simplified algorithm is called the transportation algorithm. It is used to solve some special cases of linear models. The name of this algorithm is derived from transport to which it was first applied to solve a problem. Let us consider an example of such a problem and explain the method of solving it.

Example 1. Three factories at different locations in the country manufacture a given product P. Each of these factories — let us call them F_1, F_2, and F_3—has a certain production capacity, e.g. factory F_1 can turn out 100 units of product P, factory F_2, 200 units and factory F_3, 50 units. These factories supply five wholesale houses which we denote by H_1, H_2, H_3, H_4 and H_5. Each wholesale house has a definite demand for product P. For H_1 it is 120; H_2, H_4 and H_5 need 45 each; and H_3 has a demand of 70. Both the production capacities and the demands refer to the same period of time, for instance, a year.

We have information concerning unit transport costs from individual factories to each of the wholesale houses. This information is presented in Table 1.11.

At the intersection of some row, e.g. F_2, with a column, e.g. H_3, we read the cost of transporting one unit of product from the given factory to the given wholesale house; e.g. the unit transport cost from F_2 to H_3 in our case is 4 money units.

TABLE 1/11

F_i \ H_j	H_1	H_2	H_3	H_4	H_5
F_1	2	5	3	4	8
F_2	1	9	4	5	10
F_3	5	6	1	7	4

Our problem is to determine the volume of supplies from individual factories to individual wholesale houses so that the total transport cost is a minimum, two conditions having to be met: a) in no case must the manufacturing capacity of

6*

a factory be exceeded, b) each wholesale house must receive full supplies to cover its demand.

If we wanted to solve this problem by means of a simplex algorithm, we would readily see that this would involve a fair number of calculations since the simplex table would contain a relatively large number of columns and rows. After solving this problem by means of the transportation algorithm, we shall compile a simplex table to prove this fact.

It should be noted that in our problem we have 15 decision variables. For we have to find the optimum supplies from factory F_1 to each of the 5 wholesale houses, the volume of supplies from factory F_2 to each wholesale house, and similarly for F_3. We denote by X_{ij} the volume of supplies from factory F_i to wholesale house H_j where $i = 1, 2, 3$, and $j = 1, 2, 3, 4, 5$.

The conditions concerning the production capacities of the individual factories will be:

$$X_{11}+X_{12}+X_{13}+X_{14}+X_{15} \leqslant 100 \tag{1}$$

$$X_{21}+X_{22}+X_{23}+X_{24}+X_{25} \leqslant 200 \tag{2}$$

$$X_{31}+X_{32}+X_{33}+X_{34}+X_{35} \leqslant 50. \tag{3}$$

Condition (1) states that the total deliveries from factory F_1 to all wholesale houses must not exceed the production capacity of that factory. Conditions (2) and (3) are similar as regards factories F_2 and F_3.

The second group of conditions concerns the demand of the wholesale houses:

$$X_{11}+X_{21}+X_{31} = 120 \tag{4}$$

$$X_{12}+X_{22}+X_{32} = 45 \tag{5}$$

$$X_{13}+X_{23}+X_{33} = 70 \tag{6}$$

$$X_{14}+X_{24}+X_{34} = 45 \tag{7}$$

$$X_{15}+X_{25}+X_{35} = 45. \tag{8}$$

Condition (4) stipulates that the total supplies from the individual factories to wholesale house H_1 should equal its demand. Conditions (5), (6), (7) and (8) postulate likewise concerning wholesale houses H_2, H_3, H_4 and H_5.

Our problem, therefore, is to determine the values of variables X_{ij} so that, in satisfying conditions (1) to (8), they will ensure minimum transport costs. The total transport costs are:

$$K = 2X_{11} + 5X_{12} + 3X_{13} + 4X_{14} + \ 8X_{15}$$
$$+ \ \ X_{21} + 9X_{22} + 4X_{23} + 5X_{24} + 10X_{25}$$
$$+ 5X_{31} + 6X_{32} + \ X_{33} + 7X_{34} + \ 4X_{35}.$$

This function, which we are to minimize, will be derived from the data concerning transport costs (Table 1.11).

We now proceed to solve the problem by means of a transportation algorithm. First of all, we must check whether the problem does afford a solution. In our case, it is extremely simple to check this. It only needs comparing the two figures: the total production capacity of all the factories $(100 + 200 + 50 = 350)$ and the total demand of all the wholesale houses $(120 + 45 + 70 + 45 + 45 = 325)$.

If the total demand does not exceed the total manufacturing capacity, the problem will afford a solution. This is so in our case. Otherwise, if total demand exceeded total production capacity, the problem would not offer a solution.

In the transportation, as in the simplex algorithm, we arrive at a solution by successive approximations. We determine, usually, some feasible solution (i.e. one which satisfies the conditions of the problem) and we improve it at consecutive stages until we obtain the optimum solution. Whereas in the case of the simplex algorithm we began by introducing slack and artificial variables and adopted zero values for the decision variables as our basic solution, in the case of the transportation algorithm any feasible solution (therefore, not necessarily zero) may be our basic solution. In order to find such an initial feasible solution, we compile a table containing as many rows as factories and as many columns as wholesale houses. Moreover, if the total production capacity exceeds the total demand, we add another column representing unused capacity. Finally, on the borders of this table in appropriate places (along the right-hand side and along the bottom) we place data on the capacities of individual factories and on the demands of individual wholesale houses. The remaining squares in the table are not filled for the time being. The situation is shown in Table 2.11.

S denotes here the column giving the unused production capacity. Knowing the overall production capacity (350) and the overall demand (325), we can determine the total unused capacity. In our case, this will be 25. We enter this number in the last, additional square of column S. The initial feasible solution may be determined in various ways. But there is a certain rule known as the rule of the northwest corner which enables to determine one of the initial solutions in a simple manner. We first consider the square in the upper left-hand corner of Table 2.11 (on a map this would be a northwest corner). We compare the two boundary values corresponding to this square. They will be 100 (the production capacity of factory F_1) and 120 (the demand of wholesale house H_1). We enter the smaller number, in our case 200, in the given square. A moment's consideration shows that if the larger number were accounted for we would fail to satisfy one of the conditions of the problem. In our case, for instance, if we allowed for 120, then the production capacity of factory F_1 would be exceeded.

TABLE 2/11

F_i \\ H_j	H_1	H_2	H_3	H_4	H_5	S	
F_1	100	/ −5	/ −2	/ −2	/ −3	/ −7	100
F_2	20	45	70	45	20	/ −6	200
F_3	/ 10	/ 3	/ 3	/ 8	25	25	50
	120	45	70	45	45	25	

After filling this first square, we move by one square to the right or by one square down. According to our rule, these are the only two permissible directions. In our case, we move one square down since all the remaining squares of the first row cannot be filled (this would mean exceeding the capacity of factory F_1). In this square $(F_2 H_1)$ we enter the number which raises 100 to 120 (provided the production capacity of factory F_2 does allow it). Since by entering 20 we have not yet exhausted the manufacturing capacity of factory F_2, we move to the right, to square $(F_2 H_2)$. According to the production capacity of F_2, we may enter the entire demand of wholesale house H_2. This will be number 45. Next, we pass to square $F_2 H_3$ in which we enter 70, in the next square $F_2 H_4$ we enter 45 and finally, we come to square $F_2 H_5$. We cannot enter here number 45 as the production capacity of factory F_2 no longer allows it since the entries in this row $20 + 45 + 70 + 45 = 180$. Therefore, we may only enter 20 in square $F_2 H_5$ and we proceed to square $F_3 H_5$. There, we enter number 25 and finally, in square $F_3 S$ we also enter 25.

We can easily check that our proposed solution is feasible (every wholesale house receives supplies to cover its demand; no factory exceeds its production capacity).

Having obtained in this way a first feasible solution, we proceed to investigate whether it could be improved and if so, how; i.e. whether the total transport costs could be reduced. In this connection, we must consider in turn all the available alternatives and select the best, in order to arrive in this manner at the next best solution. There are as many choices as unfilled squares in Table 2.11. They must all be considered in turn. Let us take square $F_1 H_2$, i.e. the capacity of factory F_1, to supply wholesale house H_2. If we sent one unit from factory F_1 to H_2 we would have a transport cost of 5 (cf. Table 1.11). It should be borne in mind, however, that an increase of deliveries by one unit from factory F_1 to H_2 must reduce the supplies from this factory to some other wholesale house (otherwise, we would exceed production capacity). The only wholesale house here is H_1. A decrease in the supplies to H_1 by 1 brings down transport costs by 2 (cf. Table 1.11). These two changes offset each other as far as the production capacity of factory F_1 is concerned. But these changes have caused: a) the supplies to H_1 to decrease by 1 unit, b) the deliveries to H_2 to rise by 1 unit. In order to offset these changes two further changes are necessary, i.e. the deliveries from F_2 to H_1 must be increased by one unit (increasing transport costs by 1) and supplies from F_2 to H_2 must be reduced by one unit (decreasing transport costs by 9).

Finally, if 1 unit were supplied from factory F_1 to wholesale house H_2 and the other deliveries were adjusted accordingly to ensure that the solution will be feasible, the transport costs would rise by $5 - 2 + 1 - 9 = -5$. A negative rise in costs means a fall in costs, so that choice $F_1 H_2$ is profitable. However, we have to check all the other choices as there may be among them some which are even more profitable than the one we have just considered.

The calculation for alternative $F_1 H_3$ is:

$$
\begin{array}{lr}
F_1 H_3 & 3 \\
\hline
F_1 H_1 & -2 \\
F_2 H_1 & 1 \\
F_2 H_3 & -4 \\
\hline
& -2 \\
\hline
\end{array}
$$

This entry should be read: the supply of 1 unit from F_1 to H_3 increases transport costs by 3; but in this connection supplies from F_1 to H_1 must be cut, increased from F_2 to H_1 and reduced from F_2 to H_3. The result is a decrease in transport costs by 2.

For convenience, these figures can be entered in Table 2.11 in the lower right-hand corner of the appropriate square.

We give below the corresponding calculations for all the other squares:

$$
\begin{array}{lr \qquad lr}
F_1 H_4 & 4 & F_1 H_5 & 8 \\
\hline
F_1 H_1 & -2 & F_1 H_1 & -2 \\
F_2 H_1 & 1 & F_2 H_1 & 1 \\
F_2 H_4 & -5 & F_2 H_5 & -10 \\
\hline
& -2 & & -3 \\
\hline
\end{array}
$$

F_1S	0		F_2S	0
F_3S	$-$ 0		F_3S	$-$ 0
F_3H_5	4		F_3H_5	4
F_2H_5	-10		F_2H_5	-10
F_2H_1	1			$-$ 6
F_1H_1	$-$ 2			
	$-$ 7			

F_3H_1	5		F_3H_2	6
F_3H_5	$-$ 4		F_3H_5	$-$ 4
F_2H_5	10		F_2H_5	10
F_2H_1	$-$ 1		F_2H_2	$-$ 9
	10			3

F_3H_3	1		F_3H_4	7
F_3H_5	$-$ 4		F_3H_5	$-$ 4
F_2H_5	10		F_2H_5	10
F_2H_3	$-$ 4		F_2H_4	$-$ 5
	3			8

In the above calculations we have assumed that "transport costs" from F_1 to S are zero. This is understandable since "transport" from F_1 to S simply means the unused production capacity of factory F_1.

Note the calculation for the choice F_1S. Introducing combination F_1S in the solution, we see that square F_3S is the only one in column S in which supplies can be reduced. In turn, we increase deliveries in square F_3H_5 of row F_3 (in the transport algorithm we do not change zero squares, i.e. empty ones); this necessitates decreasing supplies in square F_2H_5. In row F_2 we increase the supplies in square F_2H_1 (we cannot alter any other square in this row since the deliveries cannot be reduced in any other column except H_1). Finally, we reduce the deliveries in square F_1H_1. Moreover, the changes resulting from the use of alternative F_1S are somewhat more troublesome.

After carrying out the above calculations, we can easily show which is the most advantageous alternative. In our case it is F_1S.

Therefore, we enter the largest possible number in F_1S. In our case this is 20. It should be noted that it is not possible to enter a larger number than 20 since deliveries in square F_2H_5 must be reduced by the amount they were increased in F_1S. Since number 20 appears in square F_2H_5, the maximum we can enter in F_1S is 20.

In this way, we obtain a new solution which is presented in Table 3.11.

TABLE 3/11

F_i \ H_j	H_1	H_2	H_3	H_4	H_5	S	
F_1	80	/ −5	/ −2	/ −2	/ 4	20	100
F_2	40	45	70	45	/ 7	/ 1	200
F_3	/ 3	/ −4	/ −4	/ 1	45	5	50
	120	45	70	45	45	25	

We begin filling Table 3 from square F_1S in which we enter number 20. We reduce the value of square F_3S in Table 2.11 by this amount. Thus, our entry in square F_3S is $25 - 20 = 5$. Next, we increase the value of square F_3H_5 in Table 2.11 by 20, thus obtaining $25 + 20 = 45$. Square F_2H_5 will now be empty $(20 - 20 = 0)$; in square F_2H_1 we write 40 $(20 + 20)$ and in square F_1H_1 we enter 80 $(100 - 20)$. The other squares in Table 3.11 remain unchanged as compared with the squares in Table 2.11.

Now, if we want to find the next best solution, we must investigate all the alternative solutions of Table 3.11, select the most advantageous and determine the successive solutions.

Below we give the calculations connected with the evaluation of the individual alternatives:

F_1H_2	5	F_1H_3	3	F_1H_4	4
F_2H_2	−9	F_2H_3	−4	F_2H_4	−5
F_2H_1	1	F_2H_1	1	F_2H_1	1
F_1H_1	−2	F_1H_1	−2	F_1H_1	−2
	−5		−2		−2

F_1H_5	8	F_2H_5	10	F_2S	0
F_3H_5	−4	F_2H_1	−1	F_2H_1	−1
F_3S	+0	F_1H_1	2	F_1H_1	2
F_1S	−0	F_1S	−0	F_1S	−0
	4	F_3S	+0		1
		F_3H_5	−4		
			7		

$$
\begin{array}{ll}
\dfrac{F_3H_1}{} & 5 \\
F_3S & -0 \\
F_1S & +0 \\
F_1H_1 & -2 \\
\hline
& 3
\end{array}
\qquad
\begin{array}{ll}
\dfrac{F_3H_2}{} & 6 \\
F_3S & -0 \\
F_1S & +0 \\
F_1H_1 & -2 \\
F_2H_1 & 1 \\
F_2H_2 & -9 \\
\hline
& -4
\end{array}
\qquad
\begin{array}{ll}
\dfrac{F_3H_3}{} & 1 \\
F_3S & -0 \\
F_1S & +0 \\
F_1H_1 & -2 \\
F_2H_1 & +1 \\
F_2H_3 & -4 \\
\hline
& -4
\end{array}
$$

$$
\begin{array}{ll}
\dfrac{F_3H_4}{} & 7 \\
F_3S & -0 \\
F_1S & +0 \\
F_1H_1 & -2 \\
F_2H_1 & 1 \\
F_2H_4 & -5 \\
\hline
& 1
\end{array}
$$

We enter the results in the appropriate squares of Table 3.11. The best choice is combination F_1H_2. The largest number we can write in this square is 45. The new solution is given by Table 4.11.

TABLE 4/11

$F_i \diagdown H_j$	H_1	H_2	H_3	H_4	H_5	S	
F_1	35	45	⟋ 2	⟋ -2	⟋ 4	20	100
F_2	85	⟋ 5	70	45	⟋ 7	⟋ 1	200
F_3	⟋ 3	⟋ 1	⟋ -4	⟋ 1	45	5	50
	120	45	70	45	45	25	

The evaluations of individual choices should be entered in this table and we have done this. The reader can make the necessary calculations himself. The next most advantageous choice is F_3H_3. Further tables give the results of the next stages.

TABLE 5/11

F_i \ H_j	H_1	H_2	H_3	H_4	H_5	S	
F_1	30	45	−2	−2	0	25	100
F_2	90	5	65	45	3	1	200
F_3	7	5	5	5	45	4	50
	120	45	70	45	45	25	

In the present stage we have two equally advantageous choices: F_1H_3 and F_1H_4. Either of them can be selected, for instance F_1H_4.

TABLE 6/11

F_i \ H_j	H_1	H_2	H_3	H_4	H_5	S	
F_1	2	45	0	30	2	25	100
F_2	120	3	65	15	3	−1	200
F_3	7	3	5	5	45	2	50
	120	45	70	45	45	25	

The next most advantageous choice is F_2S. We introduce this in the new solution.

TABLE 7/11

F_i \ H_j	H_1	H_2	H_3	H_4	H_5	S	
F_1	1	45	−1	45	1	10	100
F_2	120	4	65	1	3	15	200
F_3	7	3	5	6	45	3	50
	120	45	70	45	45	25	

Now, the most advantageous choice is F_1H_3.

TABLE 8/11

F_i \ H_j	H_1	H_2	H_3	H_4	H_5	S	
F_1	2	45	10	45	2	1	100
F_2	120	3	55	0	3	25	200
F_3	7	3	5	5	45	3	50
	120	45	70	45	45	25	

From Table 8.11 it appears that F_2H_4 is the most advantageous choice. However, to introduce it would not bring down transport costs as in this case the increase in transport costs is 0. Therefore, the solution in Table 8.11 can be regarded as final, but there are other solutions which ensure the same transport costs as the solution in Table 8.11. Another such solution would be obtained from Table 8.11 by using alternative F_2H_4. This solution is given in Table 9.11.

TABLE 9/11

F_i \ H_j	H_1	H_2	H_3	H_4	H_5	S	
F_1	2	45	55	0	2	1	100
F_2	120	3	10	45	3	25	200
F_3	7	3	5	5	45	3	50
	120	45	70	45	45	25	

A study of the alternative solutions of Table 9.11 shows that the most advantageous is F_1H_4, even though its introduction does not reduce transport costs. Bringing in this alternative, we would again obtain the solution of Table 8.11. Therefore, our problem has two equivalent solutions given in Tables 8.11 and 9.11, which ensure minimum transport costs. Table 10.11 below gives the total transport costs for the consecutive solutions.

TABLE 10/11

Solution from table	Total transport costs
2	1,430
3	1,290
4	1,065
5	1,045
6	985
7	970
8	960
9	960

Table 10.11 illustrates the extent to which the consecutive solutions produced increasingly lower transport costs. This Table also confirms our conclusion that there are two equivalent optimum solutions (Tables 8.11 and 9.11). They both provide the same minimum transport cost equivalent to 960 money units.

It was apparent that the evaluation of individual alternatives presented the greatest difficulty in the transportation algorithm. It appears, however, that the procedure for determining the most advantageous alternative can be simplified appreciably. We shall become acquainted with this simplified procedure when solving Example 2.

However, before we proceed to this example, let us turn back for a moment to our earlier comment in connection with Example 1. We noted that the solution of that example by means of the general simplex algorithm would be much more laborious than by having recourse to the transportation algorithm just considered. This is due to the fact that the initial simplex table would have to be of a fairly considerable size. In order to compile such a table inequalities (1), (2) and (3) which appeared at the beginning of Section 11 would have to be changed to equations by bringing in appropriate slack variables S_1, S_2 and S_3, respectively. Artificial variables s_1, s_2, s_3, s_4 and s_5, would have to be introduced into equations (4) to (8) respectively.

As a result, the initial simplex table would comprise 23 columns and 8 rows. The columns would hold all the variables: 15 decision variables $X_{11}, X_{12}, \ldots\ldots\ldots$, $X_{22}, \ldots\ldots\ldots, X_{31}, X_{32}, \ldots\ldots\ldots, X_{35}$; 3 slack variables S_1, S_2 and S_3; and 5 artificial variables $s_1, \ldots\ldots\ldots, s_5$. The rows of the table would contain 3 slack and 5 artificial variables consistent with relations (1) to (8). The coefficients in this table would be zero and one. If the reader attempted to solve the above example on the basis of a table so compiled he would soon become convinced that the simplex algorithm is in this case much more time consuming than the transportation algorithm.

Example 2. Four factories, which we shall denote by Z_1, Z_2, Z_3 and Z_4, produce the same product. The unit production costs in these enterprises differ and are respectively, 2, 3, 1 and 5 zlotys. The production capacities are: Z_1 — 50 units, Z_2 — 70 units, Z_3 — 30 units and Z_4 — 50 units. These enterprises supply 4 other enterprises — N_1, N_2, N_3 and N_4, the demands of which are 25, 35, 105 and 20 units respectively. Unit transport costs from Z_i to N_j are given in Table 11.11.

TABLE 11/11

Z_i \ N_j	N_1	N_2	N_3	N_4
Z_1	1	3	5	10
Z_2	9	7	6	4
Z_3	12	2	8	11
Z_4	3	5	7	2

The volume of deliveries from individual enterprises Z_i to enterprises N_j are to be determined so that the total production and the related transport costs are minimum. Of course, deliveries must be fixed so that none of the enterprises Z_i exceed their production capacity and that every enterprise N_j receives the required supplies.

It is obvious that the problem can be solved by means of the transportation algorithm. For this purpose a new table of unit costs must be compiled, embracing both production and transport costs. These costs are given in Table 12.11.

TABLE 12/11

Z_i \ N_j	N_1	N_2	N_3	N_4
Z_1	3	5	7	12
Z_2	12	10	9	7
Z_3	13	3	9	12
Z_4	8	10	12	7

The values of the first row in this table are obtained by adding unit production costs of factory Z_1, i.e. 2 zlotys, to each value in the first row of Table 11.11. We obtain the values in the other rows in a similar fashion. Table 12.11, therefore, gives unit production and transport costs from factory Z_i to each of the factories N_j.

Having recourse to the rule of the northwest corner, we find the first feasible solution. It is given in Table 13.11. This table has an additional S column showing unutilized production capacities.

TABLE 13/11

Z_i \ N_j	N_1	N_2	N_3	N_4	S	
Z_1	25	25				50
Z_2		10	60			70
Z_3			30			30
Z_4			15	20	15	50
	25	35	105	20	15	

In order to select the most profitable alternative, we shall now proceed in a somewhat different manner than when solving Example 1.

We shall compile Table 14.11 entering unit costs (from Table 12.11) in those squares only for which the decision variables have non-zero values in the first solution (Table 13.11). Moreover, in Table 14.11 we add an extra column and an extra row (the column at the right-hand side and the row at the bottom.)

TABLE 14/11

Z_i \ N_j	N_1	N_2	N_3	N_4	S	
Z_1	3	5	4	−1	−8	0
Z_2	8	10	9	4	−3	5
Z_3	8	10	9	4	−3	5
Z_4	11	13	12	7	0	8
	3	5	4	−1	−8	

We enter any arbitrary number in any square of the additional column or row. To simplify, 0 may be used as that number. We enter zero in the first square of the additional column. Let us now consider the row in which we have entered this arbitrary number (here, zero). In our case this will be the row for factory Z_1. In this row we take into account the filled squares ($Z_1 N_1$ and $Z_1 N_2$). Square $Z_1 N_1$ contains number 3. In the last square of column N_1, therefore, we have to enter the number which, added to our arbitrary number (zero), will give us 3. This, of course, will be number 3. Similarly, in the last square of column N_2 we enter the number which, added to our arbitrary number (zero), will yield 5. Obviously, this is 5.

Next, we proceed to row Z_2. In the additional column we enter the number which, when added to 5 (the number in the last square of column N_2,) will give us 10. This is 5. Next, in the last square of column N_3 we enter 4, so that by adding it to 5 we obtain 9, i.e. the number in the Z_2N_3 square. We fill the other squares of the additional column and row in the same manner.

If we denote the numerical values in the additional column by k_i and the values in the additional row by w_j, these numbers are so selected that the unit costs C_{ij} corresponding to the non-zero values of the first solution satisfy the relation

$$C_{ij} = k_i + w_j.$$

As mentioned, in order to determine all the numbers k_i and w_j we have to choose one of them arbitrarily. In this example we assumed $k_1 = 0$.

Knowing numbers k_i and w_j, we fill the remaining squares of Table 14.11 by entering in each square the sum of the corresponding values from the additional column and row. For instance, in square Z_2N_4 we write $-1 + 5 = 4$, in square Z_3N_1 we enter $3 + 5 = 8$, etc. From the values in Table 12.11 giving unit costs we deduct the corresponding values taken from Table 14.11, bearing in mind that an additional column S must be added in Table 12.11 which will contain only zeros. After carrying out the subtractions we obtain:

TABLE 15/11

Z_i \ N_j	N_1	N_2	N_3	N_4	S
Z_1	0	0	3	13	8
Z_2	4	0	0	3	3
Z_3	5	−7	0	8	3
Z_4	−3	−3	0	0	0

The most advantageous alternative is given by the smallest number in the table thus obtained. In our case this alternative is Z_3N_2; we introduce this alternative in the new solution which is given in Table 16.11.

TABLE 16/11

Z_i \ N_j	N_1	N_2	N_3	N_4	S	
Z_1	25	25				50
Z_2			70			70
Z_3		10	20			30
Z_4			15	20	15	50
	25	35	105	20	15	

Before we proceed with the calculation, let us ascertain whether the evaluations of the alternatives obtained in Table 15.11 agree with the evaluations arrived at by direct calculations as used in Example 1. To illustrate this, let us carry out such calculations for several alternatives of the solution in Table 13.11.

Z_1N_3	7
Z_2N_3	-9
Z_2N_2	10
Z_1N_2	-5
	3

Z_1N_4	12
Z_4N_4	-7
Z_4N_3	12
Z_2N_3	-9
Z_2N_2	10
Z_1N_2	-5
	13

Z_1S	0
Z_4S	-0
Z_4N_3	12
Z_2N_3	-9
Z_2N_2	10
Z_1N_2	-5
	8

Thus, the numbers in Table 15.11 are really evaluations of the alternatives except that they have been obtained in a simpler, more mechanical way.

Having the solution from Table 16.11, we proceed to determine the most profitable alternative by repeating the procedure of the previous stage. For this purpose we compile Tables 17.11 and 18.11, in a similar manner to Tables 14.11 and 15.11.

TABLE 17/11

Z_i \ N_j	N_1	N_2	N_3	N_4	S	
Z_1	3	5	11	6	-1	0
Z_2	1	3	9	4	-3	-2
Z_3	1	3	9	4	-3	-2
Z_4	4	6	12	7	0	1
	3	5	11	6	-1	

TABLE 18/11

Z_i \ N_j	N_1	N_2	N_3	N_4	S
Z_1	0	0	-4	6	1
Z_2	11	7	0	3	-3
Z_3	12	0	0	8	3
Z_4	4	4	0	0	0

7

The smallest number of Table 18.11 is in square $Z_1 N_3$; thus, this is the most advantageous alternative, which we introduce in the new solution. For this purpose, we transform Table 16.11 accordingly. The result, i.e. the new solution, is given in Table 19.11.

TABLE 19/11

N_j / Z_i	N_1	N_2	N_3	N_4	S	
Z_1	25	5	20			50
Z_2			70			70
Z_3		30				30
Z_4			15	20	15	50
	25	35	105	20	15	

The next Tables, 20.11 and 21.11, serve to determine the best alternative solution from Table 19.11.

TABLE 20/11

N_j / Z_i	N_1	N_2	N_3	N_4	S	
Z_1	3	5	7	2	−5	0
Z_2	5	7	9	4	−3	2
Z_3	1	3	5	0	−7	−2
Z_4	8	10	12	7	0	5
	3	5	7	2	−5	

TABLE 21/11

N_j / Z_i	N_1	N_2	N_3	N_4	S
Z_1	0	0	0	10	5
Z_2	7	3	0	3	3
Z_3	12	0	4	12	7
Z_4	0	0	0	0	0

Table 21.11 shows that the solution obtained in Table 19.11 is the best. This is so because the smallest number in Table 21.11 equals zero. When this is the case, it means that no change in the solution will bring about a reduction in the total costs.

Table 23.11 gives the total costs relating to the consecutive solutions which we have obtained in the process of arriving at an optimum solution.

We can see, however, that the solution from Table 19.11 is not the only optimum one. As is evident from Table 21.11, the alternative $Z_4 N_1$, for instance, can be introduced from Table 19.11 without this causing any change in total transport and production costs. That this will be so emerges from the fact that there is a zero in square $Z_4 N_1$ of Table 21.11. To illustrate this, the solution obtained by using alternative $Z_4 N_1$ is given in Table 22.11.

TABLE 22/11

Z_i \ N_j	N_1	N_2	N_3	N_4	S	
Z_1	10	5	35			50
Z_2			70			70
Z_3		30				30
Z_4	15			20	15	50
	25	35	105	20	15	

TABLE 23/11

Solution from table	Total production and transport costs
13	1,403
16	1,360
19	1,280
22	1,280

Our method of determining the best alternative new solution in Example 2 is unquestionably faster than the direct calculations made in solving Example 1. In conclusion, we should add that the calculations would be much more laborious if we attempted to solve both examples by the simplex algorithm. We leave it to the reader to compile the initial-simplex table for Example 2.

12. Degeneracy in the transportation algorithm

In Section 10 we spoke of degeneracy in the simplex algorithm. Difficulties similar to those mentioned there may be encountered when the transportation algorithm is used.

In every transportation problem, the number of variables assuming non-zero values in the solution is equal to the sum of rows and columns in the table minus one. This may be easily verified from the examples discussed in Section 11. In Exam-

ple 1 of that Section, the table in question had 3 rows (factories) and 6 columns
(5 wholesale houses and 1 column for unutilized production capacity). Therefore,
the sum of rows and columns minus 1 was $3 + 6 - 1 = 8$. Indeed, as can be verified at each stage, the solutions have exactly 8 variables which assume non-zero
values. This is also the maximum number of variables having non-zero values in
the solution. On the other hand, it may happen that the number of non-zero values
in the solution is smaller than the sum of rows and columns minus one. We then
speak of degeneracy. It then becomes difficult to use the transportation algorithm.
It appears, however, that these difficulties can be overcome in a very simple manner.

Example 1. Four factories — F_1, F_2, F_3 and F_4 — supply three wholesale
houses — H_1, H_2 and H_3 — with a given product. The production capacities of the
individual factories are 25, 50, 50 and 100, respectively, while the requirements
of the wholesale houses are 50, 75 and 50, respectively. Knowing the unit transport
costs from the individual factories to the wholesale houses (Table 1.12), we must
determine from which factories and in what quantities the individual wholesale
houses should be supplied so that the requirement of each house is satisfied, the

TABLE 1/12

	H_1	H_2	H_3
F_1	2	1	3
F_2	7	8	10
F_3	5	4	6
F_4	8	12	11

production capacity of no factory is exceeded and the total transport costs are
kept to the minimum.

Employing the now familiar northwest corner rule, we find the first feasible
solution. Since the total production capacity is greater than the total demand
$(25 + 50 + 50 + 100 = 225 > 50 + 75 + 50)$, we add an extra column to the
table of solutions to include unutilized production capacity.

TABLE 2/12

	H_1	H_2	H_3	S	
F_1	25				25
F_2	25	25			50
F_3		50			50
F_4			50	50	100
	50	75	50	50	

There are only 6 non-zero values in Table 2.12, or fewer than the sum of rows and columns minus one $(4 + 4 - 1 = 7)$. This creates real difficulties in the determination of the next best solution. These difficulties are connected with the evaluation of individual alternatives which may be adopted in the next solution. Let us, for instance, try to determine how transport costs vary when combination $F_4 H_1$ is brought in in the new solution. One unit of the product supplied from F_4 to H_1 raises transport costs by 8. The use of this combination necessitates a cut in deliveries (by one unit) from F_2 to H_1 which reduces transport costs by 7. Next, we must increase transport from F_2 to H_2, thus increasing the costs by 8. Now, we must reduce deliveries from F_4 to H_2. Unfortunately, this is impossible since the deliveries from F_4 to H_2 are zero in the given solution, so that obviously these deliveries cannot be reduced further. We have therefore, run into a difficulty which can nevertheless be overcome in a simple manner. Let us designate by ε an arbitrarily small positive number. Let us assume that all the production capacities of the given factories have increased by this number. Then, the first solution obtained by the northwest angle method will now be somewhat different than before. This solution is given in Table 3.12.

TABLE 3/12

	H_1	H_2	H_3	S	
F_1	$25+\varepsilon$				$25+\varepsilon$
F_2	$25-\varepsilon$	$25+2\varepsilon$			$50+\varepsilon$
F_2		$50-2\varepsilon$	3ε		$50+\varepsilon$
F_4			$50-3\varepsilon$	$50+4\varepsilon$	$100+\varepsilon$
	50	75	50	$50+4\varepsilon$	

We see that quantity ε brought into the solution produced a non-degenerate case. We can therefore determine the next solution and as a result obtain the optimum solution. This optimum solution, however, will apply to a somewhat different problem than the original. The difference is that we have arbitrarily increased all the production capacities by a certain quantity ε. However, if we reduce the quantity ε to zero in the final solution, we obtain the solution of the original problem .

We give below all the calculations necessary to obtain an optimum solution.

TABLE 4/12

	H_1	H_2	H_3	S	
F_1	2	3	5	−6	0
F_2	7	8	10	−1	5
F_3	3	4	6	−5	1
F_4	8	9	11	0	6
	2	3	5	−6	

Table 4.12 is an auxiliary one, obtained in the way described in the discussion of Example 2, Section 11. From the unit costs (Table 1.12) we deduct the corresponding values of Table 4.12 to arrive at Table 5.12. This new table enables us to give the most profitable alternatives.

TABLE 5/12

	H_1	H_2	H_3	S
F_1	0	−2	−2	6
F_2	0	0	0	1
F_3	2	0	0	5
F_4	0	3	0	0

Combinations F_1H_2 or F_1H_3 are the most advantageous solutions. We can, of course, select either of these. Let us take F_1H_2, for instance. The new solution, obtained after rearranging the solution of Table 3.12 is given in Table 6.12.

TABLE 6/12

	H_1	H_2	H_3	S	
F_1		$25+\varepsilon$			$25+\varepsilon$
F_2	50	ε			$50+\varepsilon$
F_3		$50-2\varepsilon$	3ε		$50+\varepsilon$
F_4			$50-3\varepsilon$	$50+4\varepsilon$	$100+\varepsilon$
	50	75	50	$50+4\varepsilon$	

Tables 7.12 and 8.12 are auxiliary tables which enable to determine the next best alternatives.

From Table 8.12 it appears that none of the alternative solutions presented in Table 6.12 will contribute to a decrease in total transport costs. We conclude that the solution in Table 6.12 is optimum. Table 8.12, however, shows that besides that solution there are still two other optimum solutions. They can be obtained by introducing combinations $F_1 H_3$ or $F_4 H_1$ in the solution of Table 6.12 as alternatives. It is clear that the use of these alternatives will not alter total transport costs.

TABLE 7/12

	H_1	H_2	H_3	S	
F_1	0	1	3	—8	0
F_2	7	8	10	—1	7
F_3	3	4	6	—5	3
F_4	8	9	11	0	8
	0	1	3	—8	

TABLE 8/12

	H_1	H_2	H_3	S
F_1	2	0	0	8
F_2	0	0	0	1
F_3	2	0	0	5
F_4	0	3	0	0

Having obtained the solution given in Table 6.12, we can now determine the solution to the original problem. It is sufficient for this purpose to see what happens to the solution obtained when the quantity ε tends (diminishes) to zero. As a result we have the situation shown in Table 9.12.

TABLE 9/12

	H_1	H_2	H_3	S	
F_1		25			25
F_2	50				50
F_3		50			50
F_4			50	50	100
	50	75	50	50	

The above solution, obtained from Table 6.12 by substituting zero to ε, is the final solution of the problem.

To complete our remarks on degeneracy in the transportation algorithm, attention should be drawn to the case in which total production capacity is exactly equal to total demand. If, for instance, all the data in the example considered above remain the same, and only the demand of wholesale house H_3 increased from 50 to 100, we would have precisely that type of situation. Then, obviously, no additional column need be added for unutilized production capacity since the entire capacity will be in operation in this case. Hence, in a case of degeneracy, if total demand and total production capacity are to remain equal, when the production capacity is increased by ε, the demand of one wholesale house must be increased by $m\varepsilon$, where m is the number of rows. Therefore, the first feasible solution of our modified example is:

TABLE 10/12

	H_1	H_2	H_3	
F_1	$25+\varepsilon$			$25+\varepsilon$
F_2	$25-\varepsilon$	$25+2\varepsilon$		$50+\varepsilon$
F_3		$50-2\varepsilon$	3ε	$50+\varepsilon$
F_4			$100+\varepsilon$	$100+\varepsilon$
	50	75	$100+4\varepsilon$	

The final solution can be obtained by the procedure in accordance with the rule discussed in Sections 11 and 12.

13. Duality in linear programming

One of the most interesting results of the linear programming theory is the dualism theorem. For it appears that it is possible to match each linear programme with another one, known as a dual programme, that is, one for which we can immediately determine the solution, knowing the solution of the first. And vice versa, knowing the solution of the dual programme, we can immediately determine the solution of the primary programme.

This duality is an extremely important and interesting feature of linear programming. The significance of this problem is explained by at least three factors:

　　1) it appears that from the point of view of calculations there may be a substantial difference as regards the amount of work involved in solving primary and dual programmes. Therefore, when we have to solve a linear programme we can frequently reduce the calculations considerably by solving the dua programme;

2) duality in linear programming has certain far-reaching consequences of an economic character;

3) it becomes apparent that duality in linear programming makes it possible to demonstrate that each linear programme is equivalent to a two-person zero-sum game. Because of duality it can be shown that there are fairly close relations between linear programming and the theory of games.

In Section 13 we discuss duality but without dealing with the connections between linear programming and the theory of games. We shall come back to this subject in the chapter devoted to the theory of games.

Example 1. A factory makes three products: A, B and C. The machines M_1 and M_2 necessary for the manufacture of these commodities cause a bottleneck. Table 1.13 shows the time the individual machines must operate to produce one unit of the given product. The production capacities of these machines (maximum operating times in a given period) are also indicated.

TABLE 1/13

Machine	Working time per unit product			Maximum working time of machine
	A	B	C	
M_1	1	4	3	240
M_2	2	1	5	300

We must draw up a production plan that will ensure the maximum total profit, the unit profit being 2 zlotys for product A, 4 zlotys for product B and 3 zlotys for product C.

Denoting the output of commodities A, B and C by X_A, X_B and X_C, we can formulate the model of the above problem as follows:

$$X_A + 4X_B + 3X_C \leqslant 240 \tag{1}$$

$$2X_A + X_B + 5X_C \leqslant 300 \tag{2}$$

$$Z = 2X_A + 4X_B + 3X_C \text{ (maximum).} \tag{3}$$

In order to make use of the simplex algorithm, the above model is altered by introducing slack variables S_1 and S_2. As a result, we have:

$$X_A + 4X_B + 3X_C + S_1 = 240 \tag{1'}$$

$$2X_A + X_B + 5X_C + S_2 = 300 \tag{2'}$$

$$Z = 2X_A + 4X_B + 3X_C \text{ (maximum).} \tag{3'}$$

The point of departure for finding a solution is the following simplex table:

TABLE 2/13

	S_1	S_2	X_A	X_B	X_C	
S_1	1		1	4	3	240
S_2		1	2	1	5	300

We find the optimum solution in two stages. Below are the next two tables:

TABLE 3/13

	S_1	S_2	X_A	X_B	X_C		
X_B	$\dfrac{1}{4}$		$\dfrac{1}{4}$	1	$\dfrac{3}{4}$	60	$\div \dfrac{1}{4} = 240$
S_2	$-\dfrac{1}{4}$	1	$\dfrac{7}{4}$		$\dfrac{17}{4}$	240	$\div \dfrac{7}{4} = 137\dfrac{1}{7}$

TABLE 4/13

	S_1	S_2	X_A	X_B	X_C	
X_A	$\dfrac{2}{7}$	$-\dfrac{1}{7}$		1	$\dfrac{1}{7}$	$25\dfrac{5}{7}$
X_B	$-\dfrac{1}{7}$	$\dfrac{4}{7}$	1		$\dfrac{17}{7}$	$137\dfrac{1}{7}$

It is easily seen that the solution in Table 4.13 is optimum. As may be readily ascertained, none of the possible alternatives (S_1, S_2, X_C) is advantageous. The respective increments in the value of Z as a result of $S_1 = 1$, $S_2 = 1$ or $X_C = 1$ in the solution are: $-\dfrac{6}{7}$ for S_1, $-\dfrac{4}{7}$ for S_2 and $-\dfrac{17}{7}$ for X_C.

Let us write down the solution obtained, beginning from the slack variables and ending with the decision variables:

TABLE 5/13

$S_1 = 0$	$-\dfrac{6}{7}$
$S_2 = 0$	$-\dfrac{4}{7}$
$X_A = 137\dfrac{1}{7}$	0
$X_B = 25\dfrac{5}{7}$	0
$X_C = 0$	$-\dfrac{17}{7}$

In the second column of Table 5.13 we have entered the evaluation of the possible alternative optimum solutions. The numbers in this column, therefore, correspond to the increase in the value of Z caused by a unit increase in the value of the corresponding decision or slack variable.

Now let us look at the problem in Example 1 from a somewhat different point of view. To be more precise, let us formulate the problem in a somewhat different manner.

The production capacity of machines M_1 and M_2 represents a certain value because these machines can produce commodities A, B and C at a certain profit[1].

The unutilized production capacity of a machine does not represent any value to us in the sense that it does not help to create profit since it does not contribute directly to produce commodities A, B and C. This fact is expressed in our model by assuming zero values for coefficients of S_1 and S_2 in the profit function. Therefore, the profit function can be written as

$$Z = 2X_A + 4X_B + 3X_C + 0 . S_1 + 0 . S_2. \qquad (3'')$$

The unit production capacity of machine M_1 can be assigned a certain number denoting its value to us to realize profit in the manufacture of commodities A, B and C. We denote this number by w_1. Similarly, the unit production capacity of machine M_2 can be assigned a certain number — we designate it by w_2 — re-

---

[1] Of course, in a general case, we are concerned with the expression used as the criterion not with the profit.

presenting the value this unit has for us in realizing a profit by the production of commodities A, B and C.

The problem we set ourselves is to determine numbers w_1 and w_2 for an optimum production programme.

Knowing the optimum production programme, we can determine these numbers immediately. Let us turn back to Table 4.13 which contains that programme. From the first column (S_1) of this table it emerges that the equivalent of one unit production capacity of machine M_1 is 2/7th of a unit of commodity B diminished (since the coefficient 1/7 has a minus sign in front of it) by 1/7th of a unit of commodity A. This equivalent can be expressed in money units, since we know the unit profit realized by the individual products. Hence, we can write:

$$w_1 = \frac{2}{7} \cdot 4 - \frac{1}{7} \cdot 2 = \frac{6}{7}$$

In other words, when implementing a programme to ensure a maximum profit (the optimum programme), every utilized unit of the production capacity of machine M_1 will contribute to realize a profit of 6/7 zlotys.

Similarly, for machine M_2 we have

$$w_2 = -\frac{1}{7} \cdot 4 + \frac{4}{7} \cdot 2 = \frac{4}{7},$$

which means that each utilized unit of production capacity of machine M_2 enables us to obtain a profit of 4/7 zlotys.

Therefore, having the solution of the problem from Example 1, we can find the value of w_1 and w_2. It should be noted, however, that if we did not know the solution of the problem from Example 1, a linear programme could be drawn up with decision variables w_1 and w_2 and its solution would be identical to that obtained above, i.e. $w_1 = 6/7$; $w_2 = 4/7$.

Since w_1 and w_2 must correspond to the optimum production programme it follows that

$$w_1 \geqslant 0, \quad w_2 \geqslant 0.$$

We can convince ourselves of this if we recall the structure of the optimum solution. By introducing variables S_1 or S_2 into the solution, we do not contribute directly to an increase in the profit (the coefficients of these variables in formula (3″) are equal zero). On the other hand, the introduction of one unit of S_1 (the unutilized production capacity of machine M_1) produces a decrease in profit because of the need to reduce the output of other goods. We have, therefore, (on the basis of Table 4.13) an increase in profit of

$$0-\left(\frac{2}{7}.4-\frac{1}{7}.2\right).$$

If the simplex table in question (in our case 4.13) provides the optimum solution, the above expression must be negative. Nevertheless, if it were positive, it would be worth while changing the solution by bringing in a certain number of units of S_1. Therefore, in the optimum solution we must have

$$0-\left(\frac{2}{7}.4-\frac{1}{7}.2\right)\leqslant 0.$$

But the expression in brackets is simply w_1; in other words, we have the relation

$$-w_1\leqslant 0$$

or

$$w_1\geqslant 0.$$

Similarly, it can be proven that $w_1 \geqslant 0$. Therefore, we have the first group of conditions for variables w_1 and w_2:

$$w_1\geqslant 0, \quad w_2\geqslant 0. \tag{4}$$

Moreover, variables w_1 and w_2, satisfy another group of conditions. From Table 1.13 we can conclude that if some commodities, e.g. A, appear in the optimum solution, then the relation

$$1w_1+2w_2 = 2$$

will be satisfied.

This is due to the fact that a unit profit obtained from the production of a given commodity (in our case A) must equal the value of the utilized production capacity of the appropriate machines accounted for in terms of accounting prices w_1 and w_2.

If, on the other hand, some commodity, for instance C, does not appear in the optimum solution, the reason evidently must be that the resultant value of the production capacity would be higher than the profit, i.e. for commodity C,

$$3w_1+5w_2\geqslant 3.$$

If we do not know the commodities which will appear in the optimum solution, we may safeguard against error by setting for each commodity the condition giving the relationship "$\geqslant$", which means that the value of the production capacity used (in the optimum solution) is either larger than or equals the corresponding unit profit. This group of conditions may therefore be written for Example 1 as below:

$$1w_1 + 2w_2 \geqslant 2$$
$$4w_1 + 1w_2 \geqslant 4 \tag{5}$$
$$3w_1 + 5w_2 \geqslant 3.$$

Let us now assume that w_1 and w_2 take on any values that ensure the fulfilment of conditions (4) and (5). Let $\overline{X}_A$, $\overline{X}_B$ and $\overline{X}_C$ denote the output of commodities A, B and C in the optimum solution.

We multiply the first relation in the group of conditions (5) by $\overline{X}_A$:

$$\overline{X}_A . 1w_1 + \overline{X}_A . 2w_2 \geqslant 2\overline{X}_A. \tag{5'}$$

Similarly, the second relation is multiplied by $\overline{X}_B$, and the third by $\overline{X}_C$:

$$\overline{X}_B . 4w_1 + \overline{X}_B . 1w_2 \geqslant 4\overline{X}_B \tag{5''}$$
$$\overline{X}_C . 3w_1 + \overline{X}_C . 5w_2 \geqslant 3\overline{X}_C \tag{5'''}$$

On the right-hand side of each of these relations we have the overall profit from the production of the given commodity in the optimum programme; on the left-hand side, we have the corresponding outlays in terms of current prices w_1 and w_2.

Let us add the inequalities (5'), (5'') and (5'''), left side to left side, right side to right side. We obtain:

$$w_1(1\overline{X}_A + 4\overline{X}_B + 3\overline{X}_C) + w_2(2\overline{X}_A + 1\overline{X}_B + 5\overline{X}_C) \geqslant 2\overline{X}_A + 4\overline{X}_B + 3\overline{X}_C. \tag{6}$$

From Table 1.13 we see that

$$1\overline{X}_A + 4\overline{X}_B + 3\overline{X}_C \leqslant 240$$
$$2\overline{X}_A + 1\overline{X}_B + 5\overline{X}_C \leqslant 300.$$

If we replace, therefore, in relation (6) the expressions next to w_1 and w_2 by 240 and 300 respectively, we increase the left-hand side of the relation (or it may not undergo any change). Hence, we can write:

$$240w_1 + 300w_2 \geqslant 2\overline{X}_A + 4\overline{X}_B + 3\overline{X}_C. \tag{6'}$$

We denote the left-hand side of relation (6') by W:

$$W = 240w_1 + 300w_2. \tag{7}$$

The expression $2\overline{X}_A + 4\overline{X}_B + 3\overline{X}_C$ in relation (6') is precisely the total profit ensured by the optimum production programme, $\overline{X}_A$, $\overline{X}_B$, and $\overline{X}_C$.

On the other hand, w_1 and w_2 have been defined so that in the optimum production programme the unit profit for each commodity is equal to the outlays (utilization of production capacity) in terms of accounting prices w_1 and w_2. For the optimum production plan, therefore, it is possible to select w_1 and w_2 (satisfying conditions (4) and (5)) so that the sum of outlays, $W = 240w_1 + 300w_2$, is exactly equal to the profit, $2\overline{X}_A + 4\overline{X}_B + 3\overline{X}_C$. For this purpose, it is enough to minimize expression (7).

The resultant programme is a dual programme of the primary programme. Let us write the two programmes once again, side by side.

Primary programme	Dual programme
$1X_A + 4X_B + 3X_C \leqslant 240$	$1w_1 + 2w_2 \geqslant 2$
$2X_A + 1X_B + 5X_C \leqslant 300$	$4w_1 + 1w_2 \geqslant 4$
	$3w_1 + 5w_2 \geqslant 3$
$Z = 2X_A + 4X_B + 3X_C$ (maximum)	$W = 240w_1 + 300w_2$ (minimum)

Formally speaking, the dual programme is derived from the primary programme in a very simple manner. If the criterion-function in the primary programme is to be a maximum, all the relations of the model must be so transformed that the inequality relations are relations of the "$\leqslant$" type (only the free term is on the right-hand side). The coefficients of a model arranged in this way, are entered in a table. In our example this is Table 6.13.

TABLE 6/13

$\leqslant$

	X_A	X_B	X_C	
w_1	1	4	3	240
w_2	2	1	5	300
max.	2	4	3	min.

Reading this table by rows, we obtain the primary programme. Denoting the variables of the dual programme by w_1 and w_2 (their number will be the same as the number of conditions in the primary programme), we read Table 6.13 vertically.

If the primary programme were a "minimum" programme (i.e. in which the criterion-function is to be minimized), we would proceed similarly in order to obtain the dual programme. Namely, all the relations of the model would have to be so transformed that the inequalities would be relations of the "$\geqslant$" type (only free terms being on the right-hand side). The coefficients of such a model would be presented in a table similar to Table 6.13, except that they would have opposite inequality signs and that they would have a minimum where the other table shows a maximum, and vice versa.

Now, when solving directly a dual programme, we shall see that its solution can be obtained immediately if we know the solution of the primary programme. And, conversely, knowing the solution of the dual programme, we can immediately find the solution of the primary programme.

After introducing slack variables (T_1, T_2 and T_3) and artificial variables (s_1, s_2 and s_3), the dual programme has the following form:

$$1w_1 + 2w_2 - T_1 + s_1 = 2$$

$$4w_1 + 1w_2 - T_2 + s_2 = 4$$

$$3w_1 + 5w_2 - T_3 + s_3 = 3$$

$$W = 240w_1 + 300w_2 + Ms_1 + Ms_2 + Ms_3 \quad (\text{minimum})$$

where M is a sufficiently large number. Below are the successive simplex tables.

TABLE 7/13

	s_1	s_2	s_3	T_1	T_2	T_3	w_1	w_2		
s_1	1			-1			1	2	2	$\div 1 = 2$
s_2		1			-1		4	1	4	$\div 4 = 1$
s_3			1			-1	3	5	3	$\div 3 = 1$

It should be noted that in Table 7.13 we have a case of degeneracy. In Section 10 we discussed how the simplex algorithm should be modified in such cases.

TABLE 8/13

	s_1	s_2	s_3	T_1	T_2	T_3	w_1	w_2		
s'_1	1		$-\dfrac{1}{3}$	-1		$\dfrac{1}{3}$		$\dfrac{1}{3}$	1	$\div \dfrac{1}{3} = 3$
s_2		1	$-\dfrac{4}{3}$		-1	$\dfrac{4}{3}$		$-\dfrac{17}{3}$	0	$\div \dfrac{4}{3} = 0$
w_1			$\dfrac{1}{3}$			$-\dfrac{1}{3}$	1	$\dfrac{5}{3}$	1	

TABLE 9/13

	s_1	s_2	s_3	T_1	T_2	T_3	w_1	w_2		
s_1	1	$-\dfrac{1}{4}$		-1	$\dfrac{1}{4}$			$\dfrac{7}{4}$	1	$\div \dfrac{7}{4} = \dfrac{4}{7}$
T_3		$\dfrac{3}{4}$	-1		$-\dfrac{3}{4}$	1		$-\dfrac{17}{4}$	0	
w_1		$\dfrac{1}{4}$			$-\dfrac{1}{4}$		1	$\dfrac{1}{4}$	1	$\div \dfrac{1}{4} = 4$

TABLE 10/13

	s_1	s_2	s_3	T_1	T_2	T_3	w_1	w_2	
w_2	$\dfrac{4}{7}$	$-\dfrac{1}{7}$		$-\dfrac{4}{7}$	$\dfrac{1}{7}$			1	$\dfrac{4}{7}$
T_3	$\dfrac{17}{7}$	$\dfrac{1}{7}$	-1	$-\dfrac{17}{7}$	$-\dfrac{1}{7}$	1			$\dfrac{17}{7}$
w_1	$-\dfrac{1}{7}$	$\dfrac{2}{7}$		$\dfrac{1}{7}$	$-\dfrac{2}{7}$		1		$\dfrac{6}{7}$

Table 10.13 presents the final solution; from the calculation therein it appears that it is no longer profitable to introduce any alternative in the solution obtained:

$$\text{for } T_1 \qquad \frac{4}{7}.300 - \frac{1}{7}.240 = 137\frac{1}{7}$$

$$\text{for } T_2 \qquad -\frac{1}{7}.300 + \frac{2}{7}.240 = 25\frac{5}{7}.$$

Let us enter the results in Table 11.13.

TABLE 11/13

$w_1 = \dfrac{6}{7}$	0
$w_2 = \dfrac{4}{7}$	0
$T_1 = 0$	$137\dfrac{1}{7}$
$T_2 = 0$	$25\dfrac{5}{7}$
$T_3 = \dfrac{17}{7}$	0

The second column of Table 11.13 presents the evaluations of the individual alternatives which can be introduced in an optimum solution. Let us now compare Table 5.13, which gives the solution for the primary programme with Table 11.13 presenting the solution for the dual programme.

Note that for the solution of the "minimum" (dual) programme the second column of Table 5.13 should be multiplied by -1. It should also be noted that in Table 5.13 variables are so arranged that slack variables come first, then come the decision variables; in Table 11.13, on the other hand, the converse is true.

Similarly, if we are to obtain a solution for the "maximum" programme (in our case, the primary one) having the solution for the dual programme (minimum), we multiply the second column of Table 11.13 by $+1$, bearing again in mind that in one table we begin by recording the solutions for the decision variables and then proceed to the slack variables whereas in the other table we proceed in the reverse order.

The duality of linear programming is of considerable importance for various reasons. Let us point out two of them.

Firstly, in proceeding to solve a linear programme, we can always select one of two variants. We can solve either the primary or the dual programme, whichever involves less calculations.

Secondly, as we have seen from the example considered above, the dual programme may offer (though not always) an interesting economic interpretation. Valuable practical conclusions may emerge from it.

We shall now give one more example, the solution of which can be considerably simplified by having recourse to the dualism of linear programming.

Example 2. Let us prepare a fodder mixture for cattle consisting of four products: A, B, C, and D. One of the problems is to supply the cattle with certain nutrient constituents M_1, M_2, M_3 and M_4 in amounts not less than the specified minima. Table 12.13 gives these minima and the content of the nutrient constituents in the individual products.

TABLE 12/13

Nutrient	Product				Minimum
	A	B	C	D	
M_1	1	2	10	2	200
M_2	5	1	2	4	100
M_3	15	5	10	5	150
M_4	5	25	2	5	50

Sufficient quantities of products A, B, C and D must be bought to ensure a supply of the minimum amounts of nutrient constituents at the lowest cost. The sale prices of these products are 2, 5, 20 and 10 zlotys, respectively.

Moreover, when making the purchases it is necessary to ensure that product A will not exceed 20 units and in addition that the quantity of product B will be double the quantity of product C.

The model of the problem under consideration is:

$$X_A + 2X_B + 10X_C + 2X_D \geqslant 200$$
$$5X_A + X_B + 2X_C + 4X_D \geqslant 100$$
$$15X_A + 5X_B + 10X_C + 5X_D \geqslant 150 \tag{8}$$
$$5X_A + 25X_B + 2X_C + 5X_D \geqslant 50$$
$$X_A \leqslant 20$$
$$X_B = 2X_C$$
$$K = 2X_A + 5X_B + 20X_C + 10X_D \quad \text{(minimum)}. \tag{9}$$

In order to draw up a dual programme, we rearrange the system of inequalities so that: a) all the relations have the inequality sign $\geqslant$, b) the decision variables are on the left-hand sides and the slack variables on the right-hand sides, c) from the relationship having the "$=$" sign we shall determine one variable in terms of the others and substitute it in the other relations. The model transformed in this manner assumes the form:

$$X_A + 14X_C + 2X_D \geqslant 200$$
$$5X_A + 4X_C + 4X_D \geqslant 100$$
$$15X_A + 20X_C + 5X_D \geqslant 150 \tag{8'}$$
$$5X_A + 52X_C + 5X_D \geqslant 50$$
$$-X_A \geqslant -20$$
$$K = 2X_A + 30X_C + 10X_D \quad \text{(minimum)}. \tag{9'}$$

It should be remembered that in solving this model, knowing the optimum value of X_C, we can determine X_B, namely $X_B = 2X_C$.

The model obtained, or rather its coefficients, can be entered in Table 13.13.

TABLE 13/13

		X_A	X_C	X_D	
	w_1	1	14	2	200
	w_2	5	4	4	100
	w_3	15	20	5	150
	w_4	5	52	5	50
	w_5	−1	0	0	−20
$\wedge$	min.	2	30	10	max.

8*

The dual programme (with decision variables w_1, w_2, w_3, w_4 and w_5, to which we do not attribute here any real meaning) can easily be read from Table 13.13:

$$1w_1 + 5w_2 + 15w_3 + 5w_4 - w_5 \leqslant 2$$
$$14w_1 + 4w_2 + 20w_3 + 52w_4 \leqslant 30 \tag{10}$$
$$2w_1 + 4w_2 + 5w_3 + 5w_4 \leqslant 10$$
$$Z = 200w_1 + 100w_2 + 150w_3 + 50w_4 - 20w_5 \quad \text{(maximum)}. \tag{11}$$

It is not difficult to see that it will be easier to solve the dual programme, which is defined by relations (10) and (11), than the primary programme (relations (8′) and (9′)).

The simplex table for the primary programme contains 5 rows (the number of conditions) and 12 columns (3 decision, 5 slack and 4 artificial variables). The simplex table for the dual programme, however, will contain only 3 rows and 8 columns.

The solution of the dual programme by the simplex algorithm with the aid of the appropriate tables is given below.

TABLE 14/13

	S_1	S_2	S_3	w_1	w_2	w_3	w_4	w_5		
S_1	1			1	5	15	5	−1	2	$\div 1 = 2$
S_2		1		14	4	20	52		30	$\div 14 = 2\frac{1}{7}$
S_3			1	2	4	5	5		10	$\div 2 = 5$

TABLE 15/13

	S_1	S_2	S_3	w_1	w_2	w_3	w_4	w_5		
w_1	1			1	5	15	5	−1	2	
S_2	−14	1			−66	−190	−18	14	2	$\div 14 = \frac{1}{7}$
S_3	− 2		1		−6	−25	−5	2	6	$\div 2 = 3$

TABLE 16/13

	S_1	S_2	S_3	w_1	w_2	w_3	w_4	w_5	
w_1		$\dfrac{1}{14}$		1	$\dfrac{2}{7}$	$\dfrac{10}{7}$	$\dfrac{26}{7}$		$2\dfrac{1}{7}$
w_5	-1	$\dfrac{1}{14}$			$-\dfrac{33}{7}$	$-\dfrac{95}{7}$	$-\dfrac{9}{7}$	1	$\dfrac{1}{7}$
S_3		$-\dfrac{1}{7}$	1		$\dfrac{24}{7}$	$\dfrac{15}{7}$	$-\dfrac{17}{7}$		$5\dfrac{5}{7}$

The solution obtained in Table 16.13 is final. Let us write the results, beginning with the slack variables and then proceeding to the decision variables. In the extra column, moreover, we give the evaluation of the alternative optimum solutions.

TABLE 17/13

$S_1 = 0$	-20
$S_2 = 0$	$-12\dfrac{6}{7}$
$S_3 = 5\dfrac{5}{7}$	0
$w_1 = 2\dfrac{1}{7}$	0
$w_2 = 0$	$-51\dfrac{3}{7}$
$w_3 = 0$	$-407\dfrac{1}{7}$
$w_4 = 0$	$-718\dfrac{4}{7}$
$w_5 = \dfrac{1}{7}$	0

From Table 17.13 we can readily proceed to the solution of the primary programme. Entering first the consecutive decision variables and then the slack variables of the primary programme, we obtain the solution, multiplying the second column of Table 17.13 by —1 (we pass from the "maximum" to the "minimum" programme).

Therefore, the solution of the initial programme will be:

TABLE 18/13

$X_A = 20$	0
$X_C = 12\dfrac{6}{7}$	0
$X_D = 0$	$5\dfrac{5}{7}$
$T_1 = 0$	$2\dfrac{1}{7}$
$T_2 = 51\dfrac{3}{7}$	0
$T_3 = 407\dfrac{1}{7}$	0
$T_4 = 718\dfrac{4}{7}$	0
$T_5 = 0$	$\dfrac{1}{7}$

The second column of Table 18.13 gives the evaluation of the alternative optimum solutions for the primary programme.

The solution given in Table 18.13 reads as follows. The amount of product A to be bought is 20 units and of product C, 12 6/7 units, while there is no need to purchase product D. From the conditions of the problem it emerges that the quantity of product B to be bought should be double that of product C; therefore, we conclude that $X_B = 2.12\dfrac{6}{7} = 25\dfrac{5}{7}$. The solution obtained in this way is optimum; it ensures that the conditions of the problem are satisfied at the lowest costs. As may be seen from Table 18.13 the optimum solution is such that it yields some surplus for constituents M_2, M_3 and M_4 in comparison to the minimum target.

14. Influence of changes in the values of parameters on the optimum programme

The optimum values of the decision variables depend on the parameters appearing in the model. In general, it may be expected that a change of the value in at least one of the parameters will cause a change in the optimum value of one or more decision variables. The ability to investigate the effect of a change in the parameter values in the optimum programme is important for many reasons which we shall now discuss.

The simplest method of investigating this influence would be to solve a problem from the beginning, paying due attention to the new values of the parameters. However, as we have seen, the solution of a linear programme having a large number of variables and conditions is a very laborious procedure. The question, therefore, is whether a shorter way to the new optimum solution could not be found by changing the values of the parameters, knowing the optimum solution for the preceding set of parameter values.

This problem, in its general form, is not easy. In our further comments we shall therefore confine our discussion to some special cases.

The question we are considering is important for many reasons. Let us mention the two most important.

Firstly, the parameters which appear in the model may vary in time. For instance, the production capacity of a certain type of machine may change because of an increase in the number of machines; there may be a change in the coefficients (rates of transformation) determining the operating time of individual machines required to obtain one unit of the given commodity. Changes of the latter type may be due to such factors as better skill of machine operators as well as technical improvements. Finally, there may be a change in the parameters of the criterion-function, e.g. the unit cost, the unit profit, etc.

In all these cases, we should like to know how the changed parameters in question affect the optimum programme.

The second reason why the present problem deserves consideration is the fact that frequently the parameters appearing in the model are given with some approximation. In other words, the figures are not precise. In particular, as far as technical parameters are concerned, it is often quite difficult to give exact values for them. But if we know the tolerance of error with which the parameter values are given, we can investigate the effects of such error on the optimum programme.

Example 1. The work of machines M_1, M_2 and M_3, among other things, is required for the manufacture of commodities *A*, *B* and *C* in units of time shown in Table 1.14. This table also gives the production capacity of three types of machines available at the factory.

TABLE 1/14

Machine	Working time of machine for production of one unit			Production capacity of machine
	A	*B*	*C*	
M_1	2	3	10	60
M_2	5	2	5	50
M_3	4	1	6	60

Knowing the unit profit of individual products (1 zloty for A, 4 zlotys for B, 3 zlotys for C), the enterprise determines the optimum production programme. This programme, guaranteeing a maximum profit of 80 zlotys, involves manufacturing 20 units of product B. This was determined by means of the simplex algorithm. The final simplex table determining the optimum programme is given in Table 2.14.

TABLE 2/14

	S_1	S_2	S_3	X_A	X_B	X_C		
X_B	$\dfrac{1}{3}$			$\dfrac{2}{3}$	1	$\dfrac{10}{3}$	20	$\div \dfrac{2}{3} = 30$
S_2	$-\dfrac{2}{3}$	1		$\dfrac{11}{3}$		$-\dfrac{5}{3}$	10	$\div \dfrac{11}{3} = \dfrac{30}{11} = 2\dfrac{8}{11}$
S_3	$-\dfrac{1}{3}$		1	$\dfrac{10}{3}$		$\dfrac{8}{3}$	40	$\div \dfrac{10}{3} = 12$

In this table, S_1, S_2, S_3 stand for the unutilized production capacities of machines M_1, M_2, M_3.

Knowing that the unit profit of product A will shortly rise to 5 zlotys, the factory wants to draw up a new optimum production programme.

Thus, in the case in question, the value of the parameter appearing in the criterion-function has changed. It is evident that there is no need here to solve the entire problem from the beginning. A starting point can be Table 2.14 which determines the optimum production programme for the previous conditions. Now, it is only necessary to determine whether this programme can be improved as a result of a change in the parameter of the criterion-function. For this purpose, all the alternatives of the solution obtained should be considered, as is always done in the simplex algorithm. Below are given calculations which enable to evaluate the rise in profit caused by the introduction into the solution of one commodity unit not taken into account in the previous solution:

$$\text{for } S_1: \quad 0 - \frac{1}{3}.4 - \left(-\frac{2}{3}\right).0 - \left(-\frac{1}{3}\right).0 = -\frac{4}{3}$$

$$\text{for } X_A: \quad 5 - \frac{2}{3}.4 - \frac{11}{3}.0 - \frac{10}{3}.0 = 2\frac{1}{3}$$

$$\text{for } X_C: \quad 3 - \frac{10}{3}.4 - \left(-\frac{5}{3}\right).0 - \frac{8}{3}.0 = -10\frac{1}{3}.$$

These computations show that it is profitable to introduce commodity A in the solution. The maximum amount of product A which can be brought into the solution is $\frac{30}{11}$. This follows from the calculations made in Table 2.14.

Table 3.14 is a new simplex table. As may easily be ascertained, it gives a new optimum solution for the changed conditions.

TABLE 3/14

	S_1	S_2	S_3	X_A	X_B	X_C		
X_A	$\frac{5}{11}$	$-\frac{2}{11}$			1	$\frac{40}{11}$	$\frac{200}{11}$	$=18\frac{2}{11}$
X_B	$-\frac{2}{11}$	$\frac{3}{11}$		1		$-\frac{5}{11}$	$\frac{30}{11}$	$=2\frac{8}{11}$
S_3	$\frac{3}{11}$	$-\frac{10}{11}$	1			$\frac{46}{11}$	$\frac{340}{11}$	$=30\frac{10}{11}$

The new total profit is now 86 4/11.

It is easy to ascertain that the new solution obtained by the shorter procedure is really optimum. For this purpose the whole problem would have to be solved from the beginning. We leave it to the reader to check this.

Relatively little difficulty is encountered in changing the value of the parameters in the criterion-function. This is due to the fact that this change does not affect the area of feasible solutions. For this area is independent of these parameters. Thus, if we have a solution which was optimum for the previous values of the parameters in the criterion-function, we know that this solution is certainly feasible. Under the new conditions, therefore, we can accept this solution as the initial one and, using the simplex algorithm, we can quickly obtain a new optimum solution, without having to carry out the calculations again from the beginning.

The problem is not so simple when there is a change in other parameters appearing in the programme conditions but not in the criterion-function. In this case the area of feasible solutions does change. A particularly difficult case is that in which the rates of transformation vary. A relatively simpler case, and we shall only deal with this case, is when the parameters appearing as free expressions in the programme are changed.

Example 2. In a linear programme defined by the relations below

$$5X_1+X_2+2X_3+4X_4\leqslant 80 \tag{1}$$
$$X_1+2X_2+4X_3+X_4\leqslant 200 \tag{2}$$
$$2X_1+10X_2+5X_3+2X_4\leqslant 400 \tag{3}$$
$$Z = 2X_1+4X_2+5X_3+4X_4 \text{ (maximum)} \tag{4}$$

the value of the parameter on the right-hand side of inequality (1) is changed. This value increases from 80 to 150. Knowing the optimum programme for the initial problem (Table 4.14), we have to determine the optimum programme for the new conditions.

In Table 4.14 the symbols S_1, S_2 and S_3 denote the unutilized production capacities of machines M_1, M_2 and M_3.

TABLE 4/14

	S_1	S_2	S_3	X_1	X_2	X_3	X_4	
X_3	$\dfrac{2}{3}$		$-\dfrac{1}{15}$	$\dfrac{16}{5}$		1	$\dfrac{38}{15}$	$26\dfrac{2}{3}$
S_2	-2	1		-9			-7	40
X_2	$-\dfrac{1}{3}$		$\dfrac{2}{15}$	$-\dfrac{7}{5}$	1		$-\dfrac{16}{15}$	$26\dfrac{2}{3}$

Proceeding to determine the new solution, we note that the solution of Table 4.14 is valid for the new conditions. Since condition (1) is satisfied by the solution of Table 4.14, this condition will be even more satisfied when number 80 is replaced by 150, the new value of the parameter. It is only necessary to ascertain if and how the optimum programme will change in comparison with the programme determined by Table 4.14.

In the solution of Table 4.14, variable S_1 assumes 0 value. This means that the entire previous production capacity (80) is utilized.

At present we have available an additional 70 units of production capacity of machine M_1. From column S_1 of Table 4.14 it emerges that an increase in the value of S_1 by one unit in the solution, decreases the value of variable X_3 by 2/3 of a unit, and increases the value of S_2 by 2 units and the value of X_2 by 1/3. Such a unit increase in S_1 causes the profit to increase by $0 - \dfrac{2}{3} \cdot 5 - 2 \cdot 0 - \left(-\dfrac{1}{3}\right) \cdot 4 = -2$. Thus, it is unprofitable to increase S_1 as it causes a negative increment, i.e. a decrease, in the profit. It would be advantageous, however, to reduce S_1. Each reduction of S_1 by one unit would increase the profit by 2. Since we now have 70 units of S_1 in the solution, we can decrease S_1, and, as a consequence, for each unit of S_1 subtracted, there is an increase of 2/3 in X_3, a decrease of 2 in S_2 and of 1/3 in X_2.

Of course, the decrease of S_2 must not exceed 40 units and that of X_2 must not exceed 26 2/3, for if it did, S_2 or X_2 would be negative in the solution and this is impossible. By dividing 26 2/3 by 1/2, we see by how much S_1 can be reduced on account of X_2.

Since $26\frac{2}{3} \div \frac{1}{3} = 80 > 70$, S_1 can be reduced by the entire 70 units. As regards variable S_2 we have $40 \div 2 = 20 < 70$. This means that we can only reduce the value of S_1 by 20 units. For, if S_1 were decreased by more than 20 units, we would obtain a negative value for S_2, and this would be senseless. Consequently, S_1 should be reduced by 20 units.

As a result of this:

X_3 will increase by $\frac{2}{3} \cdot 20 = 13\frac{1}{3}$ and in the new solution will assume the value $26\frac{2}{3} + 13\frac{1}{3} = 40$

S_2 will decrease by $2.20 = 40$ and in the new solution will take on the value $40 - 40 = 0$

X_2 will decrease by $\frac{1}{3} \cdot 20 = 6\frac{2}{3}$ and in the new solution will assume the value $26\frac{2}{3} - 6\frac{2}{3} = 20$.

Therefore, we can compile a new simplex table. Instead of row S_2 there will now be row S_1 ($S_1 = 50$ since 20 units have already been utilized). The coefficients which we compute in the usual manner when passing from one simplex table to the next will be accordingly modified and Table 5.14 gives the new coefficients.

TABLE 5/14

	S_1	S_2	S_3	X_1	X_2	X_3	X_4		
X_3		$\frac{1}{3}$	$-\frac{1}{15}$	$\frac{1}{5}$		1	$\frac{1}{5}$	40	$\div \frac{1}{5} = 200$
S_1	1	$-\frac{1}{2}$		$\frac{9}{2}$			$\frac{7}{2}$	50	$\div \frac{7}{2} = 14\frac{2}{7}$
X_2		$-\frac{1}{6}$	$\frac{2}{15}$	$\frac{1}{10}$	1		$\frac{1}{10}$	20	$\div \frac{1}{10} = 200$

Now that we have Table 5.14, we verify whether the solution obtained can be improved. It emerges that the most advantageous alternative is to use $14\frac{2}{7}$ units of variable X_4. Table 6/14 is the new simplex table.

TABLE 6/14

	S_1	S_2	S_3	X_1	X_2	X_3	X_4	
X_3	$-\dfrac{2}{35}$	$\dfrac{38}{105}$	$-\dfrac{1}{15}$	$-\dfrac{2}{35}$		1		$37\dfrac{1}{7}$
X_4	$\dfrac{2}{7}$	$-\dfrac{1}{7}$		$\dfrac{9}{7}$			1	$14\dfrac{2}{7}$
X_2	$-\dfrac{1}{35}$	$-\dfrac{16}{105}$	$\dfrac{2}{15}$	$-\dfrac{1}{35}$	1			$18\dfrac{4}{7}$

The solution of Table 6.14, as may be verified, is the final solution. We would obtain the same result by a different and longer method if we solved anew the model defined by relations (1), (2), (3) and (4), substituting 150 for 80 in relation (1).

A similar procedure could be followed if the number 80 appearing in relation (1) of the given model instead of increasing was decreasing, e.g. to 50.

Once again, Table 4.14, which gives the optimum solution for the original problem, could serve as the starting point. From this table it emerges that $S_1=0$, in other words, all 80 units of the production capacity of machine M_1 have been utilized. In order to reduce the production capacity of machine M_1 to 50 it is necessary to calculate the change in the solution of Table 4.14 when the production capacity of machine M_1 is reduced by 30. The results of this are as follows:

$$\text{reduction of } X_3 \text{ by } \frac{2}{3} \cdot 30 = 20$$

$$\text{increase of } S_2 \text{ by } \quad 2 \cdot 30 = 60$$

$$\text{increase of } X_2 \text{ by } \frac{1}{3} \cdot 30 = 10.$$

Therefore, the new solution will be as follows:

$$X_1 = 0, \; X_2 = 26\frac{2}{3} + 10 = 36\frac{2}{3}, \; X_3 = 26\frac{2}{3} - 20 = 6\frac{2}{3},$$

$$X_4 = 0, \; S_1 = 0, \; S_2 = 100, \; S_3 = 0.$$

It can easily be verified that this is the optimum solution for the new conditions.

15. Some special cases of linear programming

Linear programming is a method which enables to solve linear models, i.e. models in which all the relations are linear. Naturally, the question arises whether there is an analogous method for non-linear models, i.e. models in which not all the relations are linear. As can easily be surmised, the solution of a non-linear model is a difficult and complex problem. Strictly speaking, at present there is no general method for solving non-linear programmes. It can hardly be expected that such a universal method could be worked out. Our present knowledge on the subject of non-linear programming can be reduced to two statements:

a) there are certain theorems concerning the conditions which the solution of a non-linear programme must satisfy,

b) methods are known for solving certain cases of non-linear programming[1]; it must be added, however, that in general these methods are complicated and quite laborious.

We shall not deal with the general case of non-linear programming. We shall discuss however a certain special case of the non-linear model which can be solved by the familiar methods of linear programming. This special case of the non-linear model consists in that the only non-linear relation in the model is the function which becomes the criterion. All the remaining relations are linear.

Example 1. Three factories — F_1, F_2 and F_3 — manufacture a certain product. This product is to be supplied to wholesale houses H_1, H_2 and H_3 in 100, 200 and 75 units, respectively. The cost of transport from each factory to each wholesale house is known. These costs are given in Table 1.15.

TABLE 1/15

F_i \ H_j	H_1	H_2	H_3
F_1	10	5	8
F_2	3	4	10
F_3	2	1	5

The unit production costs of the individual factories are not constants, independent of the volume of output, but vary with output.

This variability can be most conveniently characterized by the extent to which the increases in total costs per unit product vary with the volume of output[2].

For instance, let these increments or marginal costs for the 3 factories under consideration be as given below.

For factory F_1:

5 zlotys for an output of not more than 150.

7 zlotys for an output over 150 but not exceeding 195.

---

[1] See, for instance, H. S. Hauthakker, *The Capacity Method of Quadratic Programming*, *Econometrica*, Vol. 28, 1960.

[2] These, therefore, are so-called marginal costs.

For factory F_2:

  4 zlotys for an output of not more than 90.

  6 zlotys for an output larger than 90 but not exceeding 125.

For factory F_3:

  6 zlotys for an output of not more than 60.

  9 zlotys for an output of more than 60 but not exceeding 102.

A plan must be worked out for deliveries from factories F_1, F_2 and F_3 to the individual wholesale houses so that the total costs of production (i.e. the variable costs) and transport are as low as possible while the requirements of all the wholesale houses are met and the production capacity is not exceeded in any of the factories.

It should be noted that this example is almost identical to Example 2 which we studied in Section 11.

The sole but very essential difference is that at present the increases in costs relating to an increase in output by one unit are not constant but vary with the volume of output. As a result of this difference, in principle, our model will no longer be linear. Let us construct a model of this problem in order to ascertain this directly. By X_i we shall denote the output of factory F_i.

Let us first write the conditions which variables X_i have to satisfy in view of the production capacities of the individual factories.

$$X_1 \leqslant 195$$
$$X_2 \leqslant 125 \tag{1}$$
$$X_3 \leqslant 102.$$

Denoting by X_{ij} the volume of deliveries from factory F_i to wholesale house H_j, we can write a group of evident conditions that the aggregate deliveries from a factory to the separate wholesale houses must be equal to the output of that factory:

$$X_{11}+X_{12}+X_{13} = X_1$$
$$X_{21}+X_{22}+X_{23} = X_2 \tag{2}$$
$$X_{31}+X_{32}+X_{33} = X_3.$$

The next group of conditions concerns the satisfaction of the requirements of individual wholesale houses:

$$X_{11}+X_{21}+X_{31} = 100$$
$$X_{12}+X_{22}+X_{32} = 200 \tag{3}$$
$$X_{13}+X_{23}+X_{33} = 75.$$

Let us now consider the function of aggregate transport and production costs. This function is the criterion-function in this model. We denote by a_1 the marginal production costs of factory F_1. The value of a_1 depends here on the volume of output at this factory, which is

$$X_{11}+X_{12}+X_{13} = X_1.$$

The fact that a_1 depends on X_1 simply means that a_1 is a function of X_1, and we write this briefly $a_1(X_1)$. In our case, this relationship is very simple; it is illustrated by Fig. 1.15.

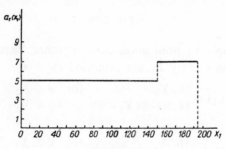

Fig. 1.15

Analytically, function $a_1(X_1)$ can be represented as follows:

$$a_1(X_1) = \begin{cases} 5 & \text{for} \quad 0 \leqslant X_1 \leqslant 150 \\ 7 & \text{for} \quad 150 < X_1 \leqslant 195. \end{cases} \tag{4}$$

Overall production costs (this is still in reference to variable costs) of factory F_1 relating to the volume of output X_1 are:

$$k_1(X_1) = \begin{cases} 5 \cdot X_1 & \text{for} \quad 0 \leqslant X_1 \leqslant 150 \\ 5 \cdot 150 + 7 \cdot (X_1 - 150) & \text{for} \quad 150 < X_1 \leqslant 195. \end{cases} \tag{4'}$$

The value of these costs (these are the total variable costs) is computed in a simple manner. Thus, as long as the output does not exceed 150, these costs are $5.X_1$ since any increase in output by one unit causes the costs to increase by 5 zlotys. On the other hand, when the output is larger than 150, the situation is somewhat different. The costs incurred in the manufacture of the first 150 units of the product come to 5.150, and each additional amount over 150, i.e. X_1—150, entails an increase of 7 zlotys per unit in the total costs. It can be easily ascertained that function $k_1(X_1)$ has the form of a broken line (Fig. 2.15).

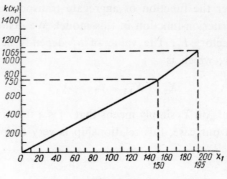

Fig. 2.16

Similar remarks apply to production costs in other factories. Thus, the total manufacturing costs in factory F_2 are expressed as

$$k_2(X_2) = \begin{cases} 4 . X_2 & \text{for } 0 \leqslant X_2 \leqslant 90 \\ 4.90 + 6(X_2 - 90) & \text{for } 90 < X_2 \leqslant 125 \end{cases} \qquad (4'')$$

and in factory F_3,

$$k_3(X_3) = \begin{cases} 6 . X_3 & \text{for } 0 \leqslant X_3 \leqslant 60 \\ 6.60 + 9(X_3 - 60) & \text{for } 60 < X_3 \leqslant 102 \end{cases} \qquad (4''')$$

where k_2 and k_3 are the total production costs in factories F_2 and F_3.

The aggregate transport and production costs connected with a certain plan of supplies may be written as

$$K = 10X_{11} + 5X_{12} + 8X_{13} + 3X_{21} + 4X_{22} + 10X_{23} + 2X_{31}$$
$$+ 1X_{32} + 5X_{33} + k_1(X_1) + k_2(X_2) + k_3(X_3). \qquad (5)$$

Finally, therefore, the problem amounts to determining the values of variables X_{11}, X_{12}, ..., etc. and variables X_1, X_2, and X_3 which satisfy the aforementioned conditions (1), (2) and (3), for which K assumes a minimum value.

As we see, function K is not linear because of components $k_1(X_1), k_2(X_2)$ and $k_3(X_3)$ and for that reason the above model cannot be solved directly by the method of linear programming. However, it is apparent that by transforming this model into a somewhat different model of equal significance it becomes possible to apply linear programming. We achieve this by introducing new variables.

We consider for instance, factory F_1. The output of this factory at marginal costs of 5 zlotys is denoted by Y_1; and at marginal costs of 7 zlotys by $\overline{Y}_1$. From the conditions of the problem it emerges that these variables have to meet the following conditions:

$$Y_1 \leqslant 150, \qquad \overline{Y}_1 \leqslant 45. \qquad (6)$$

This means that, in accordance with the assumptions of the problem, production at the lower marginal costs cannot exceed 150 units, whereas production can be increased at higher marginal costs. However, the volume of output above 150 units must not exceed 45 (this follows from the production capacities assumed).

We attach similar meanings to variables Y_2 and $\overline{Y}_2$ in reference to factory F_2 and variables Y_3 and $\overline{Y}_3$ in reference to factory F_3. These variables satisfy analogous conditions:

$$Y_2 \leqslant 90, \quad \overline{Y}_2 \leqslant 35 \tag{7}$$

$$Y_3 \leqslant 60 \quad \overline{Y}_3 \leqslant 42. \tag{8}$$

By Y_{ij} we denote the volume of deliveries from factory F_i to wholesale house H_j produced at lower marginal costs, and by $\overline{Y}_{ij}$ the volume of deliveries from factory F_i to wholesale house H_j produced at higher marginal costs. These variables must meet two groups of conditions. The first group stipulates that the aggregate output in a given factory at given marginal costs must be equal to the sum total of the factory's deliveries produced at these marginal costs.

$$
\begin{aligned}
Y_{11} + Y_{12} + Y_{13} &= Y_1 \\
\overline{Y}_{11} + \overline{Y}_{12} + \overline{Y}_{13} &= \overline{Y}_1 \\
Y_{21} + Y_{22} + Y_{23} &= Y_2 \\
\overline{Y}_{21} + \overline{Y}_{22} + \overline{Y}_{23} &= \overline{Y}_2 \\
Y_{31} + Y_{32} + Y_{33} &= Y_3 \\
\overline{Y}_{31} + \overline{Y}_{32} + \overline{Y}_{33} &= \overline{Y}_3.
\end{aligned}
\tag{9}
$$

The second group of conditions concerns the satisfaction of the requirement of each wholesale house:

$$
\begin{aligned}
Y_{11} + \overline{Y}_{11} + Y_{21} + \overline{Y}_{21} + Y_{31} + \overline{Y}_{31} &= 100 \\
Y_{12} + \overline{Y}_{12} + Y_{22} + \overline{Y}_{22} + Y_{32} + \overline{Y}_{32} &= 200 \\
Y_{13} + \overline{Y}_{13} + Y_{23} + \overline{Y}_{23} + Y_{33} + \overline{Y}_{33} &= 75.
\end{aligned}
\tag{10}
$$

The total transport and production costs will now be a linear function of the decision variables:

$$
\begin{aligned}
K = {}& 10(Y_{11} + \overline{Y}_{11}) + 5(Y_{12} + \overline{Y}_{12}) + 8(Y_{13} + \overline{Y}_{13}) + 3(Y_{21} + \overline{Y}_{21}) \\
& + 4(Y_{22} + \overline{Y}_{22}) + 10(Y_{23} + \overline{Y}_{23}) + 2(Y_{31} + \overline{Y}_{31}) \\
& + 1(Y_{32} + \overline{Y}_{32}) + 5(Y_{33} + \overline{Y}_{33}) + 5Y_1 + 7\overline{Y}_1 + 4Y_2 + 6\overline{Y}_2 + 6Y_3 + 9\overline{Y}_3.
\end{aligned}
\tag{11}
$$

The decision variables Y_{ij}, $\overline{Y}_{ij}$, Y_i, $\overline{Y}_i$ should be so selected that, while satisfying conditions (6), (7), (8), (9) and (10), they minimize function K which is defined by formula (11). Note that when proceeding to the solution, we should eliminate variables Y_i and $\overline{Y}_i$. This can easily be done by substituting for Y_i and $\overline{Y}_i$ in conditions (6), (7) and (8) the corresponding left-hand sides of equations (9). Similarly, in relation (11) we make the appropriate substitution for Y_i and $\overline{Y}_i$. Finally, Y_{ij} and $\overline{Y}_{ij}$ will be the decision variables.

The conversion of a model in which the criterion-function was not linear to a problem of linear programming can be explained by two facts.

1) Criterion-function (5) was the sum of two expressions. One expression (total transport costs) was a linear function; the other (total production costs) was the sum of functions $k_i(X_i)$, each of which was linear in its segments (cf. Fig. 2.15). This fact made it possible, by introducing new variables, to transform function (5) into a linear function.

2) The components $k_i(X_i)$ of function (5) were not only functions linear in segments, but were at the same time so-called functions convex from above[1]. The convexity consisted in that the next segment had a steeper slope to the X_i axis than the preceding segment. This feature is extremely important here. In our case, this means that the initial production conditions are more advantageous (the production costs rise more slowly as output increases) than the conditions for a larger output (production costs rise more sharply than in the initial phases for a smaller volume of output). An important conclusion from this is that until the possibilities of production at lower costs are exhausted, variables Y_i will have the value zero in the solution.

Of course, if it were otherwise, the solution would have no meaning. This explains why this convexity is so important. Hence, there is frequently talk of convex programming.

Of course, if our criterion was a non-linear function to be maximized (e.g. profit), the function would have to be convex from below[2] in order to enable the use of linear programming. The problem is that the initial conditions for realizing a profit should be more advantageous than the later conditions (e.g. for a larger volume of output). If this were not the case, we might obtain a solution that would be meaningless.

---

[1] By a function convex from above we mean one for which a segment joining any two arbitrary points of this function passes above the value which the function assumes between these two points. Cf. Fig. 3.15 a.

[2] By a function convex from below we mean a function for which the segment joining any two arbitrary points of this function passes below the value the function will assume between these two points. Cf. Fig. 3.15 b.

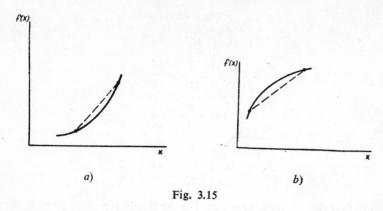

a)   b)

Fig. 3.15

Turning back to our example, we note that it can be solved by the transport method. We assume that we have six sources of supply (with three recipients H_1, H_2 and H_3). This results from "splitting" each factory in two, e.g. we split F_1 into parts which we call F_1' and F_1''. "Factory" F_1' manufactures at marginal costs of 5 zlotys and has a production capacity of 150; "factory" F_1'' produces at marginal costs of 7 zlotys and has a production capacity of 45. The situation is similar for the other two factories. The first solution obtained by the northwest corner method is given in Table 2.15.

TABLE 2/15

	H_1	H_2	H_3	N	
F_1'	100	50			150
F_1''		45			45
F_2'		90			90
F_2''		15	20		35
F_3'			55	5	60
F_3''				42	42
	100	200	75	47	

Here, the N column shows the unutilized production capacity.

Table 3.15 gives the total marginal costs for production and transport. We obtain these from Table 1.15, taking into account that each factory is "split" into two parts and knowing the unit production costs. Thus, for instance, in square $F_1'H_1$ there will be $10+5$, in square $F_1''H_1$ there will be $10+7$, etc.

9*

TABLE 3/15

	H_1	H_2	H_3	N
F_1'	15	10	13	0
F_1''	17	12	15	0
F_2'	7	8	14	0
F_2''	9	10	16	0
F_3'	8	7	11	0
F_3''	11	10	14	0

In order to find the solution, we proceed in the familiar manner given in Section 11. Below are the consecutive auxiliary tables.

TABLE 4/15

	H_1	H_2	H_3	N	
F_1'	15	10	16	5	0
F_1''	17	12	18	7	2
F_2'	13	8	14	3	-2
F_2''	15	10	16	5	0
F_3'	10	5	11	0	-5
F_3''	10	5	11	0	-5
	15	10	16	5	

TABLE 5/15

	H_1	H_2	H_3	N
F_1'	0	0	-3	-5
F_1''	0	0	-3	-7
$F_.'$	-6	0	0	-3
F_2''	-6	0	0	-5
F_3'	-2	2	0	0
F_3''	1	5	3	0

The most advantageous alternative is F_1'' N.

TABLE 6/15

	H_1	H_2	H_3	N	
F_1'	100	50			150
F_1''		40		5	45
F_2'		90			90
F_2''		20	15		35
F_3'			60		60
F_3''				42	42
	100	200	75	47	

TABLE 7/15

	H_1	H_2	H_3	N	
F_1'	15	10	16	-2	0
F_1''	17	12	18	0	2
F_2'	13	8	14	-4	-2
F_2''	15	10	16	-2	0
F_3'	10	5	11	-7	-5
F_3''	17	12	18	0	2
	15	10	16	-2	

TABLE 8/15

	H_1	H_2	H_3	N
F_1'	0	0	-3	2
F_1''	0	0	-3	0
F_2'	-6	0	0	4
F_2''	-6	0	0	2
F_3'	-2	2	0	7
F_3''	-6	-2	-4	0

Of the three most advantageous alternatives, $F_2'H_1$, $F_2''H_1$ and $F_3''H_1$, we arbitrarily select $F_2''H_1$.

TABLE 9/15

	H_1	H_2	H_3	N	
F_1'	80	70			150
F_1''		40		5	45
F_2'		90			90
F_2''	20		15		35
F_3'			60		60
F_3''				42	42
	100	200	75	47	

TABLE 10/15

	H_1	H_2	H_3	N	
F_1'	15	10	22	-2	0
F_1''	17	12	24	0	2
F_2'	13	8	20	-4	-2
F_2''	9	4	16	-8	-6
F_3'	4	-1	11	-13	-11
F_3''	17	12	24	0	2
	15	10	22	-2	

TABLE 11/15

	H_1	H_2	H_3	N
F_1'	0	0	-9	2
F_1''	0	0	-9	0
F_2'	-6	0	-6	4
F_2''	0	6	0	8
F_3'	4	8	0	13
F_3''	-6	-2	-10	0

The best alternative is $F_3''H_3$.

TABLE 12/15

	H_1	H_2	H_3	N	
F_1'	65	85			150
F_1''		25		20	45
F_2'		90			90
F_2''	35				35
F_3'			60		60
F_3''			15	27	42
	100	200	75	47	

TABLE 13/15

	H_1	H_2	H_3	N	
F_1'	15	10	12	-2	0
F_1''	17	12	14	0	2
F_2'	13	8	10	-4	-2
F_2''	9	4	6	-8	-6
F_3'	14	9	11	-3	-1
F_3''	17	12	14	0	2
	15	10	12	-2	

TABLE 14/15

	H_1	H_2	H_3	N
F_1'	0	0	1	2
F_1''	0	0	1	0
F_2'	-6	0	4	4
F_2''	0	6	10	8
F_3'	-6	-2	0	3
F_3''	-6	-2	0	0

We take $F_2' H_1$ as the most advantageous alternative.

TABLE 15/15

	H_1	H_2	H_3	N	
F_1'		150			150
F_1''		25		20	45
F_2'	65	25			90
F_2''	35				35
F_3'			60		60
F_3''			15	27	42
	100	200	75	47	

TABLE 16/15

	H_1	H_2	H_3	N	
F_1'	9	10	12	-2	0
F_1''	11	12	14	0	2
F_2'	7	8	10	-4	-2
F_2''	9	10	12	-2	0
F_3'	8	9	11	-3	-1
F_3''	11	12	14	0	2
	9	10	12	-2	

TABLE 17/15

	H_1	H_2	H_3	N
F_1'	6	0	1	2
F_1''	6	0	1	0
F_2'	0	0	4	4
F_2''	0	0	4	2
F_3'	0	-2	0	3
F_3''	0	-2	0	0

Of the two equally advantageous alternatives, $F_3'H_2$ and $F_3''H_2$, we arbitrarily choose $F_3'H_2$.

TABLE 18/15

	H_1	H_2	H_3	N	
F_1'		150			150
F_1''				45	45
F_2'	65	25			90
F_2''	35				35
F_3'		25	35		60
F_3''			40	2	42
	100	200	75	47	

TABLE 19/15

	H_1	H_2	H_3	N	
F_1'	9	10	14	0	0
F_1''	9	10	14	0	0
F_2'	7	8	12	-2	-2
F_2''	9	10	14	0	0
F_3'	6	7	11	-3	-3
F_3''	9	10	14	0	0
	9	10	14	0	

TABLE 20/15

	H_1	H_2	H_3	N
F_1'	6	0	-1	0
F_1''	8	2	1	0
F_2'	0	0	2	2
F_2''	0	0	2	0
F_3'	2	0	0	3
F_3''	2	0	0	0

The only advantageous alternative is $F_1'H_3$.

TABLE 21/15

	H_1	H_2	H_3	N	
F_1'		115	35		150
F_1''				45	45
F_2'	65	25			90
F_2''	35				35
F_3'		60			60
F_3''			40	2	42
	100	200	75	47	

TABLE 22/15

	H_1	H_2	H_3	N	
F_1'	9	10	13	−1	0
F_1''	10	11	14	0	1
F_2'	7	8	11	−3	−2
F_2''	9	10	13	−1	0
F_3'	6	7	10	−4	−3
F_3''	10	11	14	0	1
	9	10	13	−1	

TABLE 23/15

	H_1	H_2	H_3	N
F_1'	6	0	0	1
F_1''	7	1	1	0
F_2'	0	0	3	3
F_2''	0	0	3	1
F_3'	2	0	1	4
F_3''	1	−1	0	0

The only advantageous alternative is $F_3''H_2$.

TABLE 24/15

	H_1	H_2	H_3	N	
F_1'		75	75		150
F_1''				45	45
F_2'	65	25			90
F_2''	35				35
F_3'		60			60
F_3''		40		2	42
	100	200	75	47	

TABLE 25/15

TABLE 25/15

	H_1	H_2	H_3	N	
F_1'	9	10	13	0	0
F_1''	9	10	13	0	0
F_2'	7	8	11	-2	-2
F_2''	9	10	13	0	0
F_3'	6	7	10	-3	-3
F_3''	9	10	13	0	0
	9	10	13	0	

TABLE 26/15

	H_1	H_2	H_3	N
F_1'	6	0	0	0
F_1''	8	2	2	0
F_2'	0	0	3	2
F_2''	0	0	3	0
F_3'	2	0	1	3
F_3''	2	0	1	0

Table 26.15 indicates that the solution obtained in Table 24.15 is final.

It appears that factory F_1 should produce 150 units (at lower unit costs), delivering 75 units to wholesale house H_2 and 75 to H_3. There remain 45 units of unutilized production capacity in this factory. This means that factory F_1 has no need to produce on a scale which results in increased unit production costs.

Factory F_2 makes 125 units, utilizing its entire production capacity in the process. It supplies wholesale house H_1 with 100 units and H_2 with 25 units. Finally, factory F_3 turns out 100 units, leaving 2 units of its capacity unused. Factory F_3 delivers its entire output of 100 units to wholesale house H_2.

From the comments bearing on the solution of Example 1 it appears that a model in which the criterion-function is non-linear and the other functions are linear, can be transformed into a linear model, if:

a) the criterion-function is convex from above when it is to be minimized,

b) the criterion-function is convex from below when it is to be maximized.

It should be added that, in principle, in both cases the criterion-function should be linear in segments. It is easily seen, however, that every convex function can be presented with conventional accuracy as a function linear by segments. This is illustrated by Fig. 4.15 in which $f(x)$, a function convex from below, is replaced by $F(x)$, a function that closely approximates it and is linear by segments.

It appears that, in certain cases, the criterion-function cannot satisfy the convexity conditions mentioned here, and despite this the model of the given problem can be solved by linear programming methods. Examples of this type will not be discussed here. We shall merely present one more example to illustrate the applications of linear programming to cases of a non-linear criterion-function which is, or can be, approximated by an appropriate convex function, linear by segments.

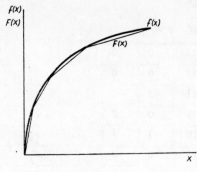

Fig. 4.15

Example 2. A factory is assigned a quarterly plan for deliveries of the products it manufactures. It has to deliver quarterly the following quantities of products in a given year:

	I	II	III	IV
	150	200	170	300

The quarterly production capacity of the factory is 250 units, and the variable production costs are expressed by the function:

$$k(x) = \begin{cases} 2x & \text{for} \quad 0 \leqslant x \leqslant 150 \\ 2 \cdot 150 + 4(x-150) & \text{for} \quad 150 < x \leqslant 200 \\ 2 \cdot 150 + 4 \cdot 50 + 5(x-200) & \text{for} \quad 200 < x \leqslant 250. \end{cases}$$

From this it follows that the increase in production costs per unit output is:
2 zlotys for an output of not more than 150 units,
4 zlotys for an output above 150 but not exceeding 200 units,
5 zlotys for an output above 200 units but not exceeding 250 units.

In selecting the optimum variant of the production plan to ensure that deliveries will be effected, we take into account the production costs connected with the implementation of the plan and the likely storage costs. For it may appear that at times it is better to satisfy the demand in a given quarter from output of earlier quarters. This, however, involves storage costs.

Let us assume that the cost of storing one unit of the product for one quarter is 3 zlotys.

Our problem may be regarded as one of transport. The output for particular quarters at specified marginal costs can be imagined to be the "suppliers". The consecutive quarters will be looked upon as the "consignees". The point will be to determine which plan of deliveries will be the optimum. Table 27.15 is our initial table for the given problem. In it we have the first solution obtained by the northwest corner rule. Since this is a case of degeneracy, quantity ε has been introduced. P_i is taken to designate the output from the quarter numbered i ($i =$ I, II, III, IV). The superscript indicates the magnitude of the marginal costs at which the production is carried out. Thus, P_i' symbolizes the output at the lowest marginal costs, i.e. at 2 zlotys, P_i'' at costs of 4 zlotys, and P_i''' at costs of 5 zlotys.

In order to be able to determine a further, and finally an optimum, solution we have to compile a table of "transport" costs. The unit "transport" costs will, in our case, represent the aggregate unit costs of production and storage. Table 28.15 gives these costs. For instance, in row P_i' they are: 2 zlotys for quarter I; 2 zlotys+3 zlotys = 5 zlotys for quarter II (in order to cover the demand in quarter II by output from quarter I, storage costs have to be incurred in addition to production costs); 2 zlotys+3 zlotys+3 zlotys = 8 zlotys for quarter III and 2 zlotys+3 zlotys+3 zlotys+3 zlotys = 11 zlotys for quarter IV. Similarly, we compute the values for the remaining rows. Note that some of the squares are not filled and this is indicated by crosses. This is because these combinations cannot enter into the solution since the demand of one quarter cannot be satisfied by production from a later period. Formally speaking, we could regard the squares filled with crosses as having infinitely large unit costs, which means that the corresponding combinations will not appear in the solution.

TABLE 27/15

	I	II	III	IV	N	
P_1'	150	ε				$150 + \varepsilon$
P_1''		$50 + \varepsilon$				$50 + \varepsilon$
P_1'''		$50 + \varepsilon$				$50 + \varepsilon$
P_2'		$100 - 3\varepsilon$	$50 + 4\varepsilon$			$150 + \varepsilon$
P_2''			$50 + \varepsilon$			$50 + \varepsilon$
P_2'''			$50 + \varepsilon$			$50 + \varepsilon$
P_3'			$20 - 6\varepsilon$	$130 + 7\varepsilon$		$150 + \varepsilon$
P_3''				$50 + \varepsilon$		$50 + \varepsilon$
P_3'''				$50 + \varepsilon$		$50 + \varepsilon$
P_4'				$70 - 9\varepsilon$	$80 + 10\varepsilon$	$150 + \varepsilon$
P_4''					$50 + \varepsilon$	$50 + \varepsilon$
P_4'''					$50 + \varepsilon$	$50 + \varepsilon$
	150	200	170	300	$180 + 12\varepsilon$	

TABLE 28/15

	I	II	III	IV	N
P_1'	2	5	8	11	0
P_1''	4	7	10	13	0
P_1'''	5	8	11	14	0
P_2'	✕	2	5	8	0
P_2''	✕	4	7	10	0
P_2'''	✕	5	8	11	0
P_3'	✕	✕	2	5	0
P_3''	✕	✕	4	7	0
P_3'''	✕	✕	5	8	0
P_4'	✕	✕	✕	2	0
P_4''	✕	✕	✕	4	0
P_4'''	✕	✕	✕	5	0

Having Table 28.15 and the initial Table 27.15, we can determine the optimum solution by the known procedure.

16. Applications of linear programming

Linear programming, as a method of solving linear programmes, can be used in various fields, such as industry, commerce, agriculture, transport, etc.

This section does not discuss typical applications of this method to the individual fields of economic activity. Such a survey would disclose that some applications to different fields have more in common than all the applications to a single specific field.

Thus, a survey of these applications by fields would result in repetition. It will, therefore, be more convenient to speak of certain typical situations to which linear programming is applied, regardless of the field it refers to. A reservation should be however made that this survey of typical situations in which linear programming can be used will by no means be complete. We shall deal only with the most frequent and best known cases.

1. The first, most typical situation to which we apply linear programming is the following.

We have many targets which can be realized with the aid of different types of resources. The feature of this is that, in general, to fulfil each individual target involves the simultaneous use of several types of resources, which may also be used to implement other targets. Moreover, the allocations of individual resources are determined in advance. This, therefore, is a situation which calls for the correct allocation of resources to achieve the individual targets. Most of the examples with which we have dealt were precisely of this type. Let us cite several such examples here by way of illustration.

Example 1. A factory produces four articles: A, B, C and D. The production of these articles entails the operation of machines M_1, M_2, M_3 and M_4, raw materials P_1, P_2 and P_3, and labour which we denote briefly by R. Having available a fixed number of machines, the factory thereby has available definite production capacities of these machines (given in hours of work per year) and a definite number of man-hours (also per year). In addition, the factory has a raw materials quota. Table 1.16 shows the working time of the machines, the quantity of raw materials and number of man-hours necessary to manufacture a unit product. The problem is to determine the optimum production plan.

TABLE 1/16

Resources	Consumption of resources per unit product				Limits on resources
	A	B	C	D	
M_1	2	5	0	0	3,000
M_2	2	3	0	4	2,500
M_3	0	6	7	3	3,200
M_4	0	0	10	15	3,600
P_1	10	15	23	16	25,000
P_2	0	10	0	20	20,000
P_3	30	0	20	5	30,000
R	10	2	3	15	100,000

In this example we have precisely the situation mentioned above. There are many targets (production of commodities A, B, C and D) which could be implemented with the aid of various resources (various machines, raw materials and labour). We must use many resources at the same time to produce each of the commodities, By determining the optimum production plan, we simultaneously establish the amounts of individual resources at our disposal to be allocated to the production of individual goods.

Of course, the optimum programme can be determined only when a criterion is given. Profit would be a relatively simple criterion. For instance, if the profits per unit of products A, B, C and D are known to be 2 zlotys, 3 zlotys, 6 zlotys and 5 zlotys, respectively, the criterion-function will have the form

$$Z = 2X_A + 3X_B + 6X_C + 5X_D$$

where X_A, X_B, X_C and X_D designate the output of individual products.

Obviously, a different criterion could be visualized. For instance, the factory may have been assigned a certain plan as to the range of products, this plan giving the proportions of the individual products to be manufactured. Let these proportions, for instance, be

$$1 \div 2 \div 1 \cdot 5 \div 0 \cdot 5.$$

This means that the output of product B should be double that of product A; the output of product C should be one and a half times that of product A and the output of product D should be half the output of product A. With this condition as to range of products, the task of the factory will be to make the best possible use of the resources at its disposal. In this situation, the complete model of the problem to be solved will be:

$$2X_A + 5X_B \leqslant 3,000$$

$$2X_A + 3X_B + 4X_D \leqslant 2,500$$

$$6X_B + 7X_C + 3X_D \leqslant 3,200$$

$$10X_C + 15X_D \leqslant 3,600$$

$$10X_A + 15X_B + 23X_C + 16X_D \leqslant 25,000 \qquad (1)$$

$$10X_B + 20X_D \leqslant 20,000$$

$$30X_A + 20X_C + 5X_D \leqslant 30,000$$

$$10X_A + 2X_B + 3X_C + 15X_D \leqslant 100,000.$$

The group of conditions (1) concerns the restraints resulting from the data in Table 1.16. A further group of conditions concerns the range:

$$X_A = \frac{1}{2}X_B \qquad X_A = \frac{1}{2}X_B$$

$$X_A = \frac{1}{1 \cdot 5}X_C \quad \text{or} \quad X_A = \frac{2}{3}X_C \qquad (2)$$

$$X_A = \frac{1}{0 \cdot 5}X_D \qquad X_A = 2X_D.$$

The output of any product may be adopted as a criterion, for instance, product A:

$$Z = X_A \text{ (maximum)}. \qquad (3)$$

Obviously, the choice of the maximum X_A, satisfying conditions (1) and (2), will give us the solution. Conditions (2) in this case guarantee the fulfilment of the task as to the range of products.

As a matter of fact, a problem so formulated becomes very simple, since in view of the group of conditions (2), conditions (1) can be transformed so as to contain only one variable: X_A. For this purpose we substitute $2X_A$ for X_B, $\dfrac{3}{2} X_A$ for X_C and $1/2X_A$ for X_D. With these substitutions, conditions (1) assume the form:

$$2X_A + 5 \cdot 2X_A = 12X_A \leqslant 3{,}000, \quad \text{i.e.} \quad X_A \leqslant 250$$

$$2X_A + 3 \cdot 2X_A + 4 \cdot \frac{1}{2}X_A = 10X_A \leqslant 2{,}500, \quad \text{i.e.} \quad X_A \leqslant 250$$

$$6 \cdot 2X_A + 7 \cdot \frac{3}{2}X_A + 3 \cdot \frac{1}{2}X_A = 24X_A \leqslant 3{,}200, \quad \text{i.e.} \quad X_A \leqslant 133\frac{1}{3}$$

$$10 \cdot \frac{3}{2}X_A + 15 \cdot \frac{1}{2}X_A = 22\frac{1}{2}X_A \leqslant 3{,}600, \quad \text{i.e.} \quad X_A \leqslant 160$$

$$10X_A + 15 \cdot 2X_A + 23 \cdot \frac{3}{2}X_A + 16 \cdot \frac{1}{2}X_A = 82\frac{1}{2}X_A \leqslant 25{,}000, \quad \text{i.e.} \quad X_A \leqslant 303\frac{1}{33} \quad (1')$$

$$10 \cdot 2X_A + 20 \cdot \frac{1}{2}X_A = 30X_A \leqslant 20{,}000, \quad \text{i.e.} \quad X_A \leqslant 666\frac{2}{3}$$

$$30 \cdot X_A + 20\frac{3}{2}X_A + 5 \cdot \frac{1}{2}X_A = 62\frac{1}{2} \leqslant 30{,}000, \quad \text{i.e.} \quad X_A \leqslant 480$$

$$10X_A + 2 \cdot 2X_A + 3 \cdot \frac{3}{2}X_A + 15 \cdot \frac{1}{2}X_A = 26X_A \leqslant 100{,}000, \quad \text{i.e.} \quad X_A \leqslant 3{,}846\frac{2}{13}$$

In accordance with criterion (3), we have to select the largest possible value for X_A which satisfies condition (1'). It is easily seen that this is $X_A = 133\ 1/3$. The "bottleneck" here is machine M_3. From conditions (2) we find

$$X_B = 2 \cdot 133\frac{1}{3} = 266\frac{2}{3}$$

$$X_C = \frac{3}{2} \cdot 133\frac{1}{3} = 200$$

$$X_D = \frac{1}{2} \cdot 133\frac{1}{3} = 66\frac{1}{2}.$$

This example illustrates that in the presence of very rigid conditions as regards the range of products, the solution of the problem becomes extremely simple.

Example 2. A farm is interested in four types of crop: U_1, U_2, U_3 and U_4. This farm has at its disposal a certain hectarage, a specified number of man-hours and certain fertilizers. Table 2.16 defines these possibilities and also gives the amount of individual resources required to obtain one ton of a given crop. The problem is to determine the optimum plan for sowing.

TABLE 2/16

Resources	Consumption of resources per ton of crop				Limits on resources
	U_1	U_2	U_3	U_4	
Hectarage	1	0·7	0·8	1·1	1,000 ha
Labour	10	3	5	4	35,000 man-hours
Fert. I	2	4	1	0	500 kg
Fert. II	0	1	0	2	250 kg
Fert. III	1	0	2	3	600 kg

Formally, the situation is entirely analogous to Example 1. Here, too, the problem is to arrive at an optimum allocation of resources which are assigned to implement individual targets. To achieve this, all that is necessary is to determine a criterion.

The type of situation which we have described here, will be called briefly the resources allocation problem. The problem is to make the best use of the available resources. Of course, the criterion determines the best use.

2. The second problem is that certain targets have been set and that for each target a minimum degree of implementation has been fixed in advance. On the other hand, the types of resources for the implementation of these targets are stipulated, but the allocation of these resources is not given. The problem is to ensure that minimum targets will at least be fulfilled with the smallest possible expenditure on resources. This is, therefore, a situation in which the resources under consideration must be allocated in such quantities as to ensure that the targets set will at least be fulfilled to the levels fixed. This type of situation is often referred to as the problem of the choice of resources. For the point is to make an optimum choice of the resources (from those taken into consideration) so as to fulfil the goals set.

We have dealt with the choice of resources in Example 2 of Sections 8 and 9, as one of the examples.

Let us cite two further examples so as to give a more thorough explanation of the problem of choice of resources.

Example 3. Three nutrient constituents M_1, M_2 and M_3 are to be supplied in the fodder to animals in amounts equal at least to the figures set in advance. Products

P_1, P_2, P_3 and P_4 contain various proportions of these nutrients. The contents of individual products in nutrients of interest to us are given in Table 3.16. An optimum plan for the purchase of products P_1, P_2, P_3 and P_4 is to be determined.

TABLE 3/16

Nutrient	Nutrient content per unit product				Minimum amount of nutrient
	P_1	P_2	P_3	P_4	
M_1	1	0·5	2	0	100
M_2	3	0·2	0	8	150
M_3	3	0·7	2	5	120

Basically, the solution of this example (at given prices for products P_1, P_2, P_3 and P_4) consists in selecting the resources (in our case, products) so that the targets set (to ensure the minimum amounts of nutrients) are achieved at the lowest cost. Therefore, this is actually a problem of the choice of resources (the products and quantities to be bought).

Example 4. A factory produces an alloy having the following properties:

a) specific weight $\leqslant 1\cdot00$

b) content of constituent $s \geqslant 10\%$

c) melting point $\geqslant 500°C$

Raw materials P_1, P_2 and P_3 having the properties indicated in Table 4.16 are the constituents involved in the production of the alloy.

TABLE 4/16

Property	Properties of raw material		
	P_1	P_2	P_3
Specific weight	0·90	0·95	1·02
Content of s	8%	12%	15%
Melting point	550°	500°	490°

The prices of the individual raw materials are: P_1 — 100 zlotys, P_2 — 300 zlotys, and P_3 — 50 zlotys.

We have to find the proportions in which P_1, P_2 and P_3 are to be used in order to obtain an alloy of the desired properties, at the lowest possible cost of raw materials.

In order to find the solution for this example, let us construct an appropriate model. The percentage contents of the individual raw materials in the alloy will be our decision variables. Let X_1, therefore, denote the percentage content of P_1 in the alloy, X_2 the percentage of P_2 and X_3 the percentage of P_3. For our decision

10

variables we could also use variables $Y_1 = \dfrac{X_1}{100}$, $Y_2 = \dfrac{X_2}{100}$, $Y_3 = \dfrac{X_3}{100}$. In principle, this second set of variables is more convenient. The condition concerning the specific weight will be

$$0{\cdot}90\,Y_1 + 0{\cdot}95\,Y_2 + 1{\cdot}02{\cdot}Y_3 \leqslant 1{\cdot}00. \tag{1}$$

Relations (2) and (3) concern the satisfaction of conditions pertaining to the content of constituents and the melting point (on the simplifying assumption that the melting points are additive)

$$8\,Y_1 + 12\,Y_2 + 15\,Y_3 \geqslant 10 \tag{2}$$

$$550\,Y_1 + 500\,Y_2 + 490\,Y_3 \geqslant 500. \tag{3}$$

There is here, of course, the additional natural condition stemming from the notations assigned the decision variables:

$$Y_1 + Y_2 + Y_3 = 1. \tag{3'}$$

From the values of variables Y_1, Y_2 and Y_3 which satisfy conditions (1), (2), (3) and (3'), let us select three for which

$$K = 100\,Y_1 + 300\,Y_2 + 50\,Y_3 \quad \text{(minimum)}. \tag{4}$$

As in the previous example, here too, the problem is one of choice of resources. We must decide upon the raw materials and the proportions in which they must be used in order to obtain the most economical alloy of the desired properties. Both of these examples can be solved by the simplex algorithm.

3. The first case which we discussed was a problem of allocation of resources. Thus, inputs of individual resources were set in advance and the problem was to allocate them for the individual goals in such a way as to achieve the highest fulfilment of the goals set.

The second case we discussed consisted in a choice of resources. Lower (and in some cases upper) limits were set in advance for individual goals and we were to determine the optimum set of resources which would enable to attain these lower limits (or not to exceed the upper limits).

The third case which we are discussing now is, in a certain sense, a synthesis of the two previous cases. Thus, on the one hand, there are allocations of resources which enable to fulfil the goals set; on the other hand, lower limits are set for the extent to which the individual goals are to be achieved. We are to make the most effective allocation of the resources for the individual goals. We shall call this type of situation the problem of allocation-choice. On the one hand (as in problem 1), we are to allocate the available resources to individual goals so as not to exceed the limit set on these resources; on the other hand (as in problem 2), we have to choose the resources for the individual goals in such a way that these goals are achieved, at least to some extent, as specified in advance.

Example 5. Factories F_1, F_2 and F_3 make a certain product to meet the demand from wholesale houses H_1, H_2, H_3 and H_4. The production capacities of the factories and the requirements of the wholesale houses are given in Table 5.16. In this table we also have the unit transport costs from each factory to each wholesale house. The problem is to establish the optimum delivery programme.

This example is a typical problem of allocations-choice. On the one hand, we have the accurate rates for achieving individual goals (the requirements of the wholesale houses) and, on the other, we have the allocations of means of production (production capacities of factories).

The goals in this case are equivalent to the delivery of the product to the four wholesale houses. The rates at which these goals are to be achieved are given by determining the volume of supplies. On the other hand, the means of production, in this case the volume of output, are limited. The individual factories cannot exceed heir production capacities. Guided by a certain criterion, in our case the transport

TABLE 5/16

F_i ╲ H_j	H_1	H_2	H_3	H_4	Production capacity
F_1	2	3	10	5	500
F_2	8	7	11	6	250
F_3	9	10	15	2	300
Supply	202	303	101	233	

costs, we have to allocate the resources, i.e. the bulk of manufactured commodities, among the wholesale houses. This allocation must be such as to ensure that the targets will be fulfilled to the specified extent, without exceeding the available resources.

The above problem, like every linear programme, can be solved by a simplex algorithm. We have seen, however, that for the solution of this special problem, which we have called the allocation-choice problem, use can be made of a special algorithm which is simpler than the simplex algorithm, namely the transportation algorithm.

A special case of the allocation-choice problem is its dynamic version. In this version the specified amounts of means are produced at different periods of time, and they can, therefore, be used to attain the respective goals within the periods of their completion. We dealt with this question in discussing non-linear programming in Section 15.

Example 6. A factory manufacturing a certain product has been assigned a plan of quarterly deliveries. The volume of deliveries which the factory must take in each quarter is given in Table 6.16.

TABLE 6/16

Quarter	Plan of supplies
I	101
II	196
III	155
IV	187

To this plan of deliveries the factory has to adjust a production plan which will: a) guarantee that the delivery plan is fulfilled, b) entail the lowest possible costs.

As a result of certain investments, the factory expands its production capacity and can produce in increasing quantity the product in each succeeding quarter at a unit cost of 10. Furthermore, the factory is able to produce some extra quantities in each quarter, but at higher unit costs of 15. The appropriate data are given in Table 7.16.

TABLE 7/16

Quarter	Production capacity at average costs of 10	Additional production capacity at average costs of 15
I	130	50
II	140	60
III	145	60
IV	150	70

The cost of storing one unit commodity for a quarter is 2 zlotys. Since the goods can be stored, the factory can produce in earlier quarters in order to make deliveries in later quarters.

The problem is one of drawing up an optimum production plan, i.e. one minimizing production costs. Furthermore, the factory is known to have available an initial stock of 15, and a stock of 20 has to be ensured for the end of the year.

This problem can easily be solved with the transportation algorithm. Table 8.16 gives the unit costs and Table 9.16 the first solution obtained by the northwest corner rule.

TABLE 8/16

Source \ Demand	I	II	III	IV	Final stock	Unutilized capacities
Initial stock	0	2	4	6	8	
I*l*.	10	12	14	16	18	0
I*h*.	15	17	19	21	23	0
II*l*.	×	10	12	14	16	0
II*h*.	×	15	17	19	21	0
III*l*.	×	×	10	12	14	0
III*h*.	×	×	15	17	19	0
IV*l*.	×	×	×	10	12	0
IV*h*.	×	×	×	15	17	0

Table 8.16 gives the unit cost involved in meeting a specified "demand" by the "supply" from a specified source. Thus, the source of supply consists of: the initial stock and the output in each quarter at the lower unit costs (we have denoted this by the letter l) and at the higher costs (symbol h).

TABLE 9/16

Source \ Demand	I	II	III	IV	Final stock	Unutilized capacity	
Initial stock	15						15
I*l*.	86	44					130
I*h*.		50					50
II*l*.		102	38				140
II*h*.			60				60
III*l*.			57	88			145
III*h*.				60			60
IV*l*.				39	20	91	150
IV*h*.						70	70
	101	196	155	187	20	161	

The interpretation of the first row is that the use of the initial stock for deliveries in the I quarter does not entail any additional costs. The use of this stock in later quarters, however, does involve storage costs. We have not filled in the last square of this row since the initial stock must either be used for deliveries or go into the final stock. The other rows are filled in a similar manner. For instance, if we take row II l the first square is not filled since the output from the second quarter cannot be used for deliveries in the I quarter.

We have entered the first feasible solution in Table 9.16 in the usual manner. Since we are seeking further solutions, we can ignore the blank spaces in Table 8.16. Formally speaking, we could say that the unit costs for the combinations corresponding to these squares are infinitely great.

4. The fourth and last situation we shall deal with here is called the assignment problem. This problem appears in many variants; let us discuss the principal ones.

The assignment problem is strictly connected with the problem of allocation. In both cases the purpose is to implement the targets by means of available resources in certain specified amounts. But the operating conditions are different. Whereas in the allocation problem each target can be attained in one way only (e.g. in the production of certain goods, a definite amount of various resources has to be used for each unit of the goods produced), in the assignment problem the individual targets can be attained in different ways (e.g. by using some quantitative combination of resources guaranteeing the output of one unit commodity).

The assignment problem is somewhat similar to the problem of choice. The chief difference is that generally in the problem of choice the assignment of resources whereby we realize the targets is not the limiting factor.

Variant A. In the simplest variant of the assignment problem, we have on the one hand a certain number of targets, for instance n, and on the other hand, the same number of different resources. Each of these n resources can be used to attain any of the n targets. An optimum assignment of resources to individual targets has to be made, and each target has to be achieved to a lesser or greater extent. Moreover, it is necessary to satisfy an additional condition which stipulates that the allocation of one resource to fulfill a given target excludes the use of this resource, even in part, for the realization of another target.

Example 7. In a certain factory the manufacture of a product calls for the production of five parts which require somewhat different skills.

Table 10.16 shows the efficiency of five different employees in making these parts.

This efficiency is given by the number of hours which the given worker requires to produce one part. In the first column of Table 10.16, for instance, we read that the first worker spends 2 hours in making one part No. 1, the second worker spends 3 hours, etc.

We are to assign workers to the production of the given parts in such a way that they spend the least possible time.

TABLE 10/16

No. of worker \ No. of parts	1	2	3	4	5
1	2	1	3	1	3
2	3	4	5	2	4
3	1	1	3	2	2
4	5	6	7	4	7
5	10	9	11	8	12

The above problem could be solved, at least theoretically, in a simple manner, by computing all the possible allocations and their efficiencies. These assignments could, for instance, be those given in Table 11.16. In this table the first three columns present, by way of example, three of the many possible assignments. They state which part will be made by each worker. Having the specified assignments on the basis of Table 10.16 we can calculate the amount of time required for all the operations.

TABLE 11/16

No. of worker \ No. of assignments	1	2	3	4	...	120
1	1	2	2			
2	2	1	1			
3	3	3	4			
4	4	4	3			
5	5	5	5			
Efficiency	25	23	25			

If we were to calculate the efficiency of each feasible assignment in this way, it would be easy to select an assignment which would give us the greatest efficiency, i.e. in our case, the least time. The difficulty involved in such a method of solution lies in the fact that there are very many possible assignments. In our case, there are 120 and, in general, there are factorial n ($n!$), i.e. the factorial of the number of targets, the number of "resources" being the same. Thus, in our case the number of ways in which the assignment can be made is:

$$5! = 5.4.3.2.1 = 120$$

We can easily see that even a slight increase in n increases sharply the number of ways in which the assignment can be made. For instance, when $n = 15$ we already have

$$15! \cong 1{,}307{,}670{,}000{,}000.$$

It appears, however, that the assignment problem can be solved in a simpler manner by linear programming. The transportation algorithm proves to be particularly useful here. Let us denote by $X_{ij} = 1$ the case in which worker i is assigned to the production of part j, and by $X_{ij} = 0$ the case in which worker i is not assigned to the production of part j. In the transportation algorithm, if the limits for the resources and the targets are integers, the solution is also given in integers[1]. Table 12.16 presents the first solution which, improved successively in the familiar manner, can be transformed into an optimum solution.

TABLE 12/16

No. of worker \ No. of parts	1	2	3	4	5	
1	1	ε				$1+\varepsilon$
2		$1-\varepsilon$	2ε			$1+\varepsilon$
3			$1-2\varepsilon$	3ε		$1+\varepsilon$
4				$1-3\varepsilon$	4ε	$1+\varepsilon$
5					$1+\varepsilon$	$1+\varepsilon$
	1	1	1	1	$1+5\varepsilon$	

Due to the special structure of the assignment problem, the transportation algorithm can be appreciably simplified in this case. But we shall not deal with this question here.

Variant B. This variant differs from variant A in that the resources are divisible. This should be taken to mean that the assignment of a factor for the purpose of fulfilling a special target does not exclude the possibility of the rest of that same factor being assigned to achieve other targets.

Example 8. Three machines (e.g. lathes) M_1, M_2 and M_3, are part of the equipment of a factory which can be used to produce (e.g. turning) four parts P_1, P_2, P_3 and P_4. These machines have certain production capacities given by the number of hours they can operate during a given period. Furthermore, we know the efficiency

---

[1] Here, X_{ij} stands for that "part" of worker i allocated to component j. Since the solutions can only be integers, X_{ij} will be either 0 or 1.

of these machines; this is the working time of each machine required to manufacture one unit of a given product. The production range is also specified in advance. Namely, the outputs of products P_1, P_2, P_3 and P_4 are to be in the proportion:

$$1 \div 3 \div 2 \div 4.$$

The problem is to arrive at such an assignment of machines for the production of each part that the production capacity of the machines is used to the best advantage. This is equivalent to the requirement that there be produced the maximum number of sets consisting of 1 unit of product P_1, 3 units of product P_2, 2 units of product P_3 and 4 of product P_4.

Table 13.16 gives the data on the efficiency of the machines and their production capacities.

TABLE 13/16

Machine \ Parts	P_1	P_2	P_3	P_4	Production capacity in machine hours
M_1	2	3	1	4	120
M_2	5	7	4	5	280
M_3	6	9	5	4	180

Attention should be paid to the correct interpretation of Table 13.16. For instance, column P_1 should be read: in order to produce one unit of P_1 we need 2 hours work by machine M_1, 5 hours by machine M_2, or 6 hours by machine M_3. The other columns should be read similarly.

We denote by X_{ij} the volume of output of commodity P_j produced by machine M_j. With these designations, the model of the problem to be solved is:

$$2X_{11}+3X_{12}+1X_{13}+4X_{14} \leqslant 120$$

$$5X_{21}+7X_{22}+4X_{23}+5X_{24} \leqslant 280 \tag{5}$$

$$6X_{31}+9X_{32}+5X_{33}+4X_{34} \leqslant 180.$$

The group of conditions (5) stipulates that the production capacities of the individual machines must not be exceeded. The second group of conditions will refer to the requirements as to range of products.

$$3(X_{11}+X_{21}+X_{31}) = X_{12}+X_{22}+X_{32} \tag{6}$$

$$2(X_{11}+X_{21}+X_{31}) = X_{13}+X_{23}+X_{33} \tag{7}$$

$$4(X_{11}+X_{21}+X_{31}) = X_{14}+X_{24}+X_{34} \tag{8}$$

Condition (6) stipulates that the total output of part P_1 by all the machines is to be one-third the total output of part P_2. Conditions (7) and (8) have a similar meaning in respect to parts P_3 and P_4.

We can take the output of any part as a criterion, e.g. P_1:

$$Z = X_{11} + X_{21} + X_{31} \text{ (maximum)}. \tag{9}$$

In this way, relations (5), (6), (7), (8) and (9) define the linear model which is to be solved. The solution can be obtained with the simplex algorithm although a certain simplified procedure can also be used here.

Variant C. This variant is even more general than the preceding. The generalization consists in that each target can be achieved by using not one factor, as in variants A and B, but by using various combinations of all or some of the available factors.

Example 9. We manufacture two products A and B by means of resources (machines, raw materials) M_1, M_2 and M_3. In order to obtain one unit of product A, one of two possible combinations of outlays of resources M_1, M_2 and M_3 can be used. One of three possible combinations of expenditure on factors of production M_1, M_2 and M_3 can be used for the production of one unit of B. These possibilities, as well as the allocation of factors, are given in Table 14.16.

TABLE 14/16

Resources	Combination of outlays	For product A		For product B			Limits on resources
		1	2	1	2	3	
M_1		2	5	4	20	10	200
M_2		3	5	15	5	3	150
M_3		6	3	18	6	9	180

We have to draw up a production plan that would enable the best possible utilization of the available resources consistent at the same time with the stipulated range. Namely, the outputs of commodities A and B to be in the ratio $1 \div 2$.

To denote the output of commodity A produced by variant No. 1 we use X_1^A and by variant No. 2, X_2^A. Similarly, the outputs of commodity B produced by the different variants are denoted by X_1^B, X_2^B and X_3^B.

With these designations the model will be:

$$2X_1^A + 5X_2^A + 4X_1^B + 20X_2^B + 10X_3^B \leqslant 200$$
$$3X_1^A + 5X_2^A + 15X_1^B + 5X_2^B + 3X_3^B \leqslant 150 \tag{10}$$
$$6X_1^A + 3X_2^A + 18X_1^B + 6X_2^B + 9X_3^B \leqslant 180.$$

By satisfying the group of conditions (10) it is ensured that the available resources are not exceeded. Condition (11) below concerns the requirements as to the range of products:

$$2(X_1^A + X_2^A) = X_1^B + X_2^B + X_3^B. \tag{11}$$

The output of any product can be taken as criterion; for instance, let us take A:

$$Z = X_1^A + X_2^A \quad \text{(maximum)}.$$

This example can also be solved by the simplex algorithm, but as in Example 8, the calculations can be simplified.

As we noted at the beginning, the aforementioned situations typical of linear programming do not exhaust all the possible situations in which the method can be applied. However, the situations mentioned above are unquestionably most characteristic and for that reason we have confined our analysis to them.

17. Bibliographical notes

At present, linear programming is one of the best developed methods of operations research. The literature on this subject is therefore appreciable. Every textbook on operations research contains more or less extensive information on this subject. Moreover, there are many special papers devoted exclusively to the theory and applications of linear programming.

Chronologically, the first bibliographical item, in linear programming, is the book by L. Kantorovich [7]. It discusses the applications of this method to a firm and gives a comprehensive exposition of the theoretical basis. It should be noted that the algorithm proposed by Kantorovich for the solution of linear programmes differs somewhat from the simplex algorithm we have presented.

An elementary exposition of linear programming is to be found in the book by R. Ferguson and L. Sargent [5] and by R. Metzger [12]. Elements of linear programming are contained in one chapter of the book by O. Lange [11]. One of the best presentations of linear programming is the book by A. Charnes, W. Cooper and A. Henderson [2]. It discusses not only the theoretical basis of this method but also its applications. However, this book requires some knowledge of linear algebra.

A detailed exposition of the mathematical foundations of linear programming is presented in the book by S. Gass [6]. It also contains a survey of the principal applications. A survey of the applications of linear programming is the sole subject of the book by S. Vajda [15].

The importance of linear programming in the theory of firms is dealt with in the book by R. Dorfman [3]. A book by three authors: R. Dorfman, P. Samuelson and R. Solow, [4] is devoted to a discussion of the role of linear programming in bourgeois economic theory.

The importance of linear programming in a planned socialist economy is dealt with in the book by L. Kantorovich [8]. In this book the reader will find much interesting material on the role which linear programming plays in the construction of a price system.

Many discussions on linear programming are contained in a collective work edited by V. Nemchinov [13].

Linear programming as connected with the theory of games is dealt with in the book by S. Vajda [14].

Many works on linear programming, its applications, the calculating technique and mathematical bases are to be found in a collective work edited by T. Koopmans [9].

A book devoted solely to special mathematical problems associated with linear programming is the collective work edited by H. Kuhn and A. Tucker [10].

The reader who wishes to learn the fundamentals of non-linear programming is referred to the book by K. J. Arrow, L. Hurwicz and H. Uzawa [1]. This book also presents algorithms according to which non-linear programmes are solved.

Papers on the subject are to be found chiefly in the journals mentioned in the bibliography of Chapter I.

In Poland, works on linear programming appear primarily in such journals as [16], [17] and [18].

It should be added that a comprehensive bibliography on linear programming is contained in the work by V. Riley and S. Gass [19].

BIBLIOGRAPHY

[1] Arrow, K. J., Hurwicz and L., Uzawa, H., *Studies in Linear and Non-linear Programming*, Stanford, 1958, Stanford Univ. Press.

[2] Charnes, A., Cooper, W. and Henderson, A., *Introduction to Linear Programming*, New York, 1953, J. Wiley.

[3] Dorfman, R., *Application of Linear Programming to the Theory of Firms*, Berkeley, 1951, Univ. of California Press.

[4] Dorfman, R., Samuelson, P. and Solow, R., *Linear Programming and Economic Analysis*, New York, 1958, McGraw-Hill.

[5] Ferguson, R. and Sargent, L., *Linear Programming — Fundamentals and Applications*, New York, 1958, McGraw-Hill.

[6] Gass, S., *Linear Programming — Methods and Applications*, New York, 1958, McGraw-Hill.

[7] Kantorovich, L., *Matematicheskiye metody organizatsiyi i planirovaniya proizvodstva (Mathematical Methods of Production and Planning)*, Leningrad, 1939, Leningradskii Gosudarstvennyi Universitet.

[8] Kantorovich, L., *Ekonomicheskii razchot nailusshego ispol'zovaniya resursov (Economic Calculation of the Best Use of Resources)*, Moscow, 1959, Izd. Akademiyi Nauk SSSR.

[9] Koopmans, T. (ed.), *Activity Analysis of Production and Allocation*, New York, 1951, J. Wiley.

[10] Kuhn, H. and Tucker, A., *Linear Inequalities and Related Systems*, Princeton, 1956, Princeton Univ. Press.

[11] Lange, O., *Introduction to Econometrics*, Warsaw–London, 1959, PWN and Pergamon Press.

[12] Metzger, R., *Elementary Mathematical Programming*, New York, 1958, J. Wiley.

[13] Nemchinov, V. (ed.), *Primeneniye matematiki v ekonomicheskikh issledovaniyakh (Applications of Mathematics in Economic Research)*, Moscow, 1959, Izd. Sotsialno-Ekonomicheskoi Literatury.

[14] Vajda, S., *The Theory of Games and Linear Programming*, London, 1956, Methuen.

[15] Vajda, S., *Readings in Linear Programming*, London, 1958, Pitman.

[16] Ekonomista.

[17] Przegląd Statystyczny (Statistical Review).

[18] Organizacja — Samorząd — Zarządzanie (Organization, Self-government, Administration).

[19] Riley, V. and Gass, S., *Bibliography on Linear Programming and Related Techniques*, Baltimore, 1958, Johns Hopkins University Press.

CHAPTER 4

Probabilistic Methods

18. Introduction to probabilistic models

This chapter is devoted to solutions of probabilistic models. Let us recall that we consider a model to be a probabilistic model when at least one of its parameters is a random variable of a known distribution. A characteristic feature of this type of situation is that for individual values of decision variables there is not only one value of the criterion-function, but that one and the same value of a decision variable may generally have many criterion-function values, occurring with varying probabilities.

Let us illustrate this with a simple example which will be considered in a more general and amplified form in the next section.

Example 1. Determine the optimum stocks of goods, knowing that the demand for these goods can be 2, 3, or 4. Table 1.18 gives the probabilities with which the demands of certain magnitudes may occur.

TABLE 1/18

Demand	Probability
2	0·1
3	0·6
4	0·3

Accumulation of stocks exceeding future demand entails losses of 10 zlotys per unit commodity. If the stocks accumulated are too small (in comparison to the demand), they must be quickly supplemented (we assume that the total demand must be satisfied), which causes an increase in costs of 5 zlotys per unit commodity as compared to the situation when provision is made for adequate stocks in advance.

How can the optimum amount of stocks be determined under such conditions? Of course, we shall regard as optimum those stocks which enable to meet demand at the lowest possible costs resulting either from a surplus of stocks over demand or from the necessity to supplement stocks if there is a rise in demand which exceeds available stocks. We denote the volume of stocks by X. It is obvious that only three values of decision variable X need be considered: 2, 3 or 4. Stocks lower than 2 are certainly unprofitable as they will have to be supplemented later to 2, 3 or 4 at an additional cost (5 zlotys per unit). Similarly, stocks larger than 4 need not

158

be considered since they would in any case entail unnecessary losses due to surplus stocks.

The difficulty which emerges when determining an optimum decision is that no single value of the criterion-function can be imputed to the individual values of the decision variable. In our case, the costs corresponding to a given stock are the criterion.

The cost function is shown in Table 2.18.

TABLE 2/18

Stock prepared \ Demand	2	3	4
2	0	5	10
3	10	0	5
4	20	10	0

When there are stocks of 2, for instance, the cost will be: 0 when the demand is 2; 5 when the demand is 3; and, finally, 10 when the demand is 4.

Similarly, there are different costs, dependent upon the actual demand, for other values of the decision variable (here the volume of accumulated stocks). Therefore, in choosing an optimum volume of stock we run into difficulty. This difficulty can be overcome by taking advantage of the fact that our parameter, the volume of demand, is a random variable of a known probability distribution, given in Table 1.18. Hence, it follows that if we establish the volume of the stock as 2, for instance, we have: a cost of 0 with a probability of $0 \cdot 1$ (such is the probability of the demand equalling 2); a cost of 5 with a probability of $0 \cdot 6$ (for such is the probability of there being a demand of 3); and finally, a cost of 10 with a probability of $0 \cdot 3$. With this information we can calculate the expected cost of accumulating a stock of 2. This will amount to:

$$0.0 \cdot 1 + 5.0 \cdot 6 + 10.0 \cdot 3 = 6.$$

In the same manner, we calculate the expected cost for a volume of stock of 3:

$$10.0 \cdot 1 + 0.0 \cdot 6 + 5.0 \cdot 3 = 2 \cdot 5.$$

And finally, the expected cost for stocks of 4 is:

$$20.0 \cdot 1 + 10.0 \cdot 6 + 0.0 \cdot 3 = 8.$$

According to the above calculations, the lowest expected cost is obtained for stocks of 3. This stock can be taken to be the optimum in regard to anticipated costs.

To summarize, it may be stated that in probabilistic models the criterion-function is a function of decision variables as well as of parameters which are random variables. The result is that for one value of the decision variable, there are various values of this function with specific probabilities. In view of this, in choosing an optimum value of the decision variable, we are not directly guided by the value of the criterion-function but by its anticipated value.

These calculations may be more or less complicated depending on the specific situation. Some of the simplest special cases, in particular, of probabilistic models met with in operations research are dealt with in subsequent sections.

19. Elementary models of stocks

In Chapter II, Section 6, Example 1 we discussed the problem of the optimum lot-size. This problem consisted in determining the size of the lot in which a given product should be manufactured when the demand for it is known. This magnitude, for a stipulated demand, depended on storage costs and fixed costs involved in starting up the production of one lot. This example can be treated as the simplest model of stocks. In practice the problem of determining an optimum volume of stocks is often more complicated owing to the element of uncertainty which arises. There can be different sources of such uncertainty. One of them is the future demand. It is often difficult to determine a unique value for the demand for a product at some future time. The delivery dates are also uncertain. For instance, if the wholesale house places an order with a factory for a lot, it must consider the possibility of delay in delivery.

There may be more sources of uncertainty of this type, depending on the concrete situation. As mentioned earlier in Chapter IV, Section 18, we shall confine ourselves to one type of uncertainty. Namely, some of the parameters which appear in the model will be treated as random variables of known probability distributions. This type of situation is troublesome in that to each of our decisions concerning the value of the decision variables there corresponds a criterion-function having not only one value but a number of values of varying probabilities. This gives rise to the principal difficulty: how is the optimum decision to be determined? One of the ways out, most often used, is to have recourse to mathematical expectancy, i.e. the mean value. An anticipated average value of a criterion-function can be determined for each possible decision. We assume that decision to be the best for which the expected value of the criterion-function becomes a minimum or maximum, depending upon the problem.

Example 1. A certain factory manufactures a perishable product. It is necessary to determine the volume of output which would ensure that the demand is met in the immediate future at the lowest possible cost. The future demand is a random variable, i.e. the probability that the demand will be lower or higher than, or equal to, a certain number x, is determined by a certain function $F(x)$[1]. This is the distribution of the random variable in question.

Let the cost of manufacturing a unit product be k_1. However, if the demand proves to be larger than the available stocks of this product, then an additional quantity must be manufactured in order to meet the full demand, this additional output being produced at a higher unit cost k_2. On the other hand, if the demand proves to be smaller than the available stocks, since the product is perishable, the factory will sustain a loss of s zlotys per unit product unsold. The magnitude of s can be equal to production costs k_1 or a figure somewhat smaller than k_1 if the spoiled product has some value.

Stocks (or volume of production) x_z should be established in such a manner that the total costs and losses involved in meeting future demand will be the lowest possible. Of course, the latter formulation will be taken to mean that anticipated costs and losses are being considered here.

In order to determine this optimum magnitude x_z, let us assume that for the time being the volume of demand is known and is x.

Two cases must be distinguished here:

a) $x_z \geqslant x$, which means that the available stocks x_z exceed the actual demand x by $(x_z - x)$. In this case the costs consist of two parts: $k_1 x$, the production costs of the part of the output sold, and $s(x_z - x)$, the losses corresponding to the surplus output above the demand.

b) $x_z < x$ which means that the available stocks x_z are $(x - x_z)$ smaller than the actual demand x. Here, too, the cost consists of two parts: $k_1 x_z$, the cost of manufacturing the available stocks and $k_2(x - x_z)$, the cost of producing an additional amount of goods.

In the first case, $(x_z \geqslant x)$, the cost amounts to

$$k_1 x + s(x_z - x) \tag{1}$$

while in the other case $(x_z < x)$,

$$k_1 x_z + k_2 (x - x_z). \tag{2}$$

Thus, if we employ the notation $dF/dx = f(x)$, the expected costs $K(x_z)$ corresponding to the volume of stocks x_z prove to be

$$E[K(x_z)] = \int_o^{x_z} [k_1 x + s(x_z - x)] f(x) \, dx + \int_{x_z}^{M} [k_1 x_z + k_2 (x - x_z)] f(x) \, dx. \tag{3}$$

---

[1] This function is assumed to be continuous.

Expression (3) constitutes a model of the problem which we are considering. Here M denotes the largest possible value of the demand. This magnitude is determined by function $F(x)$. This model contains only one relation which is, at the same time, the criterion. x_z should be so chosen that the expected costs $E[K(x_z)]$ are the lowest. The expression on the right-hand side of relation (3) is obviously a function of only one variable x_z; the other quantities, except for x, are known parameters. The variable x is an integration variable here. The whole problem, therefore, is to find the value of x_z, for which function (3) is a minimum. For this purpose, we differentiate function (3) with respect to variable x_z and set the derivative equal to zero.

It is worth while recalling here that the general formula for differentiation of function $G(x_z)$, defined by the formula

$$G(x_z) = \int_{a(x_z)}^{b(x_z)} g(x_z, x)\, dx \qquad (4)$$

is

$$\frac{dG(x_z)}{dx_z} = \int_{a(x_z)}^{b(x_z)} \frac{\partial g(x_z, x)}{\partial x_z}\, dx + g\left[x_z, b(x_z)\right] \cdot \frac{db(x_z)}{dx_z} - g\left[x_z, a(x_z)\right] \cdot \frac{da(x_z)}{dx_z}. \qquad (5)$$

We shall use this formula to differentiate expression (3).

The first term of the expression on the right-hand side of formula (3) can be written as

$$\int_0^{x_z} \left[k_1 x \cdot f(x) + sf(x) \cdot x_z - sf(x) \cdot x\right] dx = \int_0^{x_z} g(x_z, x)\, dx. \qquad (6)$$

Hence, the integrand is here function $g(x_z, x)$ from formula (4).
The limits of integration are

$$a(x_z) = 0, \qquad b(x_z) = x_z.$$

In accordance with formula (5) and by (6) we obtain

$$\frac{\partial g(x_z, x)}{\partial x_z} = sf(x).$$

$$g\left[x_z, b(x_z)\right] = k_1 x_z f(x_z) + sf(x_z) x_z - sf(x_z) x_z = k_1 x_z f(x_z)$$

$$\frac{db}{dx_z} = 1$$

$$g\left[x_z, a(x_z)\right] = 0$$

$$\frac{da}{dx_z} = 0$$

It should be noted that we obtain the expression $g[x_z, b(x_z)]$ by substituting $b(x_z) = x_z$ for x in the integrand. In a similar manner we obtain $g[x_z, a(x_z)]$. From formula (5), we find the derivative of the first term of the sum on the right-hand side of formula (3):

$$\int_0^{x_z} sf(x)\,dx + k_1 x_z f(x_z). \tag{7}$$

In a similar manner, with the aid of formula (5) we find the derivative of the second term of this sum in formula (3). Taking the integrand from the integral

$$\int_{x_z}^{M} [k_1 x_z f(x) + k_2 x f(x) - k_2 x_z f(x)]\,dx$$

for $g(x_z, x)$, we have

$$\frac{\partial g(x_z, x)}{\partial x_z} = k_1 f(x) - k_2 f(x) = (k_1 - k_2)f(x)$$

$$g(x_z, b(x_z)) = k_1 x_z f(M) + k_2 M f(M) - k_2 x_z f(M)$$

$$\frac{db(x_z)}{dx_z} = 0$$

$$g(x_z, a(x_z)) = k_1 x_z f(x_z) + k_2 x_z f(x_z) - k_2 x_z f(x_z) = k_1 x_z f(x_z)$$

$$\frac{da(x_z)}{dx_z} = 1.$$

Thus, again using (5), we find the derivative of the second term of the sum in formula (3):

$$\int_{x_z}^{M} (k_1 - k_2)f(x)\,dx - k_1 x_z f(x_z) \tag{8}$$

Taking (7) and (8) into account, we finally obtain

$$\frac{dE[K(x_z)]}{dx_z} = \int_0^{x_z} sf(x)\,dx + k_1 x_z f(x_z) + \int_{x_z}^{M} (k_1 - k_2)f(x)\,dx - k_1 x_z f(x_z)$$

$$= s\int_0^{x_z} f(x)\,dx + (k_1 - k_2)\int_{x_z}^{M} f(x)\,dx$$

Setting the derivative obtained above to equal zero, we have

$$s\int_0^{x_z} f(x)\,dx + (k_1 - k_2)\int_{x_z}^{M} f(x)\,dx = 0. \tag{9}$$

From the definition of the distribution it follows that

$$\int_0^{x_z} f(x)\,dx = F(x_z)$$

$$\int_{x_z}^{M} f(x)\,dx = 1 - F(x_z).$$

Thus, equation (9) can be written as

$$sF(x_z) + (k_1 - k_2)[1 - F(x_z)] = 0.$$

Removing the square brackets, we have

$$sF(x_z) + k_1 - k_1F(x_z) - k_2 + k_2F(x_z) = 0$$

and, therefore,

$$F(x_z)(s - k_1 + k_2) = k_2 - k_1$$

that is,

$$F(x_z) = \frac{k_2 - k_1}{s - k_1 + k_2} = \frac{k_2 - k_1}{s + k_2 - k_1}. \tag{10}$$

The interpretation of formula (10) is simple. The magnitude of production (or stocks) x_z should be so established that the probability of x_z units or less being sold equals the ratio

$$\frac{k_2 - k_1}{s + k_2 - k_1}$$

This ratio has a quite simple interpretation. In the numerator we have $k_2 - k_1$, i.e. the difference between the unit production cost when stocks are too small in comparison to demand and the unit production cost when adequate stocks are accumulated in advance. This difference can therefore be treated as a loss per unit, resulting from the actual surplus demand over the available stock. In the denominator we have $s + (k_2 - k_1)$, i.e. the sum of unit losses resulting from a surplus and deficit of stocks in relation to demand.

When the function $F(x)$ and the appropriate parameters are known, it is easy to determine an optimum volume of stocks from formula (10).

Let $F(x)$ be the distributant of the normal distribution with an average value of $m = 2,000$ and a standard deviation $\sigma = 10$. In other words, the demand for the production in question has a normal distribution with the parameters as given above. Let unit production costs be $k_1 = 1,000$ zlotys and let any additional production be at a unit cost of $k_2 = 1,200$ zlotys. Finally, let $s = 800$ zlotys. This means that when the output is greater than the actual demand we lose 800 zlotys per unit of the unsold product.

Making use of the distribution function tables for a normal distribution, we can easily determine the optimum x_z. From formula (10) we have

$$F\left(\frac{x_z-2,000}{10}\right) = \frac{1,200-1,000}{800+1,200-1,000} = \frac{200}{1,000} = 0\cdot2.$$

We have written here $\dfrac{x_z - 2,000}{10}$, as the argument of function F, hence a normalized quantity. We did this because the tables for the normal distribution give the values of a distribution function which has an average value of 0 and a standard deviation of 1. We read from these tables that the argument of function F corresponds to the value $0\cdot2$ of the distribution function.

$$\frac{x_z-2,000}{10} = -0\cdot842$$

that is,

$$x_z-2,000 = -8\cdot42$$

thus

$$x_z = 2,000-8\cdot42 = 1,991\cdot58.$$

We find, therefore, that for parameters having values as given above, stocks should amount to $x_z = 1,991\cdot58$. Stocks of this size will ensure that the anticipated costs involved in meeting the demand, which shows a normal average distribution of 2,000 and a standard deviation of 10, are the lowest.

Let us now consider a somewhat different example concerning the problem of stocks.

Example 2. A certain piece of equipment is manufactured. The production is not in series. This means that this particular piece of equipment is manufactured one at a time to order. This type of production involves certain consequences, as far as spare parts are concerned. The problem is that a certain number of spare parts must be produced at the same time as the equipment which is being manufactured. Otherwise, should it become necessary after some time of operation to replace a component, this will have to be manufactured additionally. As a rule, such production entails higher costs than when the whole equipment is produced at the same time.

Here the problem arises as to the number of spare parts to be provided for any necessary replacements. On the one hand, too large a stock of spare parts means unjustified costs; on the other hand, the lack of such parts may lead to the shutting down of the entire plant for some time and may involve higher costs for the production of the spare part.

Of course, the main difficulty in determining the correct number of spare parts is that the number required in the future is not uniquely determined. However, having experience of the operation of similar plants, we are often in a position to determine the probability of having to replace a certain number of parts during the operation of the equipment. To focus attention, let us assume that we are to determine the volume of stock for one spare part only. Let the probability distribution $P(z)$, defining the demand for this part in the course of operation, be, for example, as follows:

$$P(z = 0) = 0\cdot80$$

$$P(z = 1) = 0\cdot10$$

$$P(z = 2) = 0\cdot05$$

$$P(z = 3) = 0\cdot03$$

$$P(z = 4) = 0\cdot01$$

$$P(z = 5) = 0\cdot01$$

$$P(z \geqslant 6) = 0\cdot00.$$

From the probability distribution given above, it follows that the probability that no units of the given spare part will be required is $0\cdot80$, the probability of one part being required is $0\cdot10$, etc.

Let the cost of one spare part (when the entire piece of equipment is being manufactured) be $k_1 = 50,000$ zlotys. Let the loss due to the lack of an appropriate spare part be $k_2 = 500,000$ zlotys. This sum includes the additional sum of producing the spare part (usually higher than k_1). The problem is to establish a stock X, i.e. such a number of spare parts, for which the costs resulting from surplus stocks of these parts and the probable losses due to shortage are the lowest. Since these losses will depend not only on our decision concerning the value of X, but also (among other things) on the future demand z which is a random variable, we proceed as in the previous example. Namely, let us determine the magnitude of X which gives us the lowest anticipated loss. Two cases should be distinguished here:

a) either $X \geqslant z$, i.e. the available stock is larger than, or equal to, the demand,

b) or, $X < z$, i.e. the available stock is smaller than the actual demand.

In the first case, the loss will amount to $(X-z)k_1$, while in the second it will be $(z-X)k_2$. Thus, the expected loss, $E[K(X)]$, will be

$$E[K(X)] = \sum_{z=0}^{X} k_1(X-z) . P(z) + \sum_{z=X+1}^{M} k_2(z-X)P(z). \tag{11}$$

In formula (11) we took M as the upper limit of summation in the second sum, i.e. the largest of the values which variable z can assume. In our case $M = 5$, which follows from the probability distribution $P(z)$ as assumed by us.

If $E[K(X)]$ were a continuous function of X (as in the previous example), it would be easy to determine the minimum of this function by differential calculus. In our example, however, X (the number of parts) is not a continuous variable. The volume of stock can only be 0, 1,..., or 5. Therefore, to determine optimum X, we shall use a somewhat different technique[1]. Namely, we shall try to determine such an X^* that

$$E[K(X^* - j)] \geqslant E[K(X^*)] \leqslant E[K(X^* + i)] \tag{12}$$

for $j = 1, 2, ...; \; i = 1, 2, ...$

This means, we want to determine such an optimum stock X^* that a decrease or increase in it will cause an increase (or possibly no change) in the expected costs. For this purpose we compute the value of the expressions $E[K(X-1)]$ and $E[K(X+1)]$.

Let us substitute $X-1$ to X in formula (11):

$$E[K(X-1)] = \sum_{z=0}^{X-1} k_1(X-1-z)P(z) + \sum_{z=X}^{M} k_2(z-X+1)P(z) \tag{13}$$

Adding the term $k_1(X-1-X) P(X) = -k_1 P(X)$ to the first sum on the right-hand side, we have $\sum_{z=0}^{X} k_1(X-1-z)P(z)$. Similarly, subtracting the term $k_2(X-X+1)$ $P(X) = k_2 P(X)$ from the second sum, we obtain $\sum_{z=X+1}^{M} k_2(z-X+1)P(z)$. Therefore, we can write (12) as

$$E[K(X-1)] = \sum_{z=0}^{X} k_1(X-1-z)P(z) = k_1 P(X) + \sum_{z=X+1}^{M} k_2(z-X+1)P(z) + k_2 P(X).$$

The two sums can be broken up into separate terms of the type $k_1 P(z)$ and $k_2 P(z)$. As a result, we obtain

$$\sum_{z=0}^{X} k_1(X-z)P(z) - \sum_{z=0}^{X} k_1 P(z) + k_1 P(X)$$

$$+ \sum_{z=X+1}^{M} k_2(z-X)P(z) + \sum_{z=X+1}^{M} k_2 P(z) + k_2 P(X).$$

---

[1] See C. Churchman, R. Ackoff, E. Arnoff, *Introduction to Operations Research.*

But

$$\sum_{z=0}^{X} k_1 P(z) = k_1 \sum_{z=0}^{X} P(z)$$

and

$$\sum_{z=X+1}^{M} k_2 P(z) = k_2 \sum_{z=X+1}^{M} P(z) = k_2 \left[1 - \sum_{z=0}^{X} P(z)\right].$$

Therefore

$$E[K(X-1)] = \sum_{z=0}^{X} k_1(X-z)P(z) + \sum_{z=X+1}^{M} k_2(z-X)P(z)$$

$$-k_1 \sum_{z=0}^{X} P(z) + k_1 P(X) + k_2 - k_2 \sum_{z=0}^{X} P(z) + k_2 P(X).$$

The first two sums are identical to expression (11). Taking into account this fact and making certain algebraic transformations, we obtain

$$E[K(X-1)] = E[K(X)] - (k_1+k_2)\sum_{z=0}^{X-1} P(z) + k_2.$$

Remembering that

$$\sum_{z=0}^{X-1} P(z) = P(z \leqslant X-1),$$

we finally have

$$E[K(X-1)] = E[K(X)] - (k_1+k_2)P(z \leqslant X-1) + k_2. \tag{14}$$

Proceeding similarly, i.e. substituting $X+1$ for X in formula (11) and making transformations similar to the above, we obtain

$$E[K(X+1)] = E[K(X)] + (k_1+k_2)P(z \leqslant X) - k_2. \tag{15}$$

If X^* is the optimum volume of stock, we have, according to formula (12),

$$E[K(X^*-1)] \geqslant E[K(X^*)] \leqslant E[K(X^*+1)].$$

Substituting X^* to X in formula (14) and remembering that the inequality should be

$$E[K(X^*-1)] \geqslant E[K(X^*)],$$

we obtain the condition

$$-(k_1+k_2)P(z \leqslant X^*-1) + k_2 \geqslant 0. \tag{16}$$

Similarly, substituting X^* for X in equation (15) and remembering that

$$E[K(X^*+1)] \geqslant E[K(X^*)],$$

we obtain the condition

$$(k_1+k_2)P(z \leqslant X^*)-k_2 \geqslant 0. \tag{17}$$

Since X^* satisfies conditions (16) and (17), it will be the optimum volume of stock since it ensures minimum expected losses.

Condition (16) can be rewritten as

$$P(z \leqslant X^*-1) \leqslant \frac{k_2}{k_1+k_2}$$

and condition (17) as

$$P(z \leqslant X^*) \geqslant \frac{k_2}{k_1+k_2}$$

which together yield

$$P(z \leqslant X^*-1) \leqslant \frac{k_2}{k_1+k_2} \leqslant P(z \leqslant X^*). \tag{18}$$

Formula (18) is the solution to the problem. With it we can easily determine an optimum X^*. Let us illustrate this with the aid of the numbers given at the beginning of the example.

First of all, a distribution must be constructed. Using the numerical data given previously, we have

$$P(z \leqslant 0) = 0.80$$

$$P(z \leqslant 1) = 0.90$$

$$P(z \leqslant 2) = 0.95$$

$$P(z \leqslant 3) = 0.98$$

$$P(z \leqslant 4) = 0.99$$

$$P(z \leqslant 5) = 1.00$$

Next, bearing in mind that $k_1 = 50,000$ zlotys and $k_2 = 500,000$ zlotys, we obtain

$$\frac{k_2}{k_1+k_2} = \frac{500,000}{550,000} \cong 0.91.$$

Investigating the successive values of the distribution function for $z = 0, 1, 2, ...$, note (in keeping with formula (18)) that:

$$0.90 = P(z \leqslant 1) \leqslant 0.91 \leqslant P(z \leqslant 2) = 0.95.$$

Thus, the optimum volume of stock is $X^* = 2$.

In conclusion, it is worthwhile pointing out that the model of optimum volume of stock illustrated by Example 2 may raise some doubts of a practical nature. This model contains parameter k_2 which denotes the loss due to the lack of the spare part in question. As we have shown, this parameter includes not only the costs of producing this part (higher than under normal conditions), but also the losses resulting from the whole equipment standing idle because of the temporary lack of the spare part. Now, it is often argued that it is practically impossible to estimate the losses resulting from the equipment being out of operation. We cannot agree with this argument.

What would indeed become of the problem if we did not estimate these losses? In one way or another, a decision must be made as to the number of spare parts to be produced as stock. Suppose that the person making the decision has set this stock at $X = 4$. If someone makes a decision, it is to be believed that in his conviction, it is the optimum for the given conditions. However, from the fact that stock $X = 4$ has been acknowledged to be the optimum, it is possible to deduce how the losses k_2 must have been estimated for this decision to be regarded as truly optimum.

Taking into account formula (18), we note that the new X^* is known (equal to 4), while on the other hand, our unknown is k_2. Therefore, considering the appropriate values of the distribution function, we have

$$P(z \leqslant 3) = 0.98 \leqslant \frac{k_2}{50,000 + k_2} \leqslant P(z \leqslant 4) = 0.99.$$

That is

$$0.98 \leqslant \frac{k_2}{50,000 + k_2} \leqslant 0.99.$$

Considering the first part of this double inequality, we have

$$0.98\,(50,000 + k_2) \leqslant k_2$$

thus,

$$49,000 \leqslant k_2 - 0.98\,k_2 = 0.02\,k_2,$$

that is,

$$2,450,000 \leqslant k_2.$$

On the other hand, if we consider the second part of the given inequality, we obtain

$$k_2 \leqslant 0.99\,(50{,}000 + k_2)$$

thus

$$k_2 \leqslant 49{,}500 + 0.99\,k_2$$

or

$$k_2 - 0.99\,k_2 \leqslant 49{,}500$$

therefore,

$$0.01\,k_2 \leqslant 49{,}500.$$

Hence, finally,

$$k_2 \leqslant 4{,}950{,}000.$$

The two inequalities thus obtained indicate that the decision tacitly assumed concerning the volume of stock $X = 4$ gives the result that

$$2{,}450{,}000 \leqslant k_2 \leqslant 4{,}950{,}000.$$

Hence, in reality, whether implicit or explicit, the value of the parameter must affect the decision on stocks. It seems better to do this consciously.

In concluding this section, we should like to add that the subject of the optimum volume of stock is very extensive. We shall have further opportunities to return to problems concerning this subject. The purpose of the two examples which we considered above was merely to illustrate the simplest computing methods used to find solutions to probabilistic models.

20. The problem of queues

In examining many of the probabilistic models which are met with in practice, we are faced with a certain, well-known phenomenon which we call a "queue" or "line" in everyday language. In the present section we give some general comments on this phenomenon and against this background define in more detail some probabilistic models relating directly to the phenomenon of queues. We shall deal with the solution of some models of this type in subsequent sections.

Let us imagine that we have available some "installation" which can render specific services to users. For instance, an automatic telephone exchange is such an installation. Every subscriber can use the services of the exchange by means of a telephone and make a call to another subscriber. A post office is also such a service; a client calling can avail himself of the postal services (post a letter, buy stamps, send a money order, etc.). A shop is also such a laid on service where a client comes in order to purchase goods, etc.

From these few examples we see that the concept of installation is used very broadly. The situation which arises in connection with the functioning of such installations can be shown graphically (Fig. 1/20).

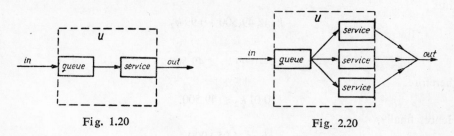

Fig. 1.20   Fig. 2.20

Every individual turning to installation U in order to receive a given service must queue up if another individual is being served. Only when the client, who has been served, leaves the installation can the next individual waiting in the queue be served. We say that this type of installation is a single channel service. Such installations can, of course, provide more than a single channel service (see Fig. 2/20). In such multi-channel installations the client waits in a queue for service only when all the channels are already busy serving other clients.

In the case of a multi-channel installation we can speak not only of queues waiting for service. It may so happen that as a result of a small number of applications, a queue may form at the other end, namely, a queue of waiting channels to serve.

It would be relatively simple to analyse the operations of the installations in question if it were known at what intervals of time the various clients will be calling and how long it takes to attend to each client. Having such information, it would be possible to make an analysis of the operation of the installation and, as a result, arrive at a conclusion as to whether the number of channels available is sufficient. Very often, however, the lapse of time between one client and the next, as well as the time of service are random variables.

Under these conditions, the decision concerning the optimum number of service channels becomes quite complicated. Before we proceed to the problem of determining an optimum decision concerning the number of channels, let us make a more detailed analysis of the operation of service installations, assuming that the number of channels is fixed in advance. The problem is, here, to examine in the first place the mechanism of queue formation.

We start from the problem of clients coming to an installation to receive a certain service.

Since the clients arrive at unpredictable times, the manner of their arrival can be described by means of an appropriate probability distribution. Let $A_0(t)$ stand for the probability that time t or less will elapse between the arrival of two successive clients. Therefore, if X denotes the time between two consecutive arrivals, we have

$$A_0(t) = P(X \leqslant t). \tag{1}$$

Therefore, function $A_0(t)$ is the distribution which we call the arrival distribution. It will be more convenient, however, instead of using distribution $A_0(t)$ to operate with function $W_0(t)$ defined by the formula:

$$W_0(t) = 1 - A_0(t) = 1 - P(X \leqslant t) = P(X > t). \tag{2}$$

$W_0(t)$ is the probability that a period of time larger than t elapses between two consecutive arrivals. This can be expressed in a different manner by the statement that $W_0(t)$ is the probability of an event that no client will arrive at the installation within the period of time equal t.

If by $a(t)$ we define the density of the probability of arrivals, i.e.

$$a(t) = \frac{dA_0(t)}{dt}, \tag{3}$$

it follows from formula (2) that

$$\frac{dW_0(t)}{dt} = -a(t). \tag{4}$$

Using the definition of the distribution function, we can write

$$A_0(t) = \int_0^t a(t)\,dt$$

and, after substituting this in formula (2), we have

$$W_0(t) = 1 - \int_0^t a(t)\,dt = \int_t^\infty a(t)\,dt \tag{5}$$

We shall now show that the average period of time T between two consecutive arrivals is

$$T = \int_0^\infty W_0(t)\,dt.$$

Note that, from the definition of the mean value, it is

$$T = \int_0^\infty t\,a(t)\,dt.$$

Making use of formula (4), we obtain

$$T = -\int_0^\infty t\,\frac{dW_0(t)}{dt}\,dt.$$

We can use here the formula for integration by parts. As a result, we obtain

$$T = -tW_0(t)\Big|_0^\infty + \int_0^\infty W_0(t)\,dt.$$

The expression $-tW_0(t)\Big|_0^\infty$ causes some difficulty. Let us make the assumption here that this expression equals zero.

Therefore, in conclusion, we have

$$T = \int_0^\infty W_0(t)\,dt. \tag{6}$$

Thus, the integral of function $W_0(t)$ is found to be the average time between two consecutive arrivals.

It is more convenient to use the inverse of the average

$$\lambda = \frac{1}{T}. \tag{7}$$

Parameter λ can be interpreted as the average rate of arrivals. For instance, if $T = 1/2$ minute, this means that there is a new arrival, on the average, every half minute. Or, in other words, there is an average of 2 arrivals per minute $\left(\lambda = \dfrac{1}{\dfrac{1}{2}} = 2\right)$,

i.e. the average rate of arrivals is 2.

Function $A_0(t)$ is a distribution function. Hence, this is a non-diminishing function of variable t. An example of such a function is given in Fig. 3/20. When function $A_0(t)$ is known, it is easy to determine function $W_0(t)$ by using formula (2). Graphically it is simple to attribute an appropriate $W_0(t)$ value to each t_0 point on Fig. 3.20, bearing in mind that $W_0(t_0) = -A_0(t_0)$. Thus, function $W_0(t)$ can easily be shown graphically on a separate diagram (Fig. 4.20).

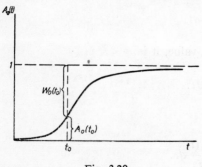

Fig. 3.20

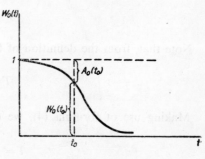

Fig. 4.20

In accordance with formula (6), the average time between two consecutive arrivals is given by the integral of function $W_0(t)$. Hence, in a graphical representation this is the area under the curve $W_0(t)$, and, in conformity with formula (7), λ is the inverse of the surface of this area.

In many applications function $W_0(t)$ takes on a certain specific form.

Let us make the following assumptions as to the arrivals of clients to obtain the services at a given installation.

a) The number of arrivals in an arbitrary period of time is independent of the number of arrivals at a different period of time (assuming that the two periods do not even partially overlap).

b) The probability of a definite number of arrivals depends only on the length of the time interval, but does not depend on when it begins or ends.

c) The possibility of two or more arrivals at the same moment is excluded, while the probability of one arrival in a sufficiently short period of time Δt is equal to $\lambda \Delta t$, where λ is a constant.

It can be shown that as a result of these three assumptions function $W_0(t)$ has the form

$$W_0(t) = e^{-\lambda t}$$

and hence,

$$a(t) = -\frac{dW_0(t)}{dt} = \lambda e^{-\lambda t} \tag{8}$$

where λ has the connotation assigned it previously, that is $\lambda = 1/T$.

If $W_0(t)$ is defined by formula (8), we say that the arrivals have a Poisson distribution. It should be added here that when the three assumptions formulated above are fulfilled, namely, when the arrivals have a Poisson distribution, function $W_0(t)$ has a broader interpretation than we originally ascribed to it. Previously we said that $W_0(t)$ is the probability that a period of time longer than t elapses between one arrival and the next. In the case of the Poisson distribution, $W_0(t)$ can have a broader interpretation. Namely, it is also the probability that the time from an arbitrary moment to the nearest arrival is longer than t.

If the arrivals have a Poisson distribution, the probability that n arrivals will be recorded in the t period of time will be expressed by formula

$$W_n(t) = \frac{(\lambda t)^n}{n!} e^{-\lambda t}. \tag{9}$$

It is easy to see that formula (8) previously quoted is a special case of formula (9) when $n = 0$.

The phenomena concerning the service offered to calling clients can be described in the above manner. For the time being, we are concerned with the services rendered only by one channel.

We have made the assumption that the time required to serve one client is a random variable. Let $B_0(t)$ stand for the probability that the time to serve one client will be equal to, or be less than t. Denoting the time of service by Y, we can write this as

$$B_0(t) = P(Y \leqslant t). \tag{10}$$

As in the case of arrivals, here too, it will be more convenient to use a function analogous to $W_0(t)$ and not the distribution $B_0(t)$; in this case, we denote this function as $V_0(t)$;

$$V_0(t) = 1 - B_0(t) = 1 - P(Y \leqslant t) = P(Y > t). \tag{11}$$

Therefore, $V_0(t)$ is the probability that the service provided to one individual will take longer than t. Denoting by $b(t)$ the probability of density of service

$$b(t) = \frac{dB_0(t)}{dt}, \tag{12}$$

we obtain from formula (11)

$$\frac{dV_0(t)}{dt} = -b(t). \tag{13}$$

Since function $b(t)$ is the probability of density of service, distribution $B_0(t)$ can be written in the form

$$B_0(t) = \int_0^t b(t)\, dt \tag{14}$$

and function $V_0(t)$ can be presented by means of formulae (11) and (14) as

$$V_0(t) = 1 - \int_0^t b(t)\, dt = \int_t^\infty b(t)\, dt.$$

We can calculate the average time of service for one client in a manner similar to that used in the case of the average time between two arrivals. We denote the average time of service by U. From the definition of the mean value, we have

$$U = \int_0^\infty t\, b(t)\, dt.$$

Using formula (13), we obtain

$$U = -\int_0^\infty t\, \frac{dV_0(t)}{dt}\, dt.$$

and, after integrating by parts (as in the case of formula (6)), we have

$$U = -tV_0(t)\Big|_0^\infty + \int_0^\infty V_0(t)\,dt$$

and finally

$$U = \int_0^\infty V_0(t)\,dt. \tag{15}$$

Let us denote by μ the inverse of the average time of service U:

$$\mu = \frac{1}{U}. \tag{16}$$

We shall call the quantity μ the average rate of service. The value of this parameter defines the average number of clients attended to per unit time. Thus, for example, if $U = 2$ min., then $\mu = 1/2$; i.e. within one minute an average of 1/2 individual is attended to.

In one particular case, function $V_0(t)$ can be given a somewhat broader interpretation. We stated earlier that $V_0(t)$ is the probability that the time of serving one client is longer than t. However, we may be interested in the probability that the channel already engaged in attending to a client will continue to be occupied for a period longer than t. This second interpretation can be given to function $V_0(t)$ if it can be presented as

$$V_0(t) = e^{-\mu t}. \tag{17}$$

It follows that in this case

$$b(t) = -\frac{dV_0(t)}{dt} = \mu e^{-\mu t}. \tag{18}$$

When we deal with formula (17), we say that the service time has an exponential distribution. The assumptions which must be made in order to arrive at an exponential distribution are analogous to those we made in order to obtain a Poisson distribution of arrivals. They are as follows:

a) the number of individuals already attended to at some arbitrarily chosen interval of time (during which the channel was engaged on providing service and was not standing idle) is independent of the number of clients attended to during a different interval of time,

b) the probability that a specific number of individuals will be attended to depends only on the length of the time interval; on the other hand, it is independent of the beginning and end of the interval (again, we take time interval to mean only the period of time during which the channel was used to render services, disregarding the periods of standing idle),

c) the possibility of two or more clients leaving a service channel simultaneously is precluded, while the possibility of one client leaving a service channel in a sufficiently short period of time Δt during which the channel was occupied is $\mu\Delta t$.

In principle, such exponential distribution could be called the Poisson distribution, but it has been agreed here not to use this name because in this case we generally do not use function $V_n(t)$ which is similar to function (9). Although theoretically function $V_n(t)$ could be constructed here, nonetheless, since it is of no major practical significance — and this precisely justifies the name of "Poisson distribution" — we shall use in this case the name "exponential distribution".

We have already described the mechanism of arrivals and the mechanism of service; in order to complete the description of the installation we are concerned with, we still have to describe the mechanism of queue formation. We shall describe this mechanism with an example of a Poisson distribution of arrivals and an exponential distribution of service time. We thus consider the probability of the queue being of a definite length, and we shall also consider the average length of the queue. We assume a queue-length to mean the number of clients waiting for service[1].

Let us denote by $P_n(t)$ the probability that at an instant of time t there are n clients in the queue. In this number we include the client being served.

We begin our analysis from the case $n = 0$, i.e. we want to calculate the value of the expression $P_0(t)$. For this purpose let us take an instant of time $t+\Delta t$, very close to t, where Δt is sufficiently small, and let us compute $P_0(t+\Delta t)$, i.e. the probability that at instant $t+\Delta t$ there are 0 individuals in the queue. Since we have assumed that Δt is a very short interval of time, then, according to the assumptions of the Poisson distribution of arrivals, at most one client can arrive during the period Δt. Hence, in order to have 0 individuals in the system at the instant $t+\Delta t$, it is necessary that there shall be:

either 0 clients in the system at instant t
and 0 arrivals in time Δt,

or, 1 client in the system at instant t and

0 arrivals within the time Δt and one client attended to within the time Δt.

The probability of the first contingency is

$$P_0(t)(1-\lambda\Delta t) \tag{19}$$

the probability of the other is

$$P_1(t)(1-\lambda\Delta t)\mu\Delta t. \tag{20}$$

In order to obtain these relationships we make use of the aforementioned properties of the distributions of arrivals and service times.

---

[1] Strictly speaking, this is the sum of waiting clients and clients being attended to.

Relation (19) is the product of the probability $P_0(t)$ that there are zero clients in the system at instant t and the probability $(1-\lambda\Delta t)$ that there will be no arrivals within the time Δt[1].

Relation (20) has a similar interpretation.

The fact that there are 0 individuals in the queue at the instant $t+\Delta t$ can be surmised from the occurrence of one of the two aforementioned events which are mutually exclusive, having probabilities defined by formulae (19) and (20); hence the probability $P_0(t+\Delta t)$ will be the sum of those two probabilities:

$$P_0(t+\Delta t) = P_0(t)(1-\lambda\Delta t)+P_1(t)(1-\lambda\Delta t)\mu\Delta t. \tag{21}$$

Carrying out the multiplication on the right-hand side of relation (21), we arrive at:

$$P_0(t+\Delta t) = P_0(t)-P_0(t)\lambda\Delta t+P_1(t)\mu\Delta t-P_1(t)\lambda\mu(\Delta t)^2.$$

If we transfer $P_0(t)$ to the left-hand side and divide both sides by Δt, we obtain

$$\frac{P_0(t+\Delta t)-P_0(t)}{\Delta t} = -\lambda P_0(t)+\mu P_1(t)-\lambda\mu P_1(t)\Delta t.$$

If the interval of time Δt is diminishing, i.e. when $\Delta t \to 0$, the left-hand side will become a derivative of function $P_0(t)$. On the right-hand side, as $\Delta t \to 0$, the expression $-\lambda\mu P_1(t)\Delta t$ will tend to zero. As a result we obtain:

$$\frac{dP_0(t)}{d(t)} = -\lambda P_0(t)+\mu P_1(t). \tag{22}$$

Assuming that $P_n(t)$ is independent of t (where n is any number), i.e. assuming that the probability of n individuals being in the queue is independent of the instant t, we have the condition:

$$\frac{dP_0(t)}{dt} = 0.$$

Setting expression (22) equal to zero, we obtain

$$\lambda P_0(t) = \mu P_1(t)$$

or

$$P_0 = \frac{\mu}{\lambda}P_1. \tag{23}$$

We enter here P_0 and P_1 in place of $P_0(t)$ and $P_1(t)$ since we are making use of the assumption just formulated that these probabilities are independent of t.

---

[1] We remember that the probability of one arrival in a sufficiently short period of time Δt is $\lambda\Delta t$.

We have therefore calculated the desired probability P_0. Unfortunately, it is expressed in terms of probability P_1 which is unknown.

We shall now calculate $P_n(t)$ when $n = 1$. Our procedure is analogous to that used before. Namely, our point of departure will be instant $t+\Delta t$ and we shall try to calculate $P_1(t+\Delta t)$. In order to have one individual in the queue at the instant $(t+\Delta t)$, one of the following mutually incompatible contingencies must occur:

1) At instant t there was one individual in the queue; during the period Δt there were no arrivals and no individuals left the system. The probability of this contingency is

$$P_1(t)(1-\lambda\Delta t)(1-\mu\Delta t) = P_1(t)-\lambda P_1(t)\Delta t-\mu P_1(t)\Delta t$$
$$+ \lambda\mu P_1(t)(\Delta t)^2.$$

2) At instant t there was one individual in the queue; during the period Δt one individual arrived and one left the system. The probability of this is

$$P_1(t)\lambda\Delta t\mu\Delta t = \lambda\mu P_1(t)(\Delta t)^2.$$

3) At instant t there were no individuals in the queue; during the period Δt one individual arrived and none left the system. The probability of this case is

$$P_0(t)\lambda\Delta t(1-\mu\Delta t) = \lambda P_0(t)\Delta t-\lambda\mu P_0(t)(\Delta t)^2.$$

4) At instant t there were two individuals in the queue; in the period Δt one left the system and none arrived. The probability of this case is

$$P_2(t)\mu\Delta t(1-\lambda\Delta t) = \mu P_2(t)\Delta t-\lambda\mu P_2(t)(\Delta t)^2.$$

Since the event of having one individual in the system at the instant $t+\Delta t$ can occur in any one of the four ways described above, the probability $P_1(t+\Delta t)$ will be the sum of the probabilities itemized there. In this sum we can disregard the expressions containing the term $(\Delta t)^2$. We can proceed in this manner since, as before, we divide both sides of the equations by Δt. In this way, the expressions containing the term $(\Delta t)^2$ will now contain the term Δt. As $\Delta t \to 0$ these terms will also tend to zero. Therefore, we can write:

$$P_1(t+\Delta t) = P_1(t)-\lambda P_1(t)\Delta t-\mu P_1(t)\Delta t+\lambda P_0(t)\Delta t+\mu P_2(t)\Delta t.$$

By transferring $P_1(t)$ to the left-hand side and dividing both sides by Δt, we obtain:

$$\frac{P_1(t+\Delta t)-P_1(t)}{\Delta t} = -\lambda P_1(t)-\mu P_1(t)+\lambda P_0(t)+\mu P_2(t)$$

or, after taking the limit when $\Delta t \to 0$,

$$\frac{dP_1(t)}{dt} = -\lambda P_1(t) - \mu P_1(t) + \lambda P_0(t) + \mu P_2(t). \tag{24}$$

From the assumption that $P_n(t)$ is independent of t, it follows that the derivative defined by formula (24) equals zero, i.e.

$$\lambda P_1 + \mu P_1 = \lambda P_0 + \mu P_2.$$

Substituting the expression defined by formula (23) for P_0, we obtain

$$\lambda P_1 + \mu P_1 = \mu P_1 + \mu P_2$$

and after reducing both terms by μP_1, we obtain

$$\lambda P_1 = \mu P_2$$

or finally

$$P_1 = \frac{\mu}{\lambda} P_2 \tag{24'}$$

Thus, we have obtained

$$P_0 = \frac{\mu}{\lambda} P_1$$

$$P_1 = \frac{\mu}{\lambda} P_2.$$

In an analogous manner, it can be proved that

$$P_2 = \frac{\mu}{\lambda} P_3$$

$$P_3 = \frac{\mu}{\lambda} P_4$$

and, generally, that

$$P_n = \frac{\mu}{\lambda} P_{n+1} \quad \text{for} \quad n = 0, 1, 2, \dots \tag{25}$$

The general formula (25) which we have obtained for the probability that there will be n individuals in the queue (including the individual being served), is inconvenient since in practice P_n cannot be calculated without knowing P_{n+1}, which in turn can be computed if P_{n+2} is known, etc. This difficulty can be overcome, however, if we take advantage of the fact that the sum of the probabilities P_n for

$n = 0, 1, 2, \ldots$ equals one. There are, indeed, in the queue, 0 or one, or two, etc. individuals. We have, therefore, the relation

$$\sum_{n=0}^{\infty} P_n = 1. \tag{26}$$

From formula (25), we note that

$$\sum_{n=0}^{\infty} P_n = \frac{\mu}{\lambda} \sum_{n=1}^{\infty} P_n$$

If we want to extend the sum on the right-hand side to $n = 0$, the first term will be $\mu/\lambda P_0$. Thus, we can write

$$\sum_{n=0}^{\infty} P_n = \frac{\mu}{\lambda} \sum_{n=0}^{\infty} P_n - \frac{\mu}{\lambda} P_0$$

or, using condition (26)

$$1 = \frac{\mu}{\lambda} - \frac{\mu}{\lambda} P_0.$$

Thus, the result is

$$P_0 = 1 - \frac{\lambda}{\mu}. \tag{27}$$

Note that P_0 is a probability, therefore, a non-negative number. It follows from this that $1 - \frac{\lambda}{\mu} \geqslant 0$, or $\frac{\lambda}{\mu} \leqslant 1$. This formula is valid only for this case[1]. Hence we have obtained a form of the formula for P_0 in which P_1 does not appear.

Substituting the expression from formula (27) for P_0 in formula (23), we can determine P_1:

$$1 - \frac{\lambda}{\mu} = \frac{\mu}{\lambda} P_1,$$

thus

$$P_1 = \frac{\lambda}{\mu}\left(1 - \frac{\lambda}{\mu}\right). \tag{28}$$

In turn, from the formula

$$P_1 = \frac{\mu}{\lambda} P_2$$

---

[1] If the opposite were true, i.e. if $\frac{\lambda}{\mu} > 1$ or $\lambda > \mu$, this would mean that the clients would arrive at the system at a higher average rate than the rate at which they leave; therefore, the length of the queue would grow to infinity.

P_2 can be determined by substituting the expression defined by formula (28) for P_1:

$$\frac{\lambda}{\mu}\left(1 - \frac{\lambda}{\mu}\right) = \frac{\mu}{\lambda} P_2$$

$$P_2 = \left(\frac{\lambda}{\mu}\right)^2 \left(1 - \frac{\lambda}{\mu}\right). \tag{29}$$

Proceeding further in this way, we obtain a general formula

$$P_n = \left(\frac{\lambda}{\mu}\right)^n \left(1 - \frac{\lambda}{\mu}\right) \quad \text{for} \quad n = 0, 1, 2, \ldots \tag{30}$$

Let us emphasize that this formula also holds for $n = 0$, since

$$P_0 = \left(\frac{\lambda}{\mu}\right)^0 \left(1 - \frac{\lambda}{\mu}\right) = 1 - \frac{\lambda}{\mu}$$

and therefore, this expression is identical to that obtained in formula (27).

Attention should be drawn to the need to strengthen the assumption that $\frac{\lambda}{\mu} \leqslant 1$, made in connection with the derivation of the formula for P_0. Namely, the probability of $\frac{\lambda}{\mu} = 1$ should be excluded. If this were so, all the probabilities P_n would equal zero and, hence, their sum would also equal zero. Therefore, it is necessary to make the assumption that $\frac{\lambda}{\mu} < 1$, i.e. $\lambda < \mu$. This means that the average rate of arrivals is lower than the average rate of service.

It is simple now to find the anticipated length of the queue. We denote the length of the queue by the number of waiting individuals plus the individuals being attended to. Of course, this quantity n is a random variable and its expected value is by definition determined from formula

$$E(n) = \sum_{n=0}^{\infty} n P_n. \tag{31}$$

Utilizing formula (30), we can convert expression (31) to obtain

$$E(n) = \sum_{n=0}^{\infty} n \left(\frac{\lambda}{\mu}\right)^n \left(1 - \frac{\lambda}{\mu}\right) = \left(1 - \frac{\lambda}{\mu}\right) \sum_{n=0}^{\infty} n \left(\frac{\lambda}{\mu}\right)^n$$

If, as we assumed, $\dfrac{\lambda}{\mu} < 1$, then the series

$$\sum_{n=0}^{\infty} n\left(\frac{\lambda}{\mu}\right)^n$$

is convergent[1] and its value is

$$\frac{\dfrac{\lambda}{\mu}}{\left(1 - \dfrac{\lambda}{\mu}\right)^2} .$$

Therefore, we have

$$E(n) = \left(1 - \frac{\lambda}{\mu}\right)\frac{\dfrac{\lambda}{\mu}}{\left(1 - \dfrac{\lambda}{\mu}\right)^2} = \frac{\dfrac{\lambda}{\mu}}{1 - \dfrac{\lambda}{\mu}} = \frac{\lambda}{\mu - \lambda}. \tag{32}$$

To conclude the present section, it should be stressed that the formulae we have obtained for the probability of various queue-lengths and for the average queue-length have limited application. All the assumptions which we formulated in the course of our reasoning must namely be fulfilled.

The problem becomes much more involved when these assumptions are not fulfilled. Whilst we shall not elaborate here or in the following sections a mathematical theory for a more general case, we shall later give a practical procedure to follow in those cases to which the assumptions formulated above do not apply. This will concern the so-called Monte Carlo method.

21. Uses of the theory of queues

In order to illustrate the simplest uses of the theory of queues, described in Section 20, we shall discuss two examples. Further examples will be given in subsequent sections.

Example 1. In a large factory, a certain number of machines of a similar type are in operation. From time to time these machines have minor breakdowns. The probability distribution of these breakdowns is a Poisson distribution, i.e. the probability of there being n breakdowns in a period of time t is:

$$W_n(t) = \frac{(\lambda t)^n}{n!} e^{-\lambda t} .$$

---

[1] The reader will find proof of this in most textbooks on differential calculus.

where $\lambda = 2$ and this means that there is an average of 2 breakdowns per unit time (e.g. per hour).

In this particular factory there is a repair squad, but in view of the installation necessary for the repair of machines, repairs can be carried out on one machine only at a time. The distribution of service time is exponential, i.e. the probability that it will take longer than time t to repair a machine is

$$V_0(t) = e^{-\mu t}$$

in which $\mu = 3$, i.e. an average of 3 machines are attended to within a unit time (one hour).

The factory is examining the possibility of decreasing or increasing the size of the repair squad. This, of course, affects coefficient μ. The problem is to establish such a value of μ (hence, indirectly the size of the repair squad) that the sum of costs consisting of the repair squad's wages and the losses due to machines standing idle while waiting for repairs, is the lowest possible.

Let

$$\mu(k) = 0\cdot1 + 0\cdot001 \cdot k \quad \text{for} \quad k > 1,900 \tag{1}$$

where k stands for the monthly cost of maintaining a squad to ensure that the value of coefficient μ is at the level $\mu(k)$. Since $\mu(k)$ must be larger than $\lambda = 2$, there is a limitation on k ($k > 1,900$).

Although this example is highly simplified and naive, its solution will give us an insight into the method of solving problems of this type.

The decision variable here is the monthly costs k of maintaining the repair squad (indirectly, this variable is the value μ). For every magnitude k, hence for every value of coefficient μ, there is a certain expected cost (loss) connected with the machines standing idle. For instance, assuming that one machine standing idle for one hour results in a loss of 500 zlotys. The average number of idle machines (waiting for repairs and being repaired), in accordance with formula (32) of the previous section, is

$$E(n) = \frac{\lambda}{\mu - \lambda}.$$

Therefore, for an 8-hour working day the resultant average losses amount to

$$S_1 = 8 \cdot \frac{\lambda}{\mu - \lambda} \cdot 500$$

which, after expression (1) is substituted for μ and the value 2 for λ, yields

$$S_1 = 4,000 \cdot \frac{2}{0\cdot1 + 0\cdot001\,k - 2}. \tag{2}$$

The daily cost of maintaining a repair squad is $k/30$, assuming 30 days in a month. Therefore, the sum of the average (expected) daily losses and costs per squad is

$$S_2 = S_1 + \frac{k}{30} \quad \text{where} \quad k > 1{,}900. \tag{3}$$

The problem is to determine such a magnitude for k that expression (3) is a minimum, on condition that $k > 1{,}900$.

Substituting the value from formula (2) for S_1, we have

$$S_2 = 4{,}000 \cdot \frac{2}{0 \cdot 1 + 0 \cdot 001\,k - 2} + \frac{k}{30}$$

that is,

$$S_2 = \frac{8{,}000}{0 \cdot 001\,k - 1 \cdot 9} + \frac{k}{30}. \tag{3'}$$

The value of k should be so chosen that expression S_2 is a minimum. For this purpose function S_2 must be differentiated and its derivative equated to zero:

$$\frac{dS_2}{dk} = -\frac{8{,}000 \cdot 0 \cdot 001}{(0 \cdot 001\,k - 1 \cdot 9)^2} + \frac{1}{30} = \frac{-8}{(0 \cdot 001\,k - 1 \cdot 9)^2} + \frac{1}{30}.$$

Equating the derivative to zero, we have the equation:

$$\frac{-8}{(0 \cdot 001\,k - 1 \cdot 9)^2} + \frac{1}{30} = 0$$

or

$$\frac{8}{(0 \cdot 001\,k - 1 \cdot 9)^2} = \frac{1}{30}.$$

After conversion we obtain a quadratic equation

$$0 \cdot 000001\,k^2 - 0 \cdot 0038\,k - 236 \cdot 39 = 0$$

or

$$k^2 - 3{,}800\,k - 236{,}390{,}000 = 0.$$

After finding the square root of this equation's discriminant, we arrive at the solution

$$k = \frac{3{,}800 + 30{,}984}{2} = 17{,}392.$$

It can be ascertained that function S_2 actually reaches its minimum when $k = 17{,}392$. The value obtained for k is the final solution of the problem since the condition that $k > 1{,}900$ is also met.

The interpretation of our solution is as follows. At the outset we assumed that μ is 3. It followed therefrom (relation (1)) that

$$3 = 0{\cdot}1 + 0{\cdot}001\,k,$$

Therefore, $k = 2,900$ and the wages of the repair squad are 2,900 zlotys monthly. The total average daily losses due to machines standing idle plus the daily wages of the repair squad according to formula (3) amount to

$$S_2 = 8 \cdot \frac{2}{3-2} \cdot 500 + \frac{2,900}{30} = 8,096{\cdot}6\,.$$

For the optimum solution, the coefficient μ changes, namely:

$$\mu = 0{\cdot}1 + 0{\cdot}001\,.\,17{,}392 = 17{,}492$$

Thus

$$S_2 = 8 \cdot \frac{2}{17{,}492 - 2} \cdot 500 + \frac{17{,}392}{30} = 1,096{\cdot}1\,.$$

Hence, by increasing the number of the repair squad, the total anticipated daily losses due to machines standing idle and daily wages, dropped more than seven-fold.

Example 2. A factory has an installation to deal with repairs of machines that have broken down. This installation cannot handle more than one machine at a time. We assume that the efficiency of this installation, measured by coefficient μ, is 2. In other words, this installation can repair an average of 2 machines per hour. Coefficient λ equals $1{\cdot}5$ which means that $1{\cdot}5$ machines break down within an hour on an average. The factory has the possibility of building another, identical installation, with the same coefficient 2. The question is whether it is profitable to construct a second installation.

In order to arrive at a decision on this we require information on the loss per hour involved in one machine standing idle, and the hourly cost of operating one installation. Let this loss be, say, 400 zlotys. Let the latter operating cost be 500 zlotys (this includes all costs, i.e. amortization, labour, servicing, etc.).

First of all, we compute by the known method the average sum of losses and costs incurred by the factory when one installation is available.

According to formula (32) of the previous section, the anticipated queue-length (including the machines in repair) amounts to

$$E(n) = \frac{\lambda}{\mu - \lambda} = \frac{1{\cdot}5}{2 - 1{\cdot}5} = 3\,.$$

Therefore, the cost of machines standing idle during an 8-hour working day is:

$$8\,.\,400 \text{ zlotys}\,.\,3 = 9,600 \text{ zlotys}.$$

After adding $8 \cdot 500$ zlotys $= 4,000$ zlotys, which is the daily cost of the installation for servicing the machines, we have a total of 13,600 zlotys which is the sum of the anticipated daily losses and costs involved in the repair of machines in one installation. We must calculate, further, the anticipated queue-length when two installations are available and the corresponding anticipated daily losses and costs. Comparing the two above sums, we readily arrive at a decision whether it would be profitable for the factory to build a second installation.

First, it is necessary to compute the probabilities $P_n^{(2)}$ that in a two-channel installation the queue will consist of n machines. We start by calculating $P_0^{(2)}$, proceeding as before. Namely, let us consider the instant $t+\Delta t$, where Δt is a sufficiently short interval of time so that there can be only one "arrival" and possibly one "exit" for a machine from a servicing "channel".

We compute the value of the probability $P_0^{(2)}$ $(t+\Delta t)$ as in Section 20.

A situation may arise when there will be 0 units at moment $t+\Delta t$ in one of the following events:

1) at instant t there are 0 units in the queue and no unit arrives during the period Δt;

2) at instant t there is 1 unit in the queue and during the period Δt 1 unit leaves and 0 arrive;

3) at instant t there are 2 units in the queue and during the period Δt 0 units arrive and 2 leave.

It is possible here for 2 units to leave during period Δt because there are 2 channels. The probability of 2 units leaving during period Δt, is, of course, $(\mu\Delta t)^2$.

After calculating the probabilities of the three events listed above and adding them together, we finally obtain

$$P_0^{(2)} = \frac{\mu}{\lambda} P_1^{(2)}. \tag{4}$$

The probability $P_1^{(2)}$ $(t+\Delta t)$ is calculated in a similar fashion.

In order to have one unit in the queue at the instant $t+\Delta t$, one of the following situations must be present:

1) At instant t there are 0 units, and during the period Δt, 1 unit arrived. The probability of this case is

$$P_0^{(2)}(t)\lambda\Delta t.$$

2) At instant t there is 1 unit, and during the period Δt nothing was added and nothing taken away. The corresponding probability is

$$P_1^{(2)}(t)(1-\lambda\Delta t)(1-\mu\Delta t) \cong P_1^{(2)}(t) - \mu P_1^{(2)}(t)\Delta t - \lambda P_1^{(2)}(t)\Delta t.$$

On the right-hand side of the above equation, the term with the factor $(\Delta t)^2$ was left out for similar reasons as before. Namely, after dividing this term by Δt and on passing to the limit ($\Delta t \to 0$), we find that this term disappears.

3) At instant t there is 1 unit, while during the period Δt, 1 unit arrives and 1 leaves. The appropriate probability is

$$P_1^{(2)}(t)\,\mu\Delta t\lambda\Delta t \cong 0.$$

4) At instant t there are 2 units, and during the period Δt, 1 unit leaves and 0 arrive.

This probability amounts to

$$P_2^{(2)}(t)\,2\,\mu\Delta t\,(1-\lambda\Delta t) \cong 2\,\mu P_2^{(2)}(t)\,\Delta t\,.$$

Attention must be drawn to the fact that since there were 2 units at the initial point t and there are two channels, a departure could take place either in one channel with a probability of $\mu\Delta t$ or in the other with the same probability. Hence, in this case the probability of a departure of one unit is

$$\mu\Delta t + \mu\Delta t = 2\mu\Delta t\,.$$

5) At instant t there are 3 units, and in period Δt, 2 units leave and 0 arrive. Here is the probability of this occurrence:

$$P_3^{(2)}(t)\,(\mu\Delta t)^2\,(1-\lambda\Delta t) \cong 0.$$

Finally, we have

$$P_1^{(2)}(t+\Delta t) = P_1^{(2)}(t) - \lambda P_1^{(2)}(t)\Delta t - \mu P_1^{(2)}(t)\Delta t$$
$$+ \lambda P_0^{(2)}(t)\Delta t + 2\,\mu P_2^{(2)}(t)\Delta t$$

or

$$\frac{P_1^{(2)}(t+\Delta t) - P_1^{(2)}(t)}{\Delta t} = -\lambda P_1^{(2)}(t) - \mu P_1^{(2)}(t) + \lambda P_0^{(2)}(t) + 2\mu P_2^{(2)}(t).$$

Adopting the limit as $\Delta t \to 0$ and equating the resultant derivative to zero (probabilities $P_n^{(2)}$ being related to time) we obtain

$$\lambda P_1^{(2)} + \mu P_1^{(2)} = \lambda P_0^{(2)} + 2\mu P_2^{(2)}\,.$$

Substituting expression (4) for $P_0^{(2)}$ we finally obtain

$$P_1^{(2)} = 2\frac{\mu}{\lambda}P_2^{(2)}\,. \tag{5}$$

Let us also make similar calculations for the case $n = 2$. As usual, we start by calculating the probability $P_2^{(2)}(t+\Delta t)$.

Below we give the circumstances, one of which must happen, to have 2 units at the instant $t+\Delta t$. The respective probabilities for each case are also given.

1) There was 1 unit at time t, and 1 unit arrived and 0 left during the period Δt.

$$P_1^{(2)}(t)\lambda\Delta t(1-\mu\Delta t) \cong \lambda P_1^{(2)}(t)\Delta t$$

2) At time t there were 2 units, and during the period Δt 0 arrived and 0 left.

$$P_2^{(2)}(t)(1-2\mu\Delta t)(1-\lambda\Delta t) \cong P_2^{(2)}(t)-\lambda P_2^{(2)}(t)\Delta t-2\mu P_2^{(2)}(t)\Delta t$$

3) At time t there were 2 units, and during the period Δt 1 unit left and 1 arrived.

$$P_2^{(2)}(t)2\mu\Delta t\lambda\Delta t \cong 0$$

4) There were 3 units at time t, and during the period Δt 1 unit left and 0 arrived.

$$P_3^{(2)}(t)2\mu\Delta t(1-\lambda\Delta t) \cong 2\mu P_3^{(2)}(t)\Delta t$$

5) At time t there were 3 units, and 2 units left and 1 unit arrived during the period Δt.

$$P_3^{(2)}(t)(\mu\Delta t)^2\lambda\Delta t \cong 0$$

6) There were 4 units at time t, and during the period Δt 2 units left and 0 arrived.

$$P_4^{(2)}(t)(\mu\Delta t)^2(1-\lambda\Delta t) \cong 0$$

Finally, we have

$$P_2^{(2)}(t+\Delta t) = P_2^{(2)}(t)-\lambda P_2^{(2)}(t)\Delta t-2\mu P_2^{(2)}(t)\Delta t+\lambda P_1^{(2)}(t)\Delta t+2\mu P_3^{(2)}(t)\Delta t$$

or, after transposing $P_2^{(2)}(t)$ to the left-hand side and dividing both sides by Δt:

$$\frac{P_2^{(2)}(t+\Delta t)-P_2^{(2)}(t)}{\Delta t} = -\lambda P_2^{(2)}(t)-2\mu P_2^{(2)}(t)+\lambda P_1^{(2)}(t)+2\mu P_3^{(2)}(t).$$

After taking the limit as $(\Delta t \to 0)$ and setting the resultant derivative equal to zero, we have

$$\lambda P_2^{(2)}+2\mu P_2^{(2)} = \lambda P_1^{(2)}+2\mu P_3^{(2)}.$$

In this equation we can substitute expression (5) for $P_1^{(2)}$, thus obtaining

$$P_2^{(2)} = 2\frac{\mu}{\lambda}P_3^{(2)}. \tag{6}$$

Similarly, we derive formulae for further values of n. In this manner we generally arrive at:

$$P_n^{(2)} = 2\frac{\mu}{\lambda}P_{n+1}^{(2)} \quad \text{for } n = 1, 2, \ldots \tag{7}$$

Let us recall that for $n = 0$, the formula for $P_0^{(2)}$ is determined in a different fashion (formula (4)):

$$P_0^{(2)} = \frac{\mu}{\lambda}P_1^{(2)}.$$

Now we impose the condition that

$$\sum_{n=0}^{\infty} P_n^{(2)} = 1. \tag{8}$$

Accounting for formula (7), we have

$$\sum_{n=1}^{\infty} P_n^{(2)} = 2\frac{\mu}{\lambda}\sum_{n=2}^{\infty} P_n^{(2)}$$

or

$$\sum_{n=0}^{\infty} P_n^{(2)} - P_0^{(2)} = 2\frac{\mu}{\lambda}\sum_{n=2}^{\infty} P_n^{(2)}.$$

Converting the left-hand side of the above equation and accounting for condition (8), we obtain

$$1 - P_0^{(2)} = 2\frac{\mu}{\lambda}\sum_{n=0}^{\infty} P_n^{(2)} - 2\frac{\mu}{\lambda}P_0^{(2)} - 2\frac{\mu}{\lambda}P_1^{(2)}.$$

It follows from formula (4) that $P_1^{(2)} = \frac{\mu}{\lambda}P_0^{(2)}$ and, therefore,

$$1 - P_0^{(2)} = 2\frac{\mu}{\lambda} - 2\frac{\mu}{\lambda}P_0^{(2)} - 2P_0^{(2)}.$$

Thus

$$P_0^{(2)} = \frac{2\mu - \lambda}{2\mu + \lambda}. \tag{9}$$

From formulae (4) and (9) we obtain:

$$P_1^{(2)} = \frac{\lambda}{\mu} \cdot \frac{2\mu - \lambda}{2\mu + \lambda}. \tag{10}$$

Substituting $n = 1$ in formula (7) and using formula (10), we obtain the formula for $P_2^{(2)}$:

$$P_2^{(2)} = \frac{1}{2}\left(\frac{\lambda}{\mu}\right)^2 \frac{2\mu - \lambda}{2\mu + \lambda}.$$

Similarly, for $P_3^{(2)}$ we have

$$P_3^{(2)} = \frac{1}{2^2}\left(\frac{\lambda}{\mu}\right)^3 \frac{2\mu - \lambda}{2\mu + \lambda}$$

and generally

$$P_n^{(2)} = \frac{1}{2^{n-1}}\left(\frac{\lambda}{\mu}\right)^n \frac{2\mu - \lambda}{2\mu + \lambda}. \tag{11}$$

Hence, for the case of a two-channel installation the corresponding probabilities $P_n^{(2)}$ are defined by the formulae

$$P_n^{(2)} = \left(\frac{\lambda}{\mu}\right)^n \frac{2\mu - \lambda}{2\mu + \lambda} \quad \text{for} \quad n = 0 \cdot 1 \tag{12}$$

$$P_n^{(2)} = \left(\frac{1}{2}\right)^{n-1}\left(\frac{\lambda}{\mu}\right)^n \frac{2\mu - \lambda}{2\mu + \lambda} \quad \text{for} \quad n \geqslant 2. \tag{13}$$

The anticipated queue-length, i.e. the mathematical expectation of variable n, will be expressed as follows:

$$E^{(2)}(n) = \sum_{i=0}^{\infty} i\,P_i^{(2)} = \sum_{i=0}^{1} i\left(\frac{\lambda}{\mu}\right)^i \frac{2\mu - \lambda}{2\mu + \lambda} + \sum_{i=2}^{\infty} i\left(\frac{1}{2}\right)^{i-1}\left(\frac{\lambda}{\mu}\right)^i \frac{2\mu - \lambda}{2\mu + \lambda}.$$

After the appropriate computations, we obtain

$$E^{(2)}(n) = \frac{\lambda^3}{\mu^2(4\mu^2 - \lambda^2)} + \frac{\lambda}{\mu} \tag{14}$$

It should be noted that the above reasoning holds only when $2\mu > \lambda$. Otherwise, in accordance with formulae (12) and (13), all the probabilities $P_n^{(2)}$ would be less than zero, which is impossible.

By means of formula (14), we can now calculate the average queue-length when two installations are available for the servicing of the machines:

$$E^{(2)}(n) = \frac{\lambda^3}{\mu^2(4\mu^2 - \lambda^2)} + \frac{\lambda}{\mu} = \frac{1 \cdot 5^3}{2^2(4.2^2 - 1 \cdot 5^2)} + \frac{1 \cdot 5}{2} = 0 \cdot 81137.$$

Thus the addition of a second installation reduced the average queue-length almost fourfold in comparison to the situation when there is only one installation in operation. Now the expected daily loss caused by the standstill of machines is

$$8.400 \, \text{zlotys} . 0.81137 \cong 2,596 \, \text{zlotys.}$$

The daily cost of operating the installation (of which there are two units) amounts to 8.500 zlotys $+ 8.500$ zlotys $= 8,000$ zlotys. Thus the total anticipated daily losses and costs are 8,000 zlotys$+2,596$ zlotys $= 10,596$ zlotys. This sum is larger than the corresponding sum for one installation. The conclusion from this is simple, namely, that under these conditions it is not profitable for the factory to put into operation a second installation for the servicing of machines.

The problem raised in Example 2 can be generalized. Thus, an installation with a larger number of channels can be studied. If k stands for the number of channels, similar formulae to those for the case $k = 2$ can be derived for the probability $P_n^{(k)}$ that there is a certain number of units n in the queue, as well as for the expected queue-length $E^{(k)}$. These formulae can be derived in a manner almost identical to that used before. Here are the appropriate formulae:

$$P_0^{(k)} = \frac{1}{\sum_{n=0}^{k-1} \left(\frac{\lambda}{\mu}\right)^n \Big/ n! + \left(\frac{\lambda}{\mu}\right)^k \Big/ k!\left(1 - \frac{\lambda}{k\mu}\right)} \tag{15}$$

$$P_n^{(k)} = \frac{\left(\frac{\lambda}{\mu}\right)^n}{n!} \cdot P_0^{(k)} \quad \text{for} \quad n \leqslant k \tag{16}$$

$$P_n^{(k)} = \frac{\left(\frac{\lambda}{\mu}\right)^n}{k! k^{n-k}} \cdot P_0^{(k)} \quad \text{for} \quad n > k \tag{17}$$

$$E_{(n)}^{(k)} = \frac{\lambda\mu\left(\frac{\lambda}{\mu}\right)^k}{(k-1)!(k\mu - \lambda)^2} P_0^{(k)} + \frac{\lambda}{\mu}. \tag{18}$$

The reader can verify that formulae (12), (13) and (14) which we derived for $k = 2$ in solving Example 2, are special cases of formulae (15), (16), (17) and (18).

From the examples cited above it follows that the theory of queues permits to arrive at decisions on likely changes in the coefficient μ (rate of service) or in the number of channels in the servicing installation. Other uses will be further considered in subsequent sections.

13

22. The Monte Carlo method

From the examples of probabilistic models studied so far, certain general conclusions may be drawn concerning the methods of finding their solutions. In general, we can say that probability calculus is the basis for the solution of probabilistic models. By means of the probability calculus, knowing the probability of one group of events, we can compute the probabilities of other events of interest to us. In particular, as far as the application of the theory of queues is concerned, we may recall that we started from the known "arrival" distribution and service time distribution. Knowing these distributions, we computed the probabilities of any one of these queue lengths. Sometimes, computations of this type, i.e. calculations of the probability of certain events on the basis of known probabilities of other events, become extremely complicated and tedious. This occurs, among other eventualities, in connection with the use of the theory of queues. The assumption that the distribution of arrivals is different from a Poisson distribution and that the service time distribution is not exponential usually leads to very tedious computations. In situations of this kind we often dispense with accurate computations and adopt certain approximate methods. In the case of probabilistic methods we often use what is known as the Monte Carlo method. The essence of this method consists in substituting an experimental procedure to analytical (mathematical) reasoning. The simple example below will explain this in more detail.

Example 1. Shafts of a certain diameter are turned on a lathe. In practice, the shafts always have a somewhat larger or smaller diameter than the required dimension. The distribution of the observed variations between the required and actual diameter is known to be a normal one with an average value of 0 and a standard deviation of 1. If the difference between the required and actual dimensions of the diameter exceeds $1 \cdot 7$, the shaft is not suitable for the purposes for which it is manufactured. Let us assume that in order to find the solution to a certain problem we have to know the probability that a lot of 10 will contain 2 or more unsuitable shafts, i.e. those with diameters differing from the required dimension by more than $1 \cdot 7$.

The solution of this example is very simple by means of the analytical method. However, assuming for a moment that the computations for the purpose of determining the desired probability are tedious and complicated, this probability could still be approximately estimated by some experimental procedure. Thus, it is possible to construct an artificial series having a normal distribution, a mean value of 0 and a standard deviation of 1, and from this series choose at random 10 elements at a time. For each sample of 10 elements we compute the number of observations exceeding $1 \cdot 7$. If we carried out a large number of such tests, e.g. 1,000, then as a result we would observe certain frequencies. We would namely observe a certain number of 10-element tests in which the number of unsuitable shafts would equal 0, a certain number in which it would be 1, etc. On this basis, we can evaluate the frequency of the occurrence of samples having 2 or more unsuitable shafts. This latter frequency can be accepted as an estimate of the probability in question.

A number of problems arise in connection with the Monte Carlo method but we shall not consider them in detail here. For instance, there is the problem of the number of experiments to be carried out. This, of course, is linked to the reliability of an estimate of a particular probability. There is also the problem of assembling an "artificial" series from which we make random selections. There is the problem of the sampling technique itself, etc.

At present, we shall examine an example of the application of the Monte Carlo method to solving a problem relating to the theory of queues. This is an example taken from the book by G. Churchman, R. Ackoff and E. Arnoff[1].

Example 2. A trading agency makes van deliveries of purchased goods to the homes of its customers. The problem arises as to the number of vans required by an establishment for the delivery of all parcels of purchases made in a given day to the customers' homes on the same day.

From past statistical records it is known that the daily number of parcels which are to be delivered to the customers is a random variable having a normal distribution of an average value of 1,000, and a standard deviation of 100 parcels.

As far as the parcel delivery time is concerned, it has been found that the number of parcels which one van can deliver in one day is also a random variable showing a normal distribution, an average number of 100 and a standard deviation of 10.

The maintenance cost of one van for one day's service, depreciation, etc. is estimated at 250 zlotys. We are to determine the optimum number of vans on the assumption that the establishment can use hired vans at 80 zlotys per hour.

The problem we are faced with is basically to ascertain the number of "channels" required for the installation in question, i.e. the number of vans required by the establishment. It should be remembered that the problem is formulated so that the agency can also use hired vans at a much higher cost. They are used only when the establishment's own vans cannot deliver all the parcels.

In order to solve this problem it would be necessary to calculate the expected costs which the establishment would incur for various numbers of vans, and choose the figure involving the lowest costs. Instead of these computations, it is possible to carry out an appropriate "artificial" experiment.

Let us assume for a moment that the establishment has available 5 of its own vans, and let us see what the costs will be. First, let us examine the number of parcels

---

[1] *Introduction to Operations Research,* New York, 1957, J. Wiley.

to be delivered. For this purpose, we make a random selection of a certain number of observations from the population showing a normal distribution of an average number of 1,000 and a standard deviation of 100. These selected observations will correspond to the number of parcels which we have to deliver within a certain number of days chosen at random. Let our sample consist of five days, observations. In order to adopt such a sample, use can be made of the so-called normal random deviates. These are numbers giving the results of random selection from a normal population with an average value of 0 and standard deviation of 1. The result of this kind of selection is obtained by reading the consecutive numbers given in tables of normal random deviates[1]. The results of a selection of this type are given in Table 1.22, column 2.

Since we assumed in the example that the average population is 1,000 (and not 0) while the standard deviation is 100 (and not 1) the figures in column 2 should be multiplied by 100 and then added to 1,000. The results are given in column 3, disregarding decimals. Column 3, therefore, gives the number of parcels that should be delivered within the 5 days chosen.

TABLE 1/22

No. of day	Result of sampling	Converted result	Result of sampling	Converted result	Excess of parcels	Cost of excess parcel transport
1	2	3	4	5	6	7
1	1·556	1,156	0·414	521	635	3,920
2	0·647	1,065	0·107	505	560	3,440
3	0·329	1,033	−0·497	475	558	3,680
4	−1·188	881	0·501	525	356	2,160
5	−0·917	908	−1·382	431	477	3,440
						16,640

In a similar manner, by means of normal random deviates, we select the next five numbers (column 4) which, after appropriate conversion, i.e. after multiplying by the standard deviation, equal 10 and after adding the mean value, i.e. 100, to the product of this multiplication, will give the number of parcels which a van can deliver on a given day. Since we assumed that we have 5 vans available, the results obtained should be multiplied by 5. Column 4 gives the consecutive figures read from the table of normal random deviations, while column 5 shows the converted figures, as mentioned above.

---

[1] For instance, see *Tablice statystyczne (Statistical Tables)*, edited by W. Sadowski, Warsaw, 1957, PWN.

By subtracting the figures in column 5 from the corresponding figures in column 3, we obtain the number of parcels which must be delivered by hired vans. We assume the hired vans operate under the same conditions as those of the agency. Thus, the 5 vans owned by the establishment deliver 521 parcels in a day, and therefore one van delivers $521 \div 5 \cong 104$ parcels. Assuming that a van is in operation for 8 hours, it delivers $104 \div 8 = 13$ parcels per hour. If we want to deliver 635 extra parcels, we must hire vans for the necessary number of hours, namely $635 \div 13 \cong 49$. The cost of hiring vans for 49 hours amounts to $49.80 = 3,920$ zlotys. We enter this figure in column 7 of Table 1.22. Similarly, we compute the cost of hiring vans required to deliver extra parcels on other days.

By summing up column 7, we obtain the total expenses involved in hiring vans for the delivery of extra parcels.

Similarly, calculations can be made for various numbers of vans.

Table 2.22 is constructed exactly like Table 1.22 and it refers to the case in which the establishment owns 10 vans, while Table 3.22 concerns the same case when 12 vans are owned.

TABLE 2/22

No. of day	Result of sampling	Converted result	Result of sampling	Converted result	Excess of parcels	Cost of excess parcel transport
1	2	3	4	5	6	7
1	1·556	1,156	0·414	1,041	115	720
2	0·647	1,065	0·107	1,011	54	320
3	0·329	1,033	−0·497	950	83	560
4	−1·188	881	0·501	1,050	0	0
5	−0·917	908	−1·382	862	46	320
						1,920

TABLE 3/22

No. of day	Result of sampling	Converted result	Result of sampling	Converted result	Excess of parcels	Cost of excess parcel transport
1	2	3	4	5	6	7
1	1·556	1,156	0·414	1,250	0	0
2	0·647	1,065	0·107	1,213	0	0
3	0.329	1,033	−0·497	1,140	0	0
4	−1·188	881	0·501	1,260	0	0
5	−0·917	908	−1·382	1,034	0	0
						0

Thus, by an artificial experiment we were able to compare the costs of delivering surplus parcels using additional numbers of vans.

The total (daily) costs for the delivery of parcels when five vans are owned amount to

$$5 . 250\,\text{zlotys} + \frac{16{,}640\,\text{zlotys}}{5} = 4{,}578\,\text{zlotys}.$$

This sum covers the daily cost of the establishment's own vans 5,250 zlotys = 1,250 zlotys and the daily cost of hiring vans

$$\left(\frac{16{,}640\,\text{zlotys}}{5} = 3{,}328\right).$$

The analogous sum of the costs for 10 vans is

$$10 . 250\,\text{zlotys} + \frac{1{,}920\,\text{zlotys}}{5} = 2{,}884\,\text{zlotys}.$$

And, finally, the sum of costs for the delivery of parcels using 12 vans is

$$12 . 250\,\text{zlotys} + 0 = 3{,}000\,\text{zlotys}.$$

From these computations it appears that the most advantageous of the situations examined is when the establishment owns 10 vans. It is necessary to examine further whether it would be profitable for the establishment to own 11 vans instead of 10, or perhaps a number smaller than 10. Table 4.22 gives the appropriate calculations for 11 vans.

TABLE 4/22

No. of day	Result of sampling	Converted result	Result of sampling	Converted result	Excess of parcels	Cost of excess parcel transport
1	2	3	4	5	6	7
1	1·556	1,156	0·414	1,146	10	64
2	0·647	1,065	0·107	1,112	0	0
3	0·329	1,033	−0·497	1,045	0	0
4	−1·188	881	0·501	1,155	0	0
5	−0·917	908	−1·382	948	0	0
						64

The sum of costs for 11 vans, therefore, is

$$11 . 250\,\text{zlotys} + \frac{64\,\text{zlotys}}{5} = 2{,}763\,\text{zlotys}.$$

As can be seen, this sum is smaller than the corresponding costs both for 10 and 12 vans. Thus, it may be concluded that the establishment should have 11 vans available.

Of course, in practice, the experiment should cover a period much longer than 5 days. An experiment of longer duration affords a greater certainty that the results obtained are not vitiated by random errors.

We shall return to the problem of determining the size of a sample when discussing statistical methods.

To conclude this section, it should be stated that the Monte Carlo method is very useful in practice as it allows us to solve even highly complex probabilistic models.

23. The renewal problem

The problems known under the general name of renewal form rather a specific and important field of application of probabilistic models.

The problem is that much of the equipment, such as machines, becomes "obsolete" in time. Such "obsolescence" is caused both by physical and so-called moral wear[1]. In further discussions we shall disregard the problem of moral wear. As far as physical wear is concerned, it may appear in two principal forms.

Firstly, the equipment is subject to physical wear in time. This physical wear causes more frequent breakdowns which involve corresponding costs. Many of these breakdowns can be avoided by appropriate maintenance and periodic renewals, which involve some expenses. After a time, the equipment becomes so expensive to operate that it has to be replaced. In this connection, the question arises of a proper maintenance policy and the period of time after which old equipment should be replaced by new.

Secondly, there are types of equipment the efficiency of which, from a practical point of view, does not change during the period of service. On the other hand, this equipment at some time not known in advance, loses 100 per cent of its efficiency and must be replaced by new equipment. Here, the problem is whether it is better to replace this type of equipment when it is completely worn out or to pursue a different policy.

In Section 23, the renewal problem will serve only as an illustration of the application of probabilistic methods. We shall not enter into the details of this extremely complicated and wide field of problems.

---

[1] The problem of moral wear is that, even if some equipment still displays a fairly high efficiency, it may be profitable to replace it by new equipment, more suited to the requirements of technical progress.

Example 1. Let us assume that 1,000 valves of a certain type (e.g. electronic valves) have a probability distribution that the valve after a certain life time will burn out. This distribution is given in Table 1.23.

TABLE 1/23

Period	Probability of breakdown of valves in period
1	0·01
2	0·15
3	0·50
4	0·20
5	0·09
6	0·05

This table should be interpreted to mean that the values given in the second column represent the probability of a valve fitted at moment 0 burning out in the period given in the corresponding line of the first column. The burning out of a valve entails certain costs amounting to 400 zlotys. These costs can be avoided if the old valve while still functioning is replaced by a new one. However, in such situations, there is also a certain expense due to the removal and replacement of the valve which could still work for some time. The cost of changing a valve regardless of whether or not it is damaged amounts to 10 zlotys; a new valve, on the other hand, costs 500 zlotys.

In this example, the renewal policy will be to replace immediately valves which burn out during use and, moreover, to subsitute new valves for those which have worked for k periods of time (and have not burned out). The task which we set ourselves consists in determining the optimum k, i.e. the optimum number of periods after which a valve should be replaced by a new one, even if it is still good.

We solve this problem by examining the expected costs for various values of k.

First, let us assume that $k = 6$, which means that the valves are changed only when they burn out. Thus, we calculate the number of valves expected to burn out within k periods. If we assume that at the outset of the examined sequence of periods all 1,000 valves are new, and in each period the burnt out valves are changed for new ones, then the number of valves expected to burn out in the first period is

$$n_1 = 1,000 \cdot 0 \cdot 01 = 10. \tag{1}$$

This means that when we enter the second period there will be 990 valves which have worked for one period and 10 new ones[1] which replaced those which burned out in the first period. In order to compute the expected number of valves to burn out within the second period, we determine the number of valves expected to last only two periods. Among the valves fitted at the outset, an average of $1,000 . 0 \cdot 15$ will burn out within the second period. Moreover, a valve fitted in the preceding period can also burn out. There were 10 such valves; therefore the expected number of burnt out valves from this source will amount to $10 . 0 \cdot 01$. Thus, we have altogether

$$n_2 = 1,000 . 0 \cdot 15 + 10 . 0 \cdot 01 = 150 \cdot 1. \tag{2}$$

In the third period, we have valves supplied at three intervals of time: a) valves fitted at the beginning, b) valves fitted during the first period and c) valves fitted during the second period. The number of valves expected to burn out in the third period will be

$$n_3 = 1,000 . 0 \cdot 50 + 10 . 0 \cdot 15 + 150 \cdot 1 . 0 \cdot 01 = 503. \tag{3}$$

In a similar fashion, we calculate the number of burnt out valves for the succeeding periods:

$$n_4 = 1,000 . 0 \cdot 20 + 10 . 0 \cdot 50 + 150 \cdot 1 . 0 \cdot 15 + 503 . 0 \cdot 01 = 232 \cdot 5 \tag{4}$$

$$n_5 = 1,000 . 0 \cdot 09 + 10 . 0 \cdot 20 + 150 \cdot 1 . 0 \cdot 50 + 503 . 0 \cdot 15 \tag{5}$$
$$+ 232 \cdot 5 . 0 \cdot 01 = 244 \cdot 8$$

$$n_6 = 1,000 . 0 \cdot 05 + 10 . 0 \cdot 09 + 150 \cdot 1 . 0 \cdot 20 + 503 . 0 \cdot 50 \tag{6}$$
$$+ 232 \cdot 5 . 0 \cdot 15 + 244 \cdot 8 . 0 \cdot 01 = 369 \cdot 7.$$

Note that in the next period, i.e. the seventh, there will be no valve left of those fitted at the beginning, since, as follows from Table 1.23, the probability that a valve will last longer than 6 periods equals zero.

The oldest valves which have lasted into the seventh period, therefore, must have been fitted in the second period. The expected number of burnt out valves in the seventh period will be

$$n_7 = 10 . 0 \cdot 05 + 150 \cdot 1 . 0 \cdot 09 + 503 . 0 \cdot 20 + 232 \cdot 5 . 0 \cdot 50 \tag{7}$$
$$+ 244 \cdot 8 . 0 \cdot 15 + 369 \cdot 7 . 0 \cdot 01 = 271 \cdot 3.$$

---

[1] In order to simplify the problem we assume that a valve which burns out in a certain period is replaced at the end of that period.

In the eighth period there will no longer be any valves from the initial and first periods; there may, however, be valves which were fitted in the second, third period, etc.

$$n_8 = 150{\cdot}1\,.\,0{\cdot}05 + 503\,.\,0{\cdot}09 + 232{\cdot}5\,.\,0{\cdot}20 + 244{\cdot}8\,.\,0{\cdot}50 \tag{8}$$

$$+ 369{\cdot}7\,.\,0{\cdot}15 + 271{\cdot}3\,.\,0{\cdot}01 = 279{\cdot}8\,.$$

If we denote the probabilities from Table 1.23 by p_1, p_2, p_3, p_4, p_5 and p_6, respectively, where p_i means that the valve will burn out in the i-th period of operation, then the general formulae for the expected number of burnt out valves calculated above (hence also, those replaced) in the individual periods will be:

$$n_1 = n_0 p_1$$

$$n_2 = n_0 p_2 + n_1 p_1$$

$$n_3 = n_0 p_3 + n_1 p_2 + n_2 p_1$$

$$n_4 = n_0 p_4 + n_1 p_3 + n_2 p_2 + n_3 p_1$$

$$n_5 = n_0 p_5 + n_1 p_4 + n_2 p_3 + n_3 p_2 + n_4 p_1$$

$$n_6 = n_0 p_6 + n_1 p_5 + n_2 p_4 + n_3 p_3 + n_4 p_2 + n_5 p_1$$

$$n_7 = \qquad n_1 p_6 + n_2 p_5 + n_3 p_4 + n_4 p_3 + n_5 p_2 + n_6 p_1$$

$$n_8 = \qquad n_2 p_6 + n_3 p_5 + n_4 p_4 + n_5 p_3 + n_6 p_2 + n_7 p_1$$

The figure n_0 stands here for the number of new valves fitted at the beginning. In our example we assumed that $n_0 = 1,000$.

As can be seen, the expected number of burnt out valves in the consecutive periods of time is subject to fluctuations, as illustrated in Fig. 1.23. It is found, however that the fluctuations of this number become ever smaller as the number of periods pass. It can be shown that after a sufficient number of periods have elapsed the expected number of burnt out valves will be 298. This average number of burnt out valves is inversely proportional to the expected life time of the valve[1]. According to Table 1.23 the expected life time of the valve is

$$1\,.\,0{\cdot}01 + 2\,.\,0{\cdot}15 + 3\,.\,0{\cdot}50 + 4\,.\,0{\cdot}20 + 5\,.\,0{\cdot}09 + 6\,.\,0{\cdot}05 = 3{\cdot}36\,.$$

Hence, the expected number of burnt out valves in one period is

$$1,000\,.\,\frac{1}{3{\cdot}36} = 298\,.$$

---

[1] We omit the proof of this theorem.

Thus, it follows that for $k = 6$, i.e. replacing only the burnt out valves, the expected costs for one period amount to:

$$(400 + 10 + 500) \, \text{zlotys} \, . \, 298 = 271{,}180 \, \text{zlotys}.$$

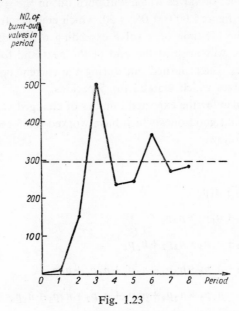

Fig. 1.23

Each burnt out valve entails the following costs: 400 zlotys if a valve burns out during operation, 10 zlotys for the cost of changing, 500 zlotys for the cost of a new valve. Therefore, the costs involved in the renewal policy for $k = 6$, amount to 271,180 zlotys.

We now follow an entirely similar reasoning for the case when $k = 5$, i.e. when we remove **both** burnt out valves and those which after having been used for 5 periods are still good.

If we start our reasoning from the beginning, i.e. immediately after fitting 1,000 valves, then the expected number of burnt out valves plus the number of good ones which worked for five periods and must be changed will be identical to the previously computed number for the first four periods. On the other hand, there will be a change in the fifth period.

The position is that at the end of the fifth period we remove all the valves which have worked for five periods and replace them by new ones. The expected number of valves to be fitted will be

$$n_5' = 1{,}000 \, . \, 0{\cdot}09 + 10 \, . \, 0{\cdot}20 + 150{\cdot}1 \, . \, 0{\cdot}50 + 503 \, . \, 0{\cdot}15 \tag{9}$$

$$+ 232{\cdot}5 \, . \, 0{\cdot}01 + 1{,}000 \, . \, 0{\cdot}05 = 294{\cdot}8 \, .$$

The value thus obtained, $n_5' = 294 \cdot 8$ differs from expression (5) only in the last term $(1,000 \cdot 0 \cdot 05)$. This is the expected number of valves which will have worked for 5 periods and could still be used further. For our conditions, this figure is equal to the expected number of valves which will burn out in the sixth and later periods. This is precisely the figure $1,000 \cdot 0 \cdot 05 = 50$, which emerges from Table 1.23 since the probability of the life-time of a valve exceeding 6 periods equals zero.

A similar situation will arise at the end of the next and following periods. Not only will those valves which burned out during the current period be replaced but also all the good valves which worked for 5 periods.

The general formulae for the expected number of changed valves (i.e. the number of burnt out valves and good ones which have worked for 5 periods) in consecutive periods will be as follows:

$$n_1 = n_0 p_1$$

$$n_2 = n_0 p_2 + n_1 p_1$$

$$n_3 = n_0 p_3 + n_1 p_2 + n_2 p_1 \tag{10}$$

$$n_4 = n_0 p_4 + n_1 p_3 + n_2 p_2 + n_3 p_1$$

$$n_5' = n_0 p_5 + n_1 p_4 + n_2 p_3 + n_3 p_2 + n_4 p_1 + n_0 p_6$$

$$n_6' = \qquad n_1 p_5 + n_2 p_4 + n_3 p_3 + n_4 p_2 + n_5' p_1 + n_1 p_6$$

$$n_7' = \qquad\qquad n_2 p_5 + n_3 p_4 + n_4 p_3 + n_5' p_2 + n_6' p_1 + n_2 p_6.$$

These formulae can be written in a somewhat different form:

$$n_1 = n_0 p_1$$

$$n_2 = n_0 p_2 + n_1 p_1$$

$$n_3 = n_0 p_3 + n_1 p_2 + n_2 p_1$$

$$n_4 = n_0 p_4 + n_1 p_3 + n_2 p_2 + n_3 p_1$$

$$n_5' = n_0 (p_5 + p_6) + n_1 p_4 + n_2 p_3 + n_3 p_2 + n_4 p_1$$

$$n_6' = \qquad n_1 (p_5 + p_6) + n_2 p_4 + n_3 p_3 + n_4 p_2 + n_5' p_1$$

$$n_7' = \qquad n_2 (p_5 + p_6) + n_3 p_4 + n_4 p_3 + n_5' p_2 + n_6' p_1.$$

In our case, the expected number of valves replaced in several consecutive periods will be

$$n_6' = 10 \cdot 0 \cdot 09 + 150 \cdot 1 \cdot 0 \cdot 20 + 503 \cdot 0 \cdot 50 + 232 \cdot 5 \cdot 0 \cdot 15 + 294 \cdot 8 \cdot 0 \cdot 01$$

$$+ 10 \cdot 0 \cdot 05 = 320 \cdot 7$$

$$n_7' = 150 \cdot 1 \cdot 0 \cdot 09 + 503 \cdot 0 \cdot 20 + 232 \cdot 5 \cdot 0 \cdot 50 + 294 \cdot 8 \cdot 0 \cdot 15 + 320 \cdot 7 \cdot 0 \cdot 01$$

$$+ 150 \cdot 1 \cdot 0 \cdot 05 = 285 \cdot 3$$

$$n_8' = 503 \cdot 0 \cdot 09 + 232 \cdot 5 \cdot 0 \cdot 20 + 294 \cdot 8 \cdot 0 \cdot 50 + 320 \cdot 7 \cdot 0 \cdot 15 + 285 \cdot 3 \cdot 0 \cdot 01$$

$$+ 503 \cdot 0 \cdot 05 = 315$$

$$n_9' = 232 \cdot 5 \cdot 0 \cdot 09 + 294 \cdot 8 \cdot 0 \cdot 20 + 320 \cdot 7 \cdot 0 \cdot 50 + 285 \cdot 3 \cdot 0 \cdot 15 + 315 \cdot 0 \cdot 01$$

$$+ 232 \cdot 5 \cdot 0 \cdot 05 = 297 \cdot 8$$

$$n_{10}' = 294 \cdot 8 \cdot 0 \cdot 09 + 320 \cdot 7 \cdot 0 \cdot 20 + 285 \cdot 3 \cdot 0 \cdot 50 + 315 \cdot 0 \cdot 15 + 297 \cdot 8 \cdot 0 \cdot 01$$

$$+ 294 \cdot 8 \cdot 0 \cdot 05 = 298 \cdot 3.$$

In spite of the fluctuations which we observe, this sequence of numbers also tends towards a limit which is inversely proportional to the anticipated life-time of the valve. The expected life-time of a valve is now shorter than before since, with the present renewal policy, a valve cannot last longer than 5 periods. The computation of the life-time of a valve is simple. It follows from Table 1.23 that $p_1 = 0 \cdot 01$, $p_2 = 0 \cdot 15$, $p_3 = 0 \cdot 50$, $p_4 = 0 \cdot 20$. In the given case, p_5' stands for the burning out of a valve either in the fifth period or at later periods. In either case the valve is withdrawn. Therefore

$$p_5' = p_5 + p_6, \text{ that is, } p_5' = 0 \cdot 09 + 0 \cdot 05 = 0 \cdot 14.$$

Thus, we have the expected life-time of a valve:

$$1 \cdot 0 \cdot 01 + 2 \cdot 0 \cdot 15 + 3 \cdot 0 \cdot 50 + 4 \cdot 0 \cdot 20 + 5 \cdot 0 \cdot 14 = 3 \cdot 31.$$

Hence, the expected number of valves to be replaced within one period is now

$$1,000 \cdot \frac{1}{3 \cdot 31} = 302.$$

True, this is a larger number of valves than before (with $k = 6$ we had 298 valves), but the expense of replacing the valves which did not burn out after five periods of use is considerably lower than that of replacing valves which burn out during such use. In this connection, it is necessary to calculate the number of valves which we expect to replace during the period, not because they burn out but because they have worked for 5 periods.

It follows from the general form of formulae (10) that the sequence of consecutive numbers of good valves which operate for 5 periods amounts to

$$n_0 p_6, \; n_1 p_6, \; n_2 p_6, \; n_3 p_6, \ldots \qquad (11)$$

Since the sequence $n_0, n_1, n_2, n_3, \ldots$ tends to the number 302, sequence (11) will tend to the limit $302 . p_6 = 302 . 0.05 = 15$. This means that of the 302 valves replaced within a period, on an average, only $302-15 = 287$ are replacements of burnt out valves while 15 are changes of good valves which have worked for 5 periods. The costs of these changes are as follows:

$$(400+10+500).287+(10+500).15 = 268{,}820 \text{ zlotys.}$$

It is found to be more advantageous to fit new valves in place of good ones having 5 periods of operation completed rather than wait until they burn out.

A similar computation should be made for $k = 4, 3, 2, 1$. This means that it is necessary to examine consecutively the costs involved in a renewal policy whereby, besides replacing burnt out valves, good valves which have worked for 3, 2, and, finally, 1 period, are also being replaced.

The general formulae for $k = 4$ then are:

$$n_1 = n_0 p_1$$

$$n_2 = n_0 p_2 + n_1 p_1$$

$$n_3 = n_0 p_3 + n_1 p_2 + n_2 p_1$$

$$n_4'' = n_0 p_4 + n_1 p_3 + n_2 p_2 + n_3 p_1 + n_0 (p_5 + p_6) \tag{12}$$

$$n_5'' = \qquad n_1 p_4 + n_2 p_3 + n_3 p_2 + n_4'' p_1 + n_1 (p_5 + p_6)$$

$$n_6'' = \qquad n_2 p_4 + n_3 p_3 + n_4'' p_2 + n_5'' p_1 + n_2 (p_5 + p_6).$$

Thus, for instance, on the right-hand side of the formula for n_4'' there is the term $n_0(p_5+p_6)$ giving the anticipated number of valves to be still good after four periods of operation (hence, these are the valves which may burn out in the fifth or sixth period). Below, we give the computations which lead to the first few values for the sequence of these numbers.

$$n_1 = 1{,}000 . 0.01 = 10$$

$$n_2 = 1{,}000 . 0.15 + 10 . 0.01 = 150.1$$

$$n_3 = 1{,}000 . 0.50 + 10 . 0.15 + 150.1 . 0.01 = 503$$

$$n_4'' = 1{,}000 . 0.20 + 10 . 0.50 + 150.1 . 0.15 + 503 . 0.01 + 1{,}000 . 0.14 = 372.5$$

$$n_5'' = 10 . 0.20 + 150.1 . 0.50 + 503 . 0.15 + 372.5 . 0.01 + 10 . 0.14 = 158.1.$$

We compute the limit of this sequence as before, i.e. we calculate the average duration of use of the valve

$$1 . 0.01 + 2 . 0.15 + 3 . 0.50 + 4(0.20 + 0.09 + 0.05) = 3.17.$$

and from this the average number of valves changed within a period is:

$$1,000 \cdot \frac{1}{3 \cdot 17} = 315.$$

We now have to compute the number of valves changed within the period only because they have worked for 4 periods (and they are still good).

The sequence of the numbers of good valves with four periods of operation completed is as follows in the various periods (this emerges from formula (12)):

$$n_0(p_5+p_6), \quad n_1(p_5+p_6), \quad n_2(p_5+p_6),\dots \tag{13}$$

The sequence $n_1, n_2, n_3 \dots$ tends to the limit of 315, hence sequence (13) will tend to the limit $315(p_5+p_6) = 315(0 \cdot 09 + 0 \cdot 05) = 44$. This means that of the 315 valves changed, 44 were good and were replaced only because they had worked for 4 periods. The total cost of replacing the valves will now be:

$$[(400 + 10 + 500) \cdot (315 - 44)] + [(10 + 500) \cdot 44] = 269{,}050 \text{ zlotys.}$$

We see that the cost of such a renewal policy is higher than for $k = 5$. It can thus be concluded that, in the given example, the best renewal policy is to replace good valves after 5 periods. For the sake of accuracy, the cost of a renewal policy for further k's, i.e. for 3, 2, and 1, should also be verified. In each of these cases the costs prove to be higher than for $k = 5$.

In our example we took into account a specific type of renewal policy; in addition to the burnt out valves, those which exceeded a certain age although still good were also replaced.

Of course, a different type of policy could be imagined, e.g. in addition to replacing burnt out valves, all the working valves might be changed for new ones after a given number of periods of operation. In this case, the question to be answered would be: after how many periods should all the valves be replaced (regardless of their age).

We shall not deal with the renewal policy for the case in which it becomes increasingly expensive in the long run to operate equipment both as a result of more frequent breakdowns, and the need for overhauls. It should be noted, however, that such problems can also be examined by the theory of queues.

The problem is that a certain piece of equipment, e.g. a machine in a given set of machinery, has a definite probability of breaking down. This probability changes, of course, in time. "Arrivals" in the language of the theory of queues form the breakdowns. "Service" consists in repairing the breakdown. A renewal policy will have to solve such problems as:

1) whether good machines should be serviced and if so, how often? (such servicing reduces the probability of breakdowns);

2) how large should the "service" be (how many channels?);

3) at what moment should an old machine be replaced by a new one?

To determine the optimum renewal policy, which is being considered here, is a fairly complicated matter, and for this reason we pass over this problem.

24. Bibliographical notes

The solution of probabilistic models consists in the application of the methods of probability calculus. We have assumed that the reader has some knowledge of this discipline.

For the reader who wishes to become more closely acquainted with the elements of probability calculus, we recommend the text-book by T. Czechowski [4] and the text-book by V. Glivenko [8] translated from Russian into Polish, both written in an easy and simple style. Moreover, attention should be drawn to the excellent book by W. Feller [5] which, in addition to an exposition of the probability calculus, contains a discussion of some of the special uses, such as, for instance, the theory of queues.

The books mentioned above do not require an extensive background in mathematics. A more advanced exposition of probability calculus is given in books by M. Fisz [6] and H. Cramér [3].

An elementary lecture on probability calculus from the point of view of its application in operations research is to be found in the book by R. Schlaifer [14]. Many interesting examples of the uses of probabilistic models in operations research can be found in this book.

Besides books devoted to the general methods of probability calculus, there are also many devoted to some special probabilistic models. In particular, there is a rather extensive literature concerning probabilistic models as applied to the theory of stocks. In this field, mention should be made first of the books by T. Within [15], J. Magee [10] and P. Massé [11].

A joint work [1] also devoted to the theory of inventories has been published under the editorship of K. Arrow, S. Karlin and H. Scarf. However, it requires a fairly thorough knowledge of mathematics to read this book.

Some sections of the interesting joint work by Guilbaud, Massé and Henon [9] also contain a discussion of inventory problems. There is also reference to other probabilistic models.

There are many books on the theory of queues. We mention the book by P. Morse [13] comprising not only an elementary exposition of this theory but also many applications, written in a clear language. A more advanced exposition of this theory, dealing also with its application to technology, is given in the book by A. Khinchin [2].

In the field of the renewal theory, there is a fairly extensive literature in the form of papers. There is no book which we could recommend here as an introduction to this problem. For readers having an adequate preparation in mathematics, we draw attention to the books by M. Frechet [7] and P. Montell [12].

BIBLIOGRAPHY

[1] Arrow, K., Karlin, S. and Scarf, H., *Studies in the Mathematical Theory of Inventory and Production,* Stanford, 1958, Stanford Univ. Press.

[2] Khinchin, A., *Matematicheskiye metody teoriyi massovovo obsluzhivaniya (Mathematical Methods of the Theory of Mass Catering),* Moscow, 1955, Izdat. Akademiyi Nauk SSSR.

[3] Cramér, H., *Mathematical Methods of Statistics,* Princeton, 1946.

[4] Czechowski, T., *Elementarny wykład rachunku prawdopodobieństwa (Elementary Probability Calculus),* Warsaw, 1958, PWN.

[5] Feller, W., *An Introduction to Probability Theory and its Applications,* Vol. I., New York 1950, J. Wiley.

[6] Fisz, M., *Rachunek prawdopodobieństwa i statystyka matematyczna (Probability Calculus, and Mathematical Statistics),* Warsaw, 1958, PWN. English translation published by McGraw Hill, 1960.

[7] Fréchet, M., *Leçons de statistique mathématique* (Course in Mathematical statistics), Paris, 1960.

[8] Glivenko, V., *Rachunek prawdopodobieństwa (Probability Calculus),* Warsaw, 1953, Polish Mathematical Society.

[9] Guilbaud, G., Massé, P. and Henon, R., *Stratégies et décisions économiques. Études théoretiques et applications aux entreprises (Economic operations and decisions. Theoretical studies as applied to an enterprise),* Paris, 1954, Centre National de la Recherche Scientifique.

[10] Magee, J., *Production Planning and Inventory Control,* New York, 1958, McGraw-Hill.

[11] Massé, P., *Les réserves et la régulation de l'avenir dans la vie économique (Inventory control in economic activity),* Vols. I and II, Paris, 1946, Herman.

[12] Montel, P., *Leçons sur les récurrences et leurs applications (Probability studies and their application),* Paris, 1957.

[13] Morse, P., *Queues, Inventories and Maintenance,* New York, 1958, J. Wiley.

[14] Schlaifer, R., *Probability and Statistics for Business Decisions,* New York, 1959, McGraw-Hill.

[15] Whitin, T., *The Theory of Inventory Management,* Princeton, 1953, Princeton Univ. Press.

14

CHAPTER 5

The Theory of Games

25. Elements of the theory of games

A characteristic feature of the models which we called *strategic models*, is that the person making a decision has relatively little information about the parameters of these models. As we recall, *deterministic models* are characterized by the fact that the parameters are constants and their values are known to the persons making a decision. In *probabilistic models*, the parameters are random variables with known distributions, i.e. the person taking the decision knows the probabilities that the parameter will assume specific values. If the model contains at least one parameter for which at the moment of the decision we know only the set of values which that parameter may assume, we say that we have a *strategic model*. If parameter a, for instance, is such a parameter, we know only that it can acquire one of the values $a_1, a_2, a_3, ..., $ or a_n. It is not difficult to surmise that in such circumstances it becomes a very complex matter to determine an optimum decision.

The situation in strategic models is such that the value of the criterion-function depends both on the decision variable (we denote it by X) and on the parameter a about which we only know that it can assume one of the values $a_1, a_2, ..., a_n$. Situations of this sort are typical of strategic games, i.e. games where the outcome is determined not only by chance (e.g. a game of heads or tails) but also by the skill of the player. The magnitude of pay-offs may be adopted as a criterion which enables the players to select a method of procedure, or to assign a value to decision variable X in strategic games. The individual values of the decision variable X which appear in strategic models are frequently called *strategies*. Of course, the player's pay-off depends not only on the strategy he chooses but also on the strategy selected by his opponent, i.e. on parameter a. Denoting by W the pay-off of a player who tries to determine the optimum value of variable X, we can write this relation symbolically as $W(X, a)$. Of course, when selecting his strategy, the player does not know the strategy of his opponent. The question therefore arises: what is the method for making an optimum choice of a strategy, or in other words, what is the optimum value of variable X? This problem is dealt with by the *theory of strategic games* which we shall henceforth briefly call the *theory of games*.

Let us now consider the simplest case of games, known as the *two-person zero-sum games*. These are games in which only two sides take part and the sum of pay-offs of both sides equals zero. This means that the pay-off of one player equals the loss of the other.

We shall consider the optimum method of choice of strategy on the basis of a simple example.

Example 1. Two players, whom we shall call G_1 and G_2, play a game. Each player, independently of the other, is to choose one of three colours: white (A), black (B) and green (C). After both players have made their independent choices of colour, the selected colours are compared. If both players have chosen white (A, A) neither has won anything. If player G_1 selects white and player G_2 black (A, B), player G_1 loses 1 zloty, hence player G_2 wins 1 zloty, etc. All possible situations are presented in Table 1.25 which is the table of pay-offs. This table can be said to determine the conditions of the game. Since the pay-off of player G_1 equals the loss of player G_2 (or vice versa), it is enough to present in the table the returns of one player. We agree to give always the pay-offs of player G_1.

TABLE 1/25

		Colour chosen by player G_2			Minimum pay-off of player G_1
		A	B	C	
Colour chosen by player G_1	A	0	−1	6	−1
	B	2	4	5	2
	C	1	−2	8	−2
Maximum loss by player G_2		2	4	8	

In Table 1.25 at the intersection of the appropriate row and column we have the pay-off of player G_1 which is at the same time the loss of player G_2. Note that in our system of entries, the pay-off can be negative (this is actually a loss).

Suppose that, together with player G_1, we consider a decision as to choice of colour. Of course, the pay-off for player G_1 forms the criterion for an evaluation of the effects of a decision. Let us denote these pay-offs by W. They depend on the decision of player G_1; we denote the decision by X. In our case X can stand for the white, black or green colours. Moreover, the pay-off, as given in Table 1.25, depends on the decision of player G_2, that is, on his choice of colour. We denote this decision by D; this too can be white, black or green. The point is to make such a choice X that the winnings W — which depend on X and D, written briefly as $W(X, D)$ — are the highest possible. Obviously, the difficulty of selecting the appropriate values of X consists in that there can be different values of W for one and the same value of X, depending on the strategy chosen by the second player.

In choosing his strategy, player G_1 can, of course, make use of the fact that the interests of player G_2 conflict with his own. Thus, in striving for his own pay-off, G_2 will automatically strive to reduce the pay-off of player G_1, and conversely.

14*

The reasoning of player G_1 may be as follows. In selecting colour A, player G_1 will win at least -1 (this is actually a loss). In choosing colour B, the player wins at least 2 and, finally, in selecting colour C, player G_1 secures for himself a pay-off of at least -2. Of these possibilities, player G_1 should select that which guarantees the largest of these minimum pay-offs. In our case, the largest of the numbers -1, 2 and -2 is 2. This means that player G_1 will do best to select colour B. This guarantees him a pay-off of at least 2. Any other decision could expose him to the risk of worse results.

Formally, the above reasoning can be written as follows:

$$v_1 = \operatorname*{Max}_{X} [\operatorname*{Min}_{D} W(X, D)]. \tag{1}$$

This simply means that player G_1 knows that player G_2, in striving for a pay-off, will strive to select his strategy so as to minimize that of player G_1. In other words, player G_2 will be trying to select D in such a way that W will be a minimum and we write this briefly as $\operatorname*{Min}_{D} W(X, D)$.

This minimum is, of course, dependent on variable X, which player G_1 can influence. He, therefore, gives variable X such a value that $\operatorname*{Min}_{D} W(X, D)$ is the largest possible value, that is,

$$\operatorname*{Max}_{X} [\operatorname*{Min}_{D} W(X, D)].$$

It is worthwhile pursuing a similar reasoning from the point of view of player G_2. Let us recall that for player G_2 the pay-offs are $-W$, and hence an effort to maximize $-W$ is equivalent to an endeavour to minimize W.

By selecting colour A, player G_2 loses at most 2. In selecting colour B, he loses at most 4 and in choosing colour C, he loses at most 8.

It seems that player G_2 will do best by selecting colour A which guarantees him a loss of at most two. Any other strategy would entail the possibility of a higher loss. Just as v_1, which is defined by formula (1), gives the minimum pay-off which player G_1 secures for himself by selecting an optimum strategy, so a formula can be presented for v_2 wherein v_2 shall denote the maximum loss which player G_2 may incur using an optimum strategy.

$$v_2 = \operatorname*{Min}_{D} [\operatorname*{Max}_{X} W(X, D)]. \tag{2}$$

In our example the optimum strategy of player G_1 is B, and the value of expression v_1 is 2, whereas the optimum strategy of player G_2 is A, and the value of expression v_2 is 2.

Let us now analyse whether the strategies we proposed are in fact optimum strategies.

If both players were to heed our advice and use the strategies we have indicated, then, as can be seen from Table 1.25, the result of the game would be that player G_1 would win 2, and G_2 would lose 2. And this much was also guaranteed them by the optimum strategies. If our players had to replay the game, neither of them would try to change his strategy. For player G_1, who had become convinced that player G_2 selected strategy A, it does not pay to change policy since he wins precisely most with strategy B (with strategy C he would win only 1, and with A only 0).

As for player G_2, seeing that player G_1 chose strategy B, it does not pay him to change strategy A to any other, since with strategy B he would lose 4 and with strategy C he would lose 5.

Neither of the players, therefore, has any reason to alter his strategy and the strategies we proposed can be regarded as optimum. Strategies determined in this manner will be called *pure minmax strategies*.

It appears that the pure minmax strategies cannot always be regarded as optimum. As we shall see later, pure minmax strategies are optimum only when $v_1 = v_2$, that is, when the condition

$$\text{Max}_{X}\left[\text{Min}_{D} W(X,D)\right] = \text{Min}_{D}\left[\text{Max}_{X} W(X,D)\right] \tag{3}$$

is satisfied.

Example 2. Players G_1 and G_2 play a game similar to that in Example 1. The difference is that pay-offs for individual results differ now from previous. Table 2.25 presents these new winnings (as usual in such tables, these are the winnings of player G_1, i.e. the losses of player G_2).

TABLE 2/25

		Colour chosen by player G_2			Minimum pay-off of player C
		A	B	C	
Colour chosen	A	−2	3	10	−2
by player G_1	B	2	−3	0	−3
	C	−1	5	8	−1
Maximum loss by player G_2		2	5	10	

Reasoning as in the preceding example, we should advise player G_1 to choose colour C, which will guarantee him a pay-off of at least −1:

$$v_1 = \text{Max}_{X}\left[\text{Min}_{D} W(X,D)\right] = -1.$$

Player G_2 should be advised to use strategy A guaranteeing him a loss of at most 2:

$$v_2 = \underset{D}{\text{Min}}\,[\underset{X}{\text{Max}}\,W(X, D)] = 2.$$

However, upon closer analysis, we find it difficult in this case to regard these strategiesas optimum. Indeed, if the players were told to repeat the game, while player G_2 would have no cause to change his strategy, player G_1 would certainly change his to B. For, knowing that in the previous round of the game player G_2 selected A, player G_1 easily notices that with a B strategy he wins 2 (whereas with C strategy he won -1). In any further round of games, player G_2 would see fit to change his strategy from A to B (as against strategy B for player G_1), etc.

Under these conditions, in the example given, the pure minmax strategies can hardly be said to be optimum. It appears that these strategies are optimum only when the condition $v_1 = v_2$ is satisfied. In the present example, however, $v_2 > v_1$.

In the next example we shall show how optimum strategies can be indicated for games in which $v_1 \neq v_2$.

Example 3. Two players G_1 and G_2 play a game similar to that in Examples 1 and 2, except that now each player selects one of two colours only. Table 3.25 gives the pay-offs of player G_1 for individual results of the game.

TABLE 3/25

		Colour chosen by player G_2		Minimum pay-off of player G_1
		A	B	
Colour chosen	A	5	-1	-1
by player G_1	B	-2	2	-2
Maximum loss by player G_2		5	2	

In this example, as in Example 2, the pure minmax strategies are not optimum strategies. As the reader may easily verify, in this case too, the inequality $v_1 \neq v_2$ is satisfied, since $v_1 = -1$, $v_2 = 2$.

In situations of this sort, the players can be offered a different way out. We propose, therefore, to player G_1 that he should decide about the choice of strategy in each case at random but so that the probability of choosing a given strategy is constant. For instance, let the probability of the choice of strategy A be p. Since there are only two strategies, then by the nature of things, the probability of the choice of a second strategy B will equal $1-p$. Let us now try to determine the magnitude of probability p so that it could be regarded as an optimum magnitude.

Let us assume that the opponent, i.e. player G_2 employs strategy A. On the basis of this assumption it is possible to calculate the expected winnings of G_1 for a definite p. They will be $E[W(X, A)]$, i.e. the mathematical expectation of expression $W(X, A)$ determining the winning of player G_1. These pay-offs, for a given strategy of player G_2 (we took $D = A$), depend only on the strategy of player G_1. But this is now a random value. It can be either A (with a probability of p) or B (with a probability of $1-p$). Hence the following calculation is understandable:

$$E[W(X, A)] = 5 \cdot p + (-2)(1-p) = 7p-2. \tag{4}$$

If player G_2 employed strategy B, then the expected pay-off of player G_1, would be

$$E[W(X, B)] = (-1)p + 2(1-p) = 2-3p. \tag{5}$$

As can be seen, the expected pay-offs of player G_1 depend on probability p and on the strategy chosen by player G_2. If player G_2 were also to choose his strategy in a similar fashion, e.g. A with a probability of q, and B with a probability of $1-q$, then the expected pay-off (let us denote it by W_1) would depend only on p and q, that is, we would have $W_1(p, q)$.

Player G_2 would select probability q so as to minimize the expected pay-off of player G_1: $\underset{q}{\text{Min }} W_1(p, q)$. Knowing this, player G_1 would select p so that $\underset{q}{\text{Min }} W_1(p, q)$ would assume a maximum value, i.e.

$$v_1' = \underset{p}{\text{Max}} \left[\underset{q}{\text{Min }} W_1(p, q) \right]. \tag{5'}$$

The optimum value of p can be determined by the graphical method in a simple manner. The appropriate construction is shown in Fig. 1.25. In this figure we have

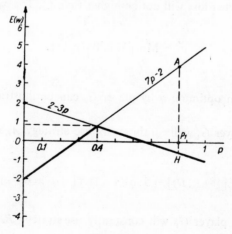

Fig. 1.25

presented graphically two lines corresponding to equations (4) and (5). A somewhat bolder (broken) line has been used to show the lowest expected pay-off for player G_1 for various strategies of player G_2 and various probabilities of p.

For instance, for a probability of $p = p_1$, player G_1 would have an expected pay-off represented by the length of segment p_1A when player G_2 uses strategy A. If player G_2 employed strategy B, player G_1 would have an expected pay-off represented by the number corresponding to the length of segment p_1H, with a minus sign. This is at the same time the lowest expected pay-off that the player can obtain with a probability of $p = p_1$.

Since player G_1 can select p freely, he sets it so that the lowest expected pay-off will be as high as possible. In our case this will be $p = 0 \cdot 4$, and the lowest expected pay-off corresponding to this is $0 \cdot 8$.

The result can be written:

$$v_1' = \underset{p}{\text{Max}} \left[\underset{q}{\text{Min}} \, W_1(p, q) \right] = 0 \cdot 8 \qquad (6)$$

where by v_1 we denote the lowest expected pay-off of player G_1, selecting the strategy in the manner given above. This strategy consists in chosing the probability of individual strategies being used. Such strategies will be called *mixed strategies* and the mixed strategy p determined by formula (6) will be called a minmax mixed strategy.

As for player G_2, he chooses the optimum decision in the same manner as player G_1. Knowing that his opponent, i.e. player G_1, selects p so as to maximize W_1, player G_2 selects q so as to minimize that maximum. Proceeding in this way, player G_2 ensures that his expected loss will not be higher than v_2'. The expression v_2' is defined by the formula

$$v_2' = \underset{q}{\text{Min}} \left[\underset{p}{\text{Max}} \, W_1(p, q) \right]. \qquad (7)$$

The selection of an optimum q by player G_2 can be illustrated graphically as in Fig. 2.25.

Assuming that player G_1 will continuously use strategy A, we can write the loss of player G_2 as

$$E[W(B, D)] = 5 \cdot q + (-1) \cdot (1 - q) = 6q - 1. \qquad (8)$$

If we assume that player G_1 will constantly use strategy B, the expected loss by player G_2 will be

$$E[W(E, D)] = -2q + 2(1-q) = 2 - 4q.$$ (9)

Both of the above equations are represented by means of appropriate lines in Fig. 2.25. As emerges from the drawing, for each value of q there is some expected definite maximum loss for player G_2.

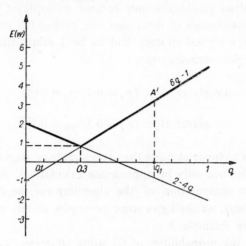

Fig. 2.25

Thus, for instance, for $q = q_1$ this expected maximum loss is represented by the length of segment $q_1 A'$. Player G_2, having a free hand in choosing probability q, selects it so that the expected maximum loss is the lowest possible. He therefore takes $q = 0 \cdot 3$, for which $v'_2 = 0 \cdot 8$, that is,

$$v'_2 = \underset{q}{\text{Min}} \left[\underset{p}{\text{Max}} \, W_1(p, q) \right] = 0 \cdot 8.$$ (10)

Since $v'_1 = v'_2$, we can regard the proposed strategies, i.e. the mixed minmax strategies, as optimum. Neither player will have cause to change the strategies for the same reason as he had no cause of changing the pure strategies when $v_1 = v_2$.

It should be noted that the concept of a mixed strategy is more general than that of a pure strategy. For a pure strategy is a special case of a mixed strategy.

For instants, turning back to Example 1, we recall that strategy B was the optimum pure strategy of player G_1. Let us denote by p_A the probability that player G_2 will use strategy A, by p_B the probability of using strategy B and p_C that of using strategy C. In this case, we can say that the optimum mixed strategy of player G_1 is ($p_A = 0$, $p_B = 1$, $p_C = 0$).

The fact that in Example 3 we obtained the result of $v'_1 = v'_2$ is by no means accidental. It appears that the equality is always satisfied[1] for each game. Hence, the conclusion that mixed minmax strategies are optimum strategies. Of course, in a special case, these mixed strategies may prove to be pure strategies.

Example 3 was solved graphically only because each player had two strategies. Thanks to this, it was enough to determine one probability only for each player (the probability of the second strategy had to be 1 minus the first probability). The optimum strategies obtained were:

$$\text{for player } G_1 \dots (p_A = 0\cdot4, \; p_B = 0\cdot6).$$

$$\text{for player } G_2 \dots (q_A = 0\cdot3, \; q_B = 0\cdot7).$$

If either player has a choice of more than two strategies, then the optimum mixed strategy can be determined only by appropriate calculations. Although we cannot give here a complete computation of the algorithm for the determination of an optimum mixed strategy, we shall give some principles of this algorithm. We shall first do this by using Example 3.

Let x_1 and x_2 be the probabilities of G_1 using strategies A and B, respectively. The magnitude of v'_1 (formula (6)) has been so determined that it is the lowest expected pay-off for the optimum choice of probabilities x_1 and x_2. In any event, the optimum strategy (x_1, x_2) guarantees at least the expected pay-off of v'_1 and this can be written as

$$x_1 5 + x_2 (-2) \geqslant v'_1 \tag{11}$$

$$x_1 (-1) + x_2 2 \geqslant v'_1.$$

Inequalities (11) refer to two possible situations: the use of strategy A or B by player G_2.

Similar inequalities can be written for player G_2. If by y_1 and y_2 we denote the probabilities of player G_2 employing strategies A and B, respectively, then for the optimum choice of these strategies he will ensure that his loss does not exceed v'_2. We therefore have two inequalities, analogous to inequalities (11):

$$y_1 5 + y_2 (-1) \leqslant v'_2 \tag{12}$$

$$y_1 (-2) + y_2 2 \leqslant v'_2.$$

---

[1] An appropriate theorem formulating more accurately the conditions under which this equality is satisfied constitutes the foundation of the theory of games.

Since we found that for optimum strategies we always have $v_1' = v_2'$, by denoting this common value of v_1' and v_2' by v, we can write the inequalities (11) and (12) as follows:

$$5x_1 - 2x_2 \geqslant v$$
$$-x_1 + 2x_2 \geqslant v$$
$$5y_1 - y_2 \leqslant v \tag{13}$$
$$-2y_1 + 2y_2 \leqslant v$$
$$x_1 + x_2 = 1$$
$$y_1 + y_2 = 1.$$

We have added two more equations to the inequalities, stipulating that for each player the sum of the appropriate probabilities must be 1. System (13) has 6 relations with 5 unknowns. This system must now be solved.

The solution of a system of this sort entails difficulties. Formally, we can proceed by changing all the inequalities to equalities and then trying to solve the system.

The system will be

$$5x_1 - 2x_2 = v$$
$$-x_1 + 2x_2 = v$$
$$5y_1 - y_2 = v \tag{14}$$
$$-2y_1 + 2y_2 = v$$
$$x_1 + x_2 = 1$$
$$y_1 + y_2 = 1$$

Let us solve the last five equations and then verify whether the first equation is satisfied by the results obtained.

From the last two equations we have

$$x_1 = 1 - x_2$$
$$y_1 = 1 - y_2.$$

Substituting these values in the second, third, and fourth equations of system (14), we have

$$-1 + x_2 + 2x_2 = v$$
$$5 - 5y_2 - y_2 = v$$
$$-2 + 2y_2 + 2y_2 = v$$

or, after simplifying

$$-1+3x_2 = v$$

$$5-6y_2 = v \qquad\qquad (15)$$

$$-2+4y_2 = v.$$

Equating the left-hand sides of the second and third equations, we obtain

$$5-6y_2 = -2+4y_2$$

or

$$7 = 10y_2$$

hence,

$$y_2 = 0.7.$$

From the third equation of system (15), we therefore have

$$-2+4.0.7 = v$$

or

$$v = 0.8.$$

And, finally, from the first equation of system (15):

$$-1+3x_2 = 0.8$$

or

$$x_2 = 0.6.$$

Since

$$y_1 = 1-y_2,$$

therefore

$$y_1 = 1-0.7 = 0.3$$

and since

$$x_1 = 1-x_2,$$

therefore

$$x_1 = 1-0.6 = 0.4.$$

We have, therefore, obtained the following solution:

$$x_1 = 0.4, \quad x_2 = 0.6, \quad y_1 = 0.3, \quad y_2 = 0.7, \quad v = 0.8. \qquad (16)$$

It is further necessary to verify whether the first equation of system (14), which we have not used, is, satisfied:

$$5.0.4 - 2.0.6 = 0.8.$$

As can be seen, this equation is satisfied and therefore solution (16) is final. It agrees with the solution obtained previously by the graphical method.

It should be emphasized that generally the determination of optimum strategies is not so simple as would appear from the example solved above.

The principle underlying the solution was that the weak inequalities $\leqslant$ or $\geqslant$ appearing in relations of type (13) were replaced by equality signs. It may prove, however, that changes of this sort lead to contradictions in that the value obtained for the probability will not lie between 0 and 1.

Such a result is a sign that one of the relations must remain an inequality. By successive eliminations we must verify in which relation this inequality should appear. If it is found that by leaving one relation with an inequality sign we do not avoid the contradictions in the solution (a probability greater than 1), this is evidence that at least two relations must have inequality signs, etc.

Before illustrating this procedure by an example, we must add that it can be shown that if some relation remains an inequality, this means that the appropriate strategy appears with a probability of 0.

For instance, let the winnings of player G_1 be as given in Table 4.25.

TABLE 4/25

		No. of strategy by player G_2					
		1	2	...	j	...	m
No. of strategy of player G_1	1	a_{11}	a_{12}		a_{1j}		a_{1m}
	2	a_{21}	a_{22}		a_{2j}		a_{2m}
	...	...	...	...	...	...	...
	i	a_{i1}	a_{i2}		a_{ij}		a_{im}
	...	...	...	...	...	...	...
	n	a_{n1}	a_{n2}		a_{nj}		a_{nm}

Let the probability of consecutive strategies being used by player G_1 be $x_1, x_2, ...,$ $x_i, ..., x_n$ and the respective probabilities of player G_2 be $y_1, y_2, ..., y_j, ... y_m$.

If it appears that there is an inequality

$$x_1a_{1j}+x_2a_{2j}+ ... +x_na_{nj} > v$$

then the conclusion is that $y_j = 0$.

Similarly, if

$$y_1a_{i1}+y_2a_{i2}+ ... +y_ma_{im} < v$$

then $x_i = 0$.

Example 4. Player G_1 has two strategies to choose from, and player G_2 has three. The winnings of player G_1 corresponding to the individual combinations of strategies employed are given in Table 5.25.

TABLE 5/25

		No. of strategy of player G_2		
		1	2	3
No. of strategy of player G_1	1	1	2	-5
	2	-2	5	2

Denoting by x_1 and x_2 the probabilities of strategies Nos. 1 and 2 being used by player G_1, and by y_1, y_2 and y_3 the respective probabilities for player G_2, and finally, denoting the value of v_1' (which is equal to v_2') by v, we obtain the following system of inequalities:

$$1x_1 - 2x_2 \geqslant v$$
$$2x_1 + 5x_2 \geqslant v$$
$$-5x_1 + 2x_2 \geqslant v$$
$$1y_1 + 2y_2 - 5y_3 \leqslant v \tag{17}$$
$$-2y_1 + 5y_2 + 2y_3 \leqslant v$$
$$x_1 + x_2 = 1$$
$$y_1 + y_2 + y_3 = 1.$$

Changing the system of relations (17) into equations, we obtain a set of seven equations with six unknowns:

$$x_1 - 2x_2 = v$$
$$2x_1 + 5x_2 = v$$
$$-5x_1 + 2x_2 = v$$
$$y_1 + 2y_2 - 5y_3 = v \tag{18}$$
$$-2y_1 + 5y_2 + 2y_3 = v$$
$$x_1 + x_2 = 1$$
$$y_1 + y_2 + y_3 = 1$$

Taking into account the first two and the last but one equations of system (18), we obtain:

$$x_1 = 1 - x_2$$

and

$$
\begin{array}{ccc}
1 - x_2 - 2x_2 = v & & 1 - 3x_2 = v \\
& \text{or} & \\
2 - 2x_2 + 5x_2 = v & & 2 + 3x_2 = v.
\end{array}
$$

Adding the last two equations by sides, we have

$$3 = 2v \text{ and, hence, } v = \frac{3}{2}.$$

Substituting this value in equation $1-3x_2 = v$, we obtain

$$1-3x_2 = \frac{3}{2} \text{ and, hence, } x_2 = -\frac{1}{6}.$$

We arrived at a contradiction since x_2, as a probability, cannot be a negative number. This contradiction shows that the assumption that all the relations of system (17) are equalities cannot be fulfilled. In view of this, it must be assumed that at least one of these relations is an inequality. For instance, let it be the first relation, that is,

$$x_1-2x_2 > v. \tag{19}$$

Let us take into account the second, third and the last but one equations of system (18), bearing in mind that the first equation in this system is replaced by relation (19). We obtain the following results:

$$x_1 = 1-x_2$$

$$2-2x_2+5x_2 = v \qquad 2+3x_2 = v$$
$$\qquad\qquad\qquad \text{or}$$
$$-5+5x_2+2x_2 = v \qquad -5+7x_2 = v.$$

Subtracting the second equation from the first by sides, we have:

$$7-4x_2 = 0 \text{ and, hence, } x_2 = \frac{7}{4}.$$

The result obtained presents again a contradiction since the probability cannot be greater than 1. Therefore, not the first but some other relation in system (17) has an inequality sign; let it be the second relation:

$$2x_1+5x_2 > v.$$

System (18) now takes the form

$$x_1-2x_2 = v$$
$$2x_1+5x_2 > v$$
$$-5x_1+2x_2 = v$$
$$y_1+2y_2-5y_3 = v \tag{20}$$
$$-2y_1+5y_2+2y_3 = v$$
$$x_1+x_2 = 1$$
$$y_1+y_2+y_3 = 1.$$

Accounting for the first, third and the last but one equations of system (20), we have

$$x_1 = 1 - x_2$$

$$1 - x_2 - 2x_2 = v \qquad\qquad 1 - 3x_2 = v$$

$$\text{or}$$

$$-5 + 5x_2 + 2x_2 = v \qquad -5 + 7x_2 = v.$$

Subtracting the second equation from the first by sides, we obtain

$$6 - 10x_2 = 0 \quad \text{and, therefore,} \quad x_2 = 0{\cdot}6.$$

This result is admissible. The remaining unknowns have now to be determined:

$$x_1 = 1 - x_2 \quad \text{and, hence,} \quad x_1 = 1 - 0{\cdot}6 = 0{\cdot}4.$$

From the first equation of system (20) we obtain

$$0{\cdot}4 - 2.0{\cdot}6 = v \quad \text{and, therefore,} \quad v = -0{\cdot}8.$$

From relation $2x_1 + 5x_2 > v$ appearing in system (20) it follows that $y_2 = 0$. Since $y_1 + y_2 + y_3 = 1$, then, $y_1 = 1 - y_3$.

The fourth equation of system (20) now assumes the form

$$1 - y_3 - 5y_3 = -0{\cdot}8 \quad \text{or} \quad 6y_3 = 1{\cdot}8$$

and hence

$$y_3 = 0{\cdot}3$$

therefore

$$y_1 = 1 - 0{\cdot}3 = 0{\cdot}7.$$

The final result, therefore, is

$$x_1 = 0{\cdot}4, \quad x_2 = 0{\cdot}6, \quad y_1 = 0{\cdot}7, \quad y_2 = 0, \quad y_3 = 0{\cdot}3.$$

It is easy to imagine how laborious calculations may become in the presence of a large number of pure strategies. There are relatively simple iteration methods for the determination of optimum mixed strategies which we shall not discuss here, but they too are quite laborious as far as calculations are concerned.

26. On the significance and applications of two-person zero-sum games

In Section 25 we considered a special type of strategic model. The characteristic feature of this model was its "conflict of interests". This was apparent in the fact that we had to deal with two subjects whose interests were contradictory. The contradiction consisted in that a successful result of an action for one side was tantamount to an unsuccessful result for the other. In other words, each of our decisions carried a result dependent on the decision of the other side whose interests were contrary to our own. Such a situation is typical of many games and for this reason the set of methods which make it possible to determine an optimum decision under these conditions is called the theory of games. Hitherto, we confined ourselves to the case of two-person zero-sum games, i.e. games in which only two sides take part and the sum of the pay-offs of the two players is zero.

The question arises as to the importance models of this kind have in operations research.

It must be stated that in conditions of a socialist economy, these models do not appear to have very wide practical use. However, the function of these models, can be much wider in conditions of a capitalist economy. In the latter case, the activity of two competing firms can at times be reduced to the model of a "game". For instance, two firms competing for a market can be compared to two players.

However, we are dealing here with the theory of games for somewhat different reasons. Firstly, because the theory of games is very closely connected with the theory of linear programming. It is evident namely that each linear programme can be represented as a two-person zero-sum game. The solution of this game is tantamount to the solution of the corresponding linear programme, and conversely. The second reason why we have devoted some space to the theory of games is that this theory constitutes a point of departure in other strategic "no-conflict" models which we shall discuss in Section 27. These strategic "no-conflict" models are frequently called games "against nature".

Finally, the theory of games has contributed to the development of statistical methods for the solution of statistical models. This will be discussed in Chapter VI.

In the subsequent pages of this Section, we shall concentrate our attention to demonstrate the equivalence of linear programmes with two-person zero-sum games. We shall not deal with this in a general manner, but shall merely demonstrate by an example how a linear programme that is equivalent to a two-person zero-sum game may be constructed.

As the starting point let us take the game from Example 4 of Section 25. Table 1.26 gives the pay-offs of player G_1.

TABLE 1/26

		No. of strategy of player G_2		
		1	2	3
No. of strategy of player G_1	1	1	2	−5
	1	−2	5	2

As before, let us denote by x_1 and x_2 the probabilities that G_1 will use strategies No. 1 and No. 2, respectively. By y_1, y_2 and y_3 we denote the respective probabilities that player G_2 will use the consecutive strategies. Let v have the same connotation as before, that is, $v = v_1' = v_2'$, where v_1' and v_2' are defined by formulae (5) and (7) of Section 25. Let us begin by considering the strategies of player G_2. The optimum strategies y_1, y_2 and y_3 must, we know, satisfy the following relations:

$$1y_1 + 2y_2 - 5y_3 \leqslant v$$
$$-2y_1 + 5y_2 + 2y_3 \leqslant v \qquad (1)$$
$$y_1 + y_2 + y_3 = 1.$$

By w we denote an arbitrary number which satisfies the condition

$$w \geqslant v.$$

Substituting w for v in relations (1), we obtain

$$1y_1 + 2y_2 - 5y_3 \leqslant w$$
$$-2y_1 + 5y_2 + 2y_3 \leqslant w \qquad (2)$$
$$y_1 + y_2 + y_3 = 1.$$

The first two inequalities of system (2) can easily be transformed into equations by introducing new variables w_1 and w_2 (of course, they can assume only non-negative values):

$$y_1 + 2y_2 - 5y_3 + w_1 = w$$
$$-2y_1 + 5y_2 + 2y_3 + w_2 = w \qquad (3)$$
$$y_1 + y_2 + y_3 = 1.$$

Writing the first equation in reverse order (first the right-hand side, then the left-hand side) and substituting the value of w from the first equation in the second, we have

$$w = y_1 + 2y_2 - 5y_3 + w_1$$
$$-2y_1 + 5y_2 + 2y_3 + w_2 = y_1 + 2y_2 - 5y_3 + w_1$$
$$y_1 + y_2 + y_3 = 1.$$

After re-arranging the components appearing on both sides of the second equation, we have

$$w = y_1 + 2y_2 - 5y_3 + w_1 \qquad (4)$$
$$-3y_1 + 3y_2 + 7y_3 - w_1 + w_2 = 0$$
$$y_1 + y_2 + y_3 = 1. \qquad (5)$$

For strategies y_1, y_2 and y_3 to be optimum, w must equal v. In other words, strategies y_1, y_2 and y_3 are optimum if they satisfy relations (2) for the lowest possible value of w. Since (4) and (5) are equivalent to system (2), the problem amounts to finding the values of y_1, y_2 and y_3 which minimize expression (4) while satisfying conditions (5). Relations (4) and (5) are a linear programme since all the variables of this programme can only assume non-negative values.

Solving this programme by the known simplex algorithm, we should obtain the same values for y_1, y_2 and y_3 as we did in solving this problem as a game, in Example 4 of Section 25.

And here is the initial simplex table. Two artificial variables, s_1 and s_2, have been introduced into the first and second equations of system (5) respectively.

When introducing the artificial variables s_1 and s_2, we must bear in mind that the function which we are to minimize will change and will take the form

$$w = y_1 + 2y_2 - 5y_3 + w_1 + Ms_1 + Ms_2 \qquad (6)$$

where M is a correspondingly large number.

TABLE 2/26

	s_1	s_2	w_1	w_2	y_1	y_2	y_3	
s_1	1	0	-1	1	-3	3	7	0	$\div 7 = 0$
s_2	0	1	0	0	1	1	1	1	$\div 1 = 1$

The solution is obtained in two stages. From Table 2.26 it appears that it is most advantageous to introduce variable y_3 in the new solution. As a result we have Table 3.26.

TABLE 3/26

	s_1	s_2	w_1	w_2	y_1	y_2	y_3	
y_3	$\dfrac{1}{7}$	0	$-\dfrac{1}{7}$	$\dfrac{1}{7}$	$-\dfrac{3}{7}$	$\dfrac{3}{7}$	1	0	
s_2	$-\dfrac{1}{7}$	1	$\dfrac{1}{7}$	$-\dfrac{1}{7}$	$\dfrac{10}{7}$	$\dfrac{4}{7}$	0	1	$\div \dfrac{10}{7} = \dfrac{7}{10}$

The next variable, to enter in the next solution, is y_1. The new coefficients of the simplex table are given in Table 4.26.

TABLE 4/26

	s_1	s_2	w_1	w_2	y_1	y_2	y_3
y_3	$\dfrac{1}{10}$	$\dfrac{3}{10}$	$-\dfrac{1}{10}$	$\dfrac{1}{10}$	0	$\dfrac{6}{10}$	1	$\dfrac{3}{10}$
y_1	$-\dfrac{1}{10}$	$\dfrac{7}{10}$	$\dfrac{1}{10}$	$-\dfrac{1}{10}$	1	$\dfrac{4}{10}$	0	$\dfrac{7}{10}$

It is easy to ascertain that the solution given in Table 4.26 is final.
We have therefore obtained the following solution:

$$y_1 = 0.7, \qquad y_2 = 0, \qquad y_3 = 0.3$$

and $w_1 = 0$, $w_2 = 0$ (moreover, $s_1 = 0$ and $s_2 = 0$).

Hence, substituting the values obtained in expression (6), we have the minimum value for w which, we recall, we denoted by v:

$$v = 0.7 + 2.0 - 5.0 \cdot 3 + 0 + M.0 + M.0 = -0.8.$$

In a similar fashion, we could construct a second linear programme which would enable to determine the optimum strategies of player G_1. The optimum strategies of player G_1 must satisfy the following conditions:

$$1x_1 - 2x_2 \geqslant v$$

$$2x_1 + 5x_2 \geqslant v \tag{7}$$

$$-5x_1 + 2x_2 \geqslant v$$

$$x_1 + x_2 = 1.$$

Denoting by w, as before, some arbitrary number that satisfies the condition

$$w \leqslant v,$$

we can rewrite system (7) as

$$x_1 - 2x_2 \geqslant w$$

$$2x_1 + 5x_2 \geqslant w \tag{8}$$

$$-5x_1 + 2x_2 \geqslant w$$

$$x_1 + x_2 = 1.$$

Introducing variables u_1, u_2 and u_3 which can assume non-negative values, we obtain the set of equations

$$x_1 - 2x_2 - u_1 = w$$

$$2x_1 + 5x_2 - u_2 = w \tag{9}$$

$$-5x_1 + 2x_2 - u_3 = w$$

$$x_1 + x_2 = 1.$$

We substitute value w from the first equation in the next two equations and we obtain

$$w = x_1 - 2x_2 - u_1$$

$$2x_1 + 5x_2 - u_2 = x_1 - 2x_2 - u_1$$

$$-5x_1 + 2x_2 - u_3 = x_1 - 2x_2 - u_1$$

$$x_1 + x_2 = 1$$

or, after re-arranging,

$$w = x_1 - 2x_2 - u_1 \tag{10}$$

$$x_1 + 7x_2 + u_1 - u_2 = 0$$

$$-6x_1 + 4x_2 + u_1 - u_3 = 0 \tag{11}$$

$$x_1 + x_2 = 1.$$

Strategies x_1 and x_2 are optimum if they satisfy conditions (8) for the largest value of w. But (10) and (11) are equivalent to system (8). The problem therefore is to select values of x_1 and x_2 for which (10) is maximum and (11) is satisfied, with a proviso that all the variables x_1, x_2, u_1, u_2 and u_3 can assume only non-negative values. Sets (10) and (11), therefore, again constitute a linear programme. It is easy to check that the solution of this programme is

$$x_1 = 0{\cdot}4, \quad x_2 = 0{\cdot}6, \quad u_1 = 0, \quad u_2 = 0, \quad u_3 = 0$$

and the maximum value of w is —0·8.

We have, therefore, demonstrated how the solution of a two-person zero-sum game can be reduced to the solution of a corresponding linear programme.

The converse theorem, stating that a linear programme can be reduced to the solution of an appropriate two-person zero-sum game, is also true.

This result is of practical and theoretical importance. The practical significance lies in the fact that when we have to solve a linear programme or game, we can always replace one problem by the other, depending which problem it is easier to solve.

The theoretical significance of the equivalence of games and linear programmes is that the solution of some deterministic models (which linear programmes are), in which all the parameters are known quantities, amounts to the solution of strategic models in which, as we know, the parameters are uncertain in the sense that at the moment the decision is taken we only know that these parameters can assume one of several predetermined values.

Unquestionably, this result is quite surprising. However, we shall not analyse here in more detail this phenomenon, but shall merely confine ourselves to stating this interesting fact that the two-person zero-sum games and linear programmes are equivalent.

27. Games against "nature"

Let us return for the moment to probabilistic models. Their characteristic feature is that all, or at least some, parameters appearing in these models are not known constant quantities but are random variables, i.e. quantities which can assume various values for given probabilities. Knowing these probabilities (strictly speaking, knowing the distribution of these variables), we can determine the values of the decision variables which can be regarded as being optimum. The problem of solving models of this type, that is, of determining optimum decisions, was dealt with in Chapter IV. However, if we assume that those probabilities of the individual parameters which can take on various values are unknown or, if these parameters are not random variables at all and we only know that they can take on a value belonging to a given set, then we can differentiate here between two cases at least. One case is that we know that the value which some single parameter assumes is determined by the given subject of activity, whose interests are completely in conflict with our own. This is the case of a two-person zero-sum game. At times, however, the situation is different in that the value which one parameter or another assumes is not determined by anyone consciously. For instance, if the decision which we have to take today, depends on tomorrow's weather[1], the appropriate model could scarcely be reduced to a two-person zero-sum game, even though some analogy could be drawn here. For, we can imagine that we have, for instance, three possible "strategies", i.e. we can take three different decisions. The effect of these decisions will depend on whether tomorrow there will be rain, or whether it will be sunny or cloudy. The difference between the situation which we have here and the two-person zero-sum game consists in the fact that nature is not interested in selecting tomorrow's weather so as to present for us the greatest possible difficulty. We can say, figuratively speaking, that for "nature" it is indifferent whether we are satisfied or dissatisfied with the weather.

Therefore, the situation as described above can be reduced to the scheme of a game with an opponent who is not interested in winning the game and is equally indifferent to losing it. "Games" of this type will be called games against "nature".

It is easily surmised that the optimum strategy in games of this sort will generally be different from the optimum strategy in two-person zero-sum games.

---

[1] Assuming that we do not make use of the weather forecast.

Example 1.[1] The problem of investments in electricity is under consideration. The sum allocated for this purpose can be used to build either a thermal power station, a hydroelectric power station with a reservoir, a hydro-electric power station on a river, or a power station with sluices. The efficiency of each of the four possible types of investments depends on several basic factors such as future price of coal, climatic conditions (floods, droughts, frosts, etc.). Let us assume that we can establish, at least roughly, four different cases, each determined by a definite set of factors which affect efficiency. We denote these cases by A, B, C and D. Table 1.27 gives the investment efficiencies of the power projects for each of the four possible cases (we do not go into the question of how that efficiency is computed).

TABLE 1/27

	A	B	C	D
Thermal power station (c)	5	2	8	4
Hydro-electric power station with reservoir (z)	2	3	4	12
River power station (r)	8	5	3	10
Power station with sluice installations (s)	1	4	2	8

The above problem can be treated as a game against "nature" in the sense that the set of conditions arising (A, B, C or D) in the course of the operation of the power station is completely independent of whether these conditions are favourable to us or not.

Of course, in games against "nature" we actually have only one "player". In the given case, the subject undertaking the decision on the type of project for investment in electricity is that player. Henceforth we shall call that subject briefly the "player".

Formally speaking, the player could employ a pure minmax strategy here.

As follows from Table 1.27, this strategy would mean taking a decision to build a river power station. It is not difficult to see that this type of strategy can in this case be termed a "pessimistic" strategy. Indeed, we are taking here as our starting point the worst case that can occur in each of our decisions. Thus, in decision c[2], the worst case is B, for which the efficiency of this investment is 2; for decision z the worst case is A, when the investment efficiency is 2, etc. Taking these least advantageous circumstances as our starting point, we select a decision which ensures at

---

[1] This is a modified example given in O. Lange's book *Introduction to Econometrics*, after the French author E. Ventura.

[2] See Table 1.27

least the best of these worst possibilities. Therefore, in deciding to build the river power station, we ensure that its efficiency will be at least 3.

It is easy to see that someone more optimistically minded might reason differently in arriving at a decision. For instance, the best, and not the worst, cases could be taken as the starting point, and of these the best could be chosen. For instance, for decision c the highest attainable efficiency is 8 (in case C), for decision z the highest attainable efficiency is 12, etc. In selecting the best of these best possibilities, we decide to build a hydro-electric power station with a reservoir, thus creating conditions for attaining maximum efficiency.

Whereas we regarded the minmax strategy as being pessimistic, the latter strategy may be considered optimistic or downright speculative. This strategy involves the risk of a much lower efficiency than 12; it is possible that, if case A is realized, the efficiency will be only 2.

Instead of these two extremes, an intermediate attitude could be taken in the choice of strategy. Thus, it is possible to adopt as a starting point not the worst or the best case, but to account for both cases simultaneously.

For instance, in decision c the best possible result is 8, and the worst 2.

As a measure of comparison of the effects of this decision with those of other decisions we could take the mean of these two figures, i.e. $1/2(8+2) = 5$. For decision z the corresponding mean is $1/2(2+12) = 7$. For decision r the mean takes on the value $1/2(3+10) = 6\cdot5$ and, finally, for decision s it is $1/2(1+8) = 4\cdot5$. Guided by this type of criterion, we should select decision z.

This sort of procedure could be generalized by attributing to the worst and best possibilities of each of the decisions different weights, e.g. 2/3 for the worst and 1/3 for the best, instead of the same weight (i.e. 1/2).

With such weights, the results of the individual decisions would be measured by the following magnitudes:

$$\text{for decision } c \quad \frac{2}{3}\cdot 2+\frac{1}{3}\cdot 8 = 4$$

$$\text{for decision } z \quad \frac{2}{3}\cdot 2+\frac{1}{3}\cdot 12 = 5\frac{1}{3}$$

$$\text{for decision } r \quad \frac{2}{3}\cdot 3+\frac{1}{3}\cdot 10 = 5\frac{1}{3}$$

$$\text{for decision } s \quad \frac{2}{3}\cdot 1+\frac{1}{3}\cdot 8 = 3\frac{1}{3}.$$

Such a criterion would offer two equally good decisions: z and r.

The choice of weights discussed here is quite a subjective matter. It is difficult, however, to imagine some objectively best decision in games against nature, for the reason that in such games our information about the results of the decisions is too meagre. In particular, we know nothing about the strategies likely to be employed by nature. Besides the afore-mentioned method of choosing the optimum strategy in games against nature, of which L. Hurwicz[1] is the author, others may be mentioned.

All of these methods are, by their nature, more or less subjective. More objective methods of determining the optimum decision could only be discussed if we knew more about the strategies of "nature". When some information about the strategies of "nature" is available we are in the presence of either a probabilistic or statistical model which will be the subject of Chapter VI.

To conclude our discussion of the theory of games it should be added that this theory also deals with games of non-zero sums. This means that the sum of pay-offs of all players does not equal zero. We have such games when the interests of the individual players are not entirely conflicting with to one another. This, in the two-person game, is expressed in that the "pay-offs" of the first player need not necessarily, equal the "loss" of the second.

In situations of this type, especially when there is a larger number of players, it is possible to form an agreement between individual players, i.e. a coalition. It may indeed prove more convenient for a certain group of players to come to an understanding among themselves and to agree upon the "division" of the total pay-off than to play singly.

The theory of non-zero games still contains many as yet unsolved problems.

28. Bibliographical notes

The theory of games has quite a wealth of literature. This literature varies, ranging from purely mathematical studies to textbooks giving the fundamentals of this theory and its applications in an accessible language.

Unquestionably, the best book in this field is at present the study by R. Luce and H. Raiffa [4]. This book can be understood by a reader without any special mathematical training. It touches upon all the essential questions pertaining to the theory of games and its applications.

A very elementary introduction to the theory of games is given in the book by J. Williams [7].

J. von Neumann was the creator of the theory of games. In a book [5] written in conjunction with O. Morgenstern, he gives an exposition of the theory of games and its applications in economics. This book does not make easy reading and requires considerable mathematical training on the part of the reader, although the formal mathematical procedures used by the authors are quite modest.

---

[1] Cf. R. Luce and H. Raiffa, *Games and Decisions*, New York, 1957, J. Wiley.

Much more readable than the book by von Neumann and Morgenstern is that by J. McKinsey [2]. This is however, rather a formal exposition of the theory of games and it discusses the mathematical aspect more than the question of applications.

An exposition relatively easy to understand, but of quite limited scope, is found in the first part of the joint work by Guilbaud, Massé and Henon [1]. The theory of games is presented therein from the point of view of its applications to economic activity.

A concise exposition of the theory of games and its links with the theory of linear programming is given in a small book by S. Vajda [6].

Finally, mention should be made of a work containing collections of mathematical dissertations devoted to the theory of games. This book [3], edited by H. Kuhn and A. Tucker, is intended solely for mathematicians.

BIBLIOGRAPHY

[1] Guilbaud, G., Massé, P. and Henon, R., *Stratégies et décision économiques. Études théoretiques et applications aux entreprises* (Economic Strategies and Decisions. Theoretical Studies as Applied to an Enterprise) Paris 1954, Centre National de la Recherche Scientifique.

[2] McKinsey, J., *Introduction to the Theory of Games,* New York, 1952, McGraw-Hill.

[3] Kuhn, H. and Tucker, A., *Contributions to the Theory of Games,* Princeton, vol. I — 1950, vol. II — 1953, Princeton Univ. Press.

[4] Luce, R. and Raiffa, H., *Games and Decisions,* New York, 1957, J. Wiley.

[5] von Neumann, J. and Morgenstern, O., *Theory of Games and Economic Behavior,* Princeton, 1944, Princeton Univ. Press.

[6] Vajda, S., *Theory of Games and Linear Programming,* New York, 1956, J. Wiley.

[7] Williams, J., *The Compleat Strategyst,* New York, 1954, McGraw-Hill.

CHAPTER 6

Statistical Methods

29. The optimum decision in statistical models

Statistical models have two essential features. One is that the values of the parameters which appear in them are, to a varying extent, unknown to the person taking the decision.

The other feature is that before a decision is taken there is a possibility of additional information (as a rule, incomplete) being obtained about these parameters Such information can be utilized in determining the optimum decision.

This possibility of additional information being obtained complicates the solution of a statistical model in that it is not sufficient to define how the optimum decision is to be determined on the basis of available information on parameter values, but it is also necessary to decide how this information is to be gathered.

We devote Section 29 to a discussion of the problems involved in the solution of statistical models.

Example 1. A consignee receives a lot of goods from a supplier. The lot comprises 10,000 metal rods. Each rod must have a specified strength[1], for instance, $W = 500$ cu. cm. The consignee can reject the lot if he considers it unsatisfactory or he can accept it if he considers it good.

Since it is difficult to imagine ideal production conditions which guarantee a strength of exactly $W = 500$ cu. cm. for all the rods, the lot may contain rods of a higher or lower strength. Such an occurrence is unavoidable in practice. Accepting this fact, both the consignee and the supplier agree what should be regarded as a good lot, i.e. one which can be accepted, and what as an unsuitable lot, i.e. which the consignee has the right to reject.

Let us assume that they agree to classify a lot as good if the number of faulty rods does not exceed 5 per cent, a rod being considered faulty if its strength is less than 450 cu. cm.

The decision to accept or reject a lot depends on the actual faultiness of the lot[2], which we shall denote as w. If the value of this parameter were known, we would

---

[1] Strength as a factor is measured in cu. cm. (See J. Nowiński and W. Sadowski's *Dobór asortymentu kształtowników walcowanych jako zagadnienie probabilistyczne (Choice of the Range of Rolled Shapes as a Probabilistic Problem)*, Przegląd Statystyczny, 1954).

[2] By faultiness of the lot we mean in this case the ratio of unsuitable rods to the total number of rods in the lot.

have a very simple deterministic model. We shall formulate this model in more detail. The difficulty is that the value of this parameter is more or less unknown. It is, however, possible to obtain additional information concerning it. This can be done by selecting in an appropriate manner, a small number of rods from the lot, say 100. Knowledge of the strength of these rods will throw more light on the unknown value of parameter w. With this kind of information it will be easier to make a correct (i.e. optimum) decision whether to accept or to reject the lot.

From this example it is seen that the solution of a statistical model requires a decision on two closely related problems:

1) how, and to what extent, additional information about the given parameter should be collected,

2) how this information should be used to determine an optimum decision.

Regarding the first problem, this additional information on the faultiness of the lot was obtained in our example by inspection of 100 of the 10,000 rods. The more representative the material on which we base our observations (in our case 100 rods), the more reliable will be this information. In our case, we could say that the 100 rods selected are quite representative of the total 10,000 rods, if the defects in the 100 rods were the same as in the 10,000 rods. However, as we do not know the defects of the entire lot, it is difficult to say whether or not the selected 100 rods are a representative sample of the whole lot. In this respect, there is only one indication on which we can rely in collecting information. Information should be collected in an unbiased manner.

Let us agree that the incomplete material which we use in the assessment of the unknown parameter shall be called a sample. Then the objective, as we said, is to select a sample which is unbiased, i.e. which is not burdened with a systematic error. When shall we consider a sample biased? Whenever the appearance or otherwise of a given unit in a sample affects the investigated feature. Thus, in our example, the feature to be investigated was the quality of the rods determined by the strength factor. Let us assume that some of the rods delivered are rusty. If all the rusty rods were selected as a sample, there would be a great danger that this sample would be biased since, undoubtedly, the fact that the rod is rusty has some bearing on its durability; (it decreases it).

In order to safeguard against biased samples, it is best to select a sample at random. There are various ways of random sampling, depending on the particular situation. One of the more widely used methods of random sampling consists in using so-called random numbers.

We shall say more about some specific problems relating to sampling in later sections. At present, we merely state that the sample must be selected at random and we assume that the size of the sample has been established beforehand.

Another problem related to the solution of a statistical model is the method of using information contained in a sample in order to determine an optimum decision. Here, two cases can be distinguished:

a) when the parameter about which we have partial information is a random variable of a known distribution,

b) when the parameter about which we have partial information is a random variable of an unknown distribution or is a constant of an unknown value.

The procedure varies somewhat according to the case. However, since both are special cases of the statistical model, they have certain features in common which we discuss below.

First of all, every statistical model, like every model in operations research, contains in addition to parameters, one or more decision variables. In our case, the decision variable can be assumed to take on only two values. Let us agree that when we decide to reject the lot, the decision variable X is 0 and when we decide to accept the lot, X equals 1.

In order to be able to find the optimum decision, i.e. to give variable X one of the two possible values, it is necessary to have appropriate criteria. Here, the point of departure will be some function dependent on variable X and on the parameters of the model. The values of this function will be decisive in the selection of values of X.

Let us assume that this function can be obtained from Table 1.29.

TABLE 1/29

X \ w	$w > 0 \cdot 05$	$w \leqslant 0 \cdot 05$
$X = 0$	0	20
$X = 1$	30	0

The values of this function (which we denote by S), determine the loss $S = g(X, w)$. That is, if $X = 0$ and we reject the lot, the value of the function is 0 for $w > 0 \cdot 05$ and 20 for $w \leqslant 0 \cdot 05$. This means that the rejection of the bad lot is a correct decision and does not entail any loss. On the other hand, if we rejected a lot which in reality was good ($w \leqslant 0 \cdot 05$), this would result in losses (transport costs, labour costs, etc.) amounting to 20 (e.g. 20,000 zlotys). Similarly, if a lot is accepted ($X = 1$) when it is actually bad ($w > 0 \cdot 05$), we incur losses which we assess at 30. The acceptance of a good lot is again a correct decision which does not involve any loss. If we knew the value of parameter w, it would be very simple to make the decision, i.e. establish the optimum value of the decision variable, X. For a specific w, S is a function of only one variable X. It is easy to see that for $w > 0 \cdot 05$ the optimum value of the decision variable is $X = 0$, while for $w \leqslant 0 \cdot 05$ it is $X = 1$. However, we do not know the value of w, but on the other hand we can obtain information about this parameter from a sample. The problem which we face in solving a statistical model is to formulate a rule which attaches a specific value of the decision variable to every possible sample. In other words, if we denote the assessed value of parameter w by $\bar{w}$, obtained from the sample, the objective is to form a function

$$X = h(\bar{w})$$

which will decide the value to be given the decision variable in relation to whatever sample is obtained.

Of course, the principal problem is to choose the form of function h. It is easy to see that the way in which function h is constructed depends to a large extent on function S. The problem is to arrive at a minimum possible loss. However, we always risk incurring some loss no matter how we construct function h. This is because the value of $\bar{w}$ does not determine a unique value of w. Therefore, one and the same value of $\bar{w}$ may correspond to different values of parameter w, or even better, for one and the same value of w several samples can be obtained and, hence, various values of $\bar{w}$.

Thus, the problem of solving a statistical model is reduced to the determination of the optimum function h, i.e. one which ensures the lowest losses. This is quite a difficult problem and for this reason, in subsequent sections, we shall confine our discussion to some basic concepts of this solution alone. This solution would become even more complicated if we disregarded the assumption that the size of the sample is predetermined, and if we wanted both to form function h and to determine the size and the method of selecting the sample. We shall not consider these two problems jointly but shall discuss each of them individually.

30. Bayes decision functions

As we established in Section 29, the principal problem which arises in the solution of statistical models is the construction of an appropriate function h, assigning a specific value of the decision variable to each possible sample. We shall call function h the decision function.

First, let us study a simple case in which the unknown parameter is a random variable with a known distribution.

To explain in more detail the procedure followed, we shall discuss a simpler example than given in Section 29. This is an artificial example; none the less it will give us a better idea of the essence of the solution of statistical models.

Example 1. An urn contains 100 balls of two types, black and white. It is known in advance that the ratio of the number of white balls to the total number in the urn, can be one of three values: 0·25, 0·50 or 0·75. The probability of the urn having one of the three aforementioned ratios of white balls is also known. Denoting the ratio of white balls by p, we write these probabilities as:

$$P(p = 0·25) = 0·1$$
$$P(p = 0·50) = 0·4$$
$$P(p = 0·75) = 0·5$$

Without examining the contents of the urn, i.e. without knowing exactly which of the three possible types of urn we are handling, we must decide the number of white balls to be added so that the number of balls in the urn including the additional ones amount to 75. We assume that our choice is limited in regard to the number of additional balls which we can prepare. This number can be either 0, 20, 40 or 60.

If the total number of balls in the urn plus the additional balls does not equal 75, we incur certain losses, irrespective as to whether the number of balls is smaller or larger than 75. Table 1.30 gives these losses. The number of balls prepared is denoted by X; this is the decision variable.

In the top left-hand corner of each square we note the number of balls we would receive for the various possible combinations of the values of X and p. We assumed that a deficiency in white balls to the desired number of 75 involved a loss of 2 zlotys per ball, while each white ball in surplus brought a loss of 1 zloty.

TABLE 1/30

X \ p	0·25		0·50		0·75	
0	25	100	50	50	75	0
20	45	60	70	10	95	20
40	65	20	90	15	115	40
60	85	10	110	35	135	60

If the ratio of white balls in the urn were known (i.e. if we knew the value of parameter p), it would be a simple matter to determine the optimum decision[1]. For instance, if it were known that $p = 0·25$, the optimum value of the decision variable X

---

[1] This emerges from the assumption that there are 100 balls in the urn; therefore, the specified ratio determines the number of white and black balls.

would be 60, ensuring the smallest possible loss (10). This would be an instance
of a deterministic model.

On the assumption that p is a random variable having a distribution as given
above, we obtain a probabilistic model. In order to determine the optimum decision
it would be necessary to calculate the expected loss for every possible decision
and to choose the case for which this loss is the lowest. In our example, the values
of expected losses would be as follows:

$$\text{for } X = 0 \quad 100.0\cdot1 + 50.0\cdot4 + 0.0\cdot5 = 30$$

$$\text{for } X = 20 \quad 60.0\cdot1 + 10.0\cdot4 + 20.0\cdot5 = 20$$

$$\text{for } X = 40 \quad 20.0\cdot1 + 15.0\cdot4 + 40.0\cdot5 = 28$$

$$\text{for } X = 60 \quad 10.0\cdot1 + 35.0\cdot4 + 60.0\cdot5 = 45.$$

In this case, the optimum value of the decision variable is $X = 20$. This value
corresponds to the lowest of the possible expected losses.

If we assume that it is possible to select a sample from the urn, e.g. four balls,
before the decision, we are in a somewhat better situation than in the case of the
probabilistic model. From the selected sample, certain conclusions can be drawn
concerning parameter p; thus, we can reach conclusions about the structure of the
balls in the urn in question. In this particular case we are dealing with a statistical
model and the entire problem may be reduced to the question as to the kind of
decisions to be attributed to the various obtainable samples. In other words, the
problem is to plot a decision function — in such a way, of course, that it can be
considered optimum.

In the example under consideration we can obtain five different samples (assuming
that the sample contains four balls):

a) 0 white and 4 black balls
b) 1 white and 3 black balls
c) 2 white and 2 black balls
d) 3 white and 1 black balls
e) 4 white and 0 black balls

We denote the sample (of four balls) containing i white balls by the symbol b_i,
in which $i = 0, 1, 2, 3, 4$. Formally, there are 1,024 different possible decision functions in our example.

Table 2.30 gives several of the possible functions by way of example.

Thus, the decision function h_1, for instance, allots only one value of the decision
variable X to every possible sample, and this value is 0. Function h_3 allots a value
of variable $X = 60$ to sample b_0, 40 to sample b_1, 40 to b_2, 20 to b_3, and zero to
sample b_4.

TABLE 2/30

Decision function \ Sample	b_0	b_1	b_2	b_3	b_4
h_1	0	0	0	0	0
h_2	20	20	20	20	20
h_3	60	40	40	20	0
h_4	40	40	20	20	0
h_5	60	40	40	20	20
h_6	0	20	40	60	60
.	.	.	.	.	.
.	.	.	.	.	.
.	.	.	.	.	.
h_{1024}	60	60	60	60	60

As is easily calculated, the number of such allocations (i.e. decision functions of specific values of variable X to the various samples will be equal to the number of five-term variations with repetitions, created from four elements. These variations are in five-terms, since there are five possible samples and every variation can be formed from four elements as there is this number of possible values of the decision variable.

In accordance with the formula for the number of k-term variations with repetitions, created from n elements, we have[1]

$$n^k = 4^5 = 1{,}024 .$$

Next, it is necessary to investigate the consequences of selecting any of the decision functions.

The point of departure for an examination of these consequences will be to calculate the probabilities of obtaining various types of samples in relation to the value of parameter p.

For instance, if $p = 0.25$, it is easy to calculate the probability that sample b_i will be obtained, i.e. a sample (of four elements) having i white balls. Assuming that the balls are drawn according to the sampling scheme in which the balls are returned after selection, we can easily determine the desired probabilities:

$$P(b_i|0.25) = \binom{4}{i} . 0.25^i (1 - 0.25)^{4-i} .$$

---

[1] A k-term variation with repetitions, created from n elements, is a k-term sequence of any of the n elements, it being understood that the elements can be repeated (See T. Czechowski, *Elementarny wykład rachunku prawdopodobieństwa (An Elementary Exposition of Probability Calculus)*, Warsaw, 1958, PWN.)

These probabilities are calculated from the well-known Bernoulli formula. The symbol $P(b_i|0.25)$ gives the probability of obtaining i white balls in a four-element sample, on the assumption that the value of parameter p is 0.25. Symbol $\binom{4}{i}$ stands for the number of so-called combinations of 4 elements by i.[1]

For instance, for $i = 0$ we have

$$P(b_0|0.25) = \binom{4}{0} 0.25^0 . 0.75^4 \cong 0.3164$$

$$\text{for } i = 1: \quad P(b_1|0.25) = \binom{4}{1} 0.25^1 . 0.75^3 \cong 0.4219$$

$$\text{for } i = 2: \quad P(b_2|0.25) = \binom{4}{2} 0.25^2 . 0.75^2 \cong 0.2109$$

$$\text{for } i = 3: \quad P(b_3|0.25) = \binom{4}{3} 0.25^3 . 0.75^1 \cong 0.0469$$

$$\text{for } i = 4: \quad P(b_4|0.25) = \binom{4}{4} 0.25^4 . 0.75^0 \cong 0.0039 .$$

The above probabilities can be read from special tables of the binomial distribution.[2]

Table 3.30 gives the appropriate probabilities of every possible sample in relation to the value of parameter p.

TABLE 3/30

b_i \\ p	0·25	0·50	0·75
b_0	0·3164	0·0625	0·0039
b_1	0·4219	0·2500	0·0469
b_2	0·2109	0·3750	0·2109
b_3	0·0469	0·2500	0·4219
b_4	0·0039	0·0625	0·3164

The probabilities from Table 3.30 make it possible to calculate expected losses in relation to the use of any of the decision functions. These losses, of course, depend on the value of parameter p.

In order to illustrate how such expected losses are assessed, we shall carry out appropriate calculations for one of the many possible decision functions, viz., for function h_3 from Table 2.30.

This function definitely determines a decision (i.e. the value of decision variable X) in relation to whatever kind of sample is taken.

---

[1] Cf. T. Czechowski, op. cit.

[2] For instance, Tables of the Binomial Probability Distribution, published by the National Bureau of Standards, Washington, 1949.

Let us assume, to begin with, that $p = 0.25$. From Table 3.30 we immediately have the probability of obtaining the various types of samples and, assuming that we are using function h_3, we also have the probability that the decision variable may assume any value. Using the decision function h_3, we arrive at the following probabilities:

$$P(X = 60) = 0.3164$$

$$P(X = 40) = 0.4219 + 0.2109 = 0.6328$$

$$P(X = 20) = 0.0469$$

$$P(X = 0) = 0.0039.$$

On the assumption that $p = 0.25$, the losses corresponding to the various decisions can be read from Table 1.30. Similarly, knowing the probabilities that particular decisions will be taken, it is possible to calculate the anticipated loss as a result of using decision function h_3 on the assumption that $p = 0.25$. This anticipated loss, denoted by S_3, amounts to

$$S_3(0.25) = 10.0.3164 + 20.0.6328 + 60.0.0469 + 100.0.0039 = 18.824.$$

Assuming that $p = 0.50$, the expected loss will be:

$$S_3(0.50) = 35.0.0625 + 15.0.6250 + 10.0.2500 + 50.0.0625 = 17.4875.$$

The above loss was calculated in a similar manner to that used previously. Namely, from Tables 2.30 and 3.30 it follows that when decision function h_3 is used, the probability of the various decisions (on the assumption that $p = 0.50$) is as follows:

$$P(X = 60) = 0.0625$$

$$P(X = 40) = 0.2500 + 0.3750 = 0.6250$$

$$P(X = 20) = 0.2500$$

$$P(X = 0) = 0.0625.$$

Making use of these probabilities and Table 1.30, we can determine the probabilities of losses of various values, and from this can be calculated the expected loss $S_3(0.50)$.

We calculate similarly the expected loss for $p = 0.75$, that is $S_3(0.75)$:

$$S_3(0.75) = 60.0.0039 + 40.0.2578 + 20.0.4219 + 0.0.3164 = 19.0040.$$

Both this result and the results of similar calculations for several other decision functions from Table 2.30, are given in Table 4.30.

This table includes the expected losses resulting from the use of the various functions in relation to the magnitude of parameter p.

TABLE 4/30

p ＼ h_i	h_3	h_1	h_2	h_4	h_5
0·25	18·8240	100	60	30·6240	18·8680
0·50	17·4875	50	10	14·0625	14·6875
0·75	19·0040	0	20	14·6880	25·3120

It is particularly easy to calculate the expected losses for such decision functions as h_1, for instance. Function h_1 allots a decision variable value 0 to every obtainable sample. This means that we always give a 0 value to this variable, i.e.

$$P(X = 0) = 1$$

$$P(X \neq 0) = 0$$

Thus,

$$S_1(0·25) = 1.100 + 0.60 + 0.20 + 0.10 = 100$$

$$S_1(0·50) = 1.50 + 0.10 + 0.15 + 0.35 = 50$$

$$S_1(0·75) = 1.0 + 0.20 + 0.40 + 0.60 = 0.$$

Considering this formally, for each of the 1,024 possible decision functions, in our case, it would be necessary to calculate the expected losses for the various values of parameter p. For obvious reasons we do not do this here. Next, we can proceed to determine the optimum decision function. Since we assumed that parameter p is a random variable determined by the probabilities as given below:

$$P(p = 0·25) = 0·1$$

$$P(p = 0·50) = 0·4$$

$$P(p = 0·75) = 0·5,$$

it is now easy to assign an expected loss to each possible decision function. On the basis of the aforementioned probabilities and data from Table 4.30, these calculations can be carried out giving the expected losses corresponding to the various functions h_i. Namely, for h_3, the expected loss S_3 amounts to

$$S_3 = 18·8240 . 0·1 + 17·4875 . 0·4 + 19·0040 . 0·5 = 18·3794$$

for h_1:
$$S_1 = 100.0 \cdot 1 + 50.0 \cdot 4 + 0.0 \cdot 5 = 30$$

for h_2:
$$S_2 = 60.0 \cdot 1 + 10.0 \cdot 4 + 20.0 \cdot 5 = 20, \quad \text{etc.}$$

In this manner, an expected loss has been attached to every possible decision function. Of course, in our view, the optimum function is the one for which the expected loss is the lowest.

A decision function chosen in this way is called *the Bayes decision function*. The name comes from the fact that the choice of this function depends on the *a priori* distribution of parameter p, i.e. the distribution which we know before the sample is taken. The problem is that if there is a change in the *a priori* distribution, generally speaking, the optimum decision function changes, too.

To summarize, we can say that the procedure used in determining the optimum Bayes decision function which gives us the solution of the statistical model, is as follows:

1. We determine the function of "losses" which attaches to every possible value of decision variable X a specific loss S, which is dependent on a certain parameter p of a known probability distribution. We denote the loss function as $S(X, p)$.

2. Having established the type of sample which can be obtained as a result of drawing lots, we determine all the possible decision functions, allotting a specific value of the decision variable to each sample. If we denote the sample by b, this relationship can be symbolically represented as

$$X = h_i(b).$$

Many such functions can be plotted: h_1, h_2, ...[1]

3. For every decision function h_i there is a certain expected loss S_i. The method of calculating these expected losses was given above. It should be mentioned that without knowing the probability distribution of parameter p it would be impossible to calculate losses S_i.

4. We take as our optimum decision function the function for which the anticipated loss S_i is the lowest. We call this the optimum Bayes decision function.

From the comments in Section 30 we became acquainted with the fundamentals of solving a statistical model when the parameter of this model is a random variable of a known distribution. On the other hand, we disregarded the technical side of the problem, i.e. we did not mention how optimum Bayes decision functions are determined in practice, or in other words, how statistical models are solved in practice.

---

[1] As we recall, there are 1,024 such functions in our example.

From the aforementioned theory it follows that it is an extremely laborious matter to solve a statistical model, involving extensive calculations. There are, however, methods which make it possible to arrive at the solution of a model in a relatively easy manner. We shall not enter into the details of these methods as this is the subject matter of mathematical statistics. It is particularly easy to solve statistical models with parameters of known distributions.

Much more trouble is encountered in the case of a statistical model in which a parameter is not a random variable but a constant (unknown), or when it is a random variable but of an unknown distribution. Some brief comments on finding solutions for statistical models of this type are given in Section 31.

31. Minmax decision functions

When the parameter of the statistical model is a random variable of an unknown distribution or an unknown constant, the statistical model has much in common with the theory of games. The situation is, in fact, quite similar to games against nature, mentioned in Chapter V.

Let us turn back for a moment to the example of the previous section and let us assume that we do not know the distribution of parameter p. Without this information it is possible to construct a function alloting an expected value of losses to each of the possible decision functions and the various values of parameter p. Table 4.30 can be regarded as giving the pay-offs by "nature", and the problem of choosing an optimum decision function can be reduced to the choice of an optimum strategy for the player. Let us suppose that one of the players is nature which can use various strategies. In our case, the strategy of nature consists in making a choice of three possible values of parameter p. The other player in this case is the statistician, i.e. the person making the decision. Let us call him the second player. The strategies of the second player are all the possible decision functions. This player is perfectly free to choose any one of them.

It might seem, as in the games against "nature" discussed previously, that the use by the second player of the minmax strategy would be unjustified insofar as it is difficult to consider nature as a player interested to defeat the opponent. As stressed before, this is so to speak a matter of complete indifference to "nature".

It appears, however, that this question is not quite so simple. We have already been able to observe that in statistical models occurring in practice, there is an infinite number of decision functions from which an optimum function must be chosen. When we know the *a priori* distribution of the parameter of a statistical model this fact does not present any major difficulty in effectively determining the optimum decision function. However, this is not so in our present case. Our problem, therefore, is how to effectively determine the decision function so that we can regard it as optimum.

Obviously, a function like h_k will not be optimum if for the various values of parameter p it gives higher losses than some other function h_l. For instance, let the losses for the two functions h_k and h_l be as given in Table 1.31.

TABLE 1/31

p ⟍ h_i	h_k	h_l
0·25	18	17
0·50	20	10
0·75	32	30

It is understood that functions with characteristics analogous to those of h_k should be disregarded in the selection of an optimum decision function. Function h_l is often said to be uniformly better than h_k. The set of decision functions for which no uniformly better functions exist is called the set of feasible decision functions and it is to this set that we confine ourselves in the search for an optimum.

Unfortunately, considerable difficulties are encountered in making an effective determination of a decision function which we know belongs to the set of feasible decision functions. These difficulties can be overcome if mixed strategies are considered. The mixed strategy of nature is a certain distribution of parameter p probabilities determining the probability of a given decision function being employed. Such mixed strategies are known as *randomized decision functions*. Of course, out of all these we can select those which create a feasible set of randomized functions, i.e. one comprising the functions for which there are no uniformly better functions.

It appears that the statistician's mixed minmax strategy, in other words, the minmax randomized decision function, has the property of belonging to the set of feasible randomized decision functions.

The theory of solving statistical models is in its infancy and even though there have been considerable theoretical achievements, there is still a lack of appropriate computational methods for the effective solution of these models. For this reason, in speaking of statistical models, we have limited ourselves to the presentation of some general information giving an insight into the problem itself without going into detail and avoiding the actual computation.

32. The problem of sample size

The sample giving some information about the parameter plays a fundamental role in the solution of statistical models.

Naturally, if the sample is small, i.e. if it comprises a small number of elements (observations), the information obtained about the parameter must necessarily be rather scanty. In this situation, the expected losses which we risk in making a decision by means of the optimum decision function, must be relatively high. These expected losses could be decreased appreciably if the sample were increased appropriately.

From these comments it emerges that the problem of solving a statistical model is not simply a matter of choosing an optimum decision function but also one of establishing the sample size.

Generally speaking, the sampling and examination of the sample entail certain costs which depend on the size of sample. The larger the sample, the higher the costs. As a result, we conclude that an increase in the size of sample, on the one hand, decreases the expected losses, but on the other hand increases the cost of examining the sample. Thus, the problem is to establish an appropriate size of the sample.

We shall discuss this problem on the basis of an example. It is connected with the problem called statistical evaluation.[1]

Example 1. A lot delivered to a consignee (e.g. electric bulbs), may contain better and worse items. For instance, some bulbs can last longer than others. We determine the value of each bulb according to the number of light-hours which the bulb provides. If, in a lot consisting of N bulbs, we know the value of each (let us denote it as x_i), then the value of the whole lot W is determined by the sum of the values x_i, that is:

$$W = \sum_{i=1}^{N} x_i. \tag{1}$$

In practice it is too tedious to check the entire lot of electric bulbs. It is possible, however, to make an approximate assessment of the value of the lot by checking a sample consisting of, say, n bulbs, chosen at random. The average value of a bulb in the sample can be denoted as $\overline{x}_n$, where

$$\overline{x}_n = \frac{1}{n} \sum_{i=1}^{n} x_i. \tag{2}$$

Let us agree that for the entire lot of bulbs the consignee pays the sum

$$Z = N \cdot \overline{x}_n. \tag{3}$$

If n is a very small number, the sum Z differs considerably from the true value W of the entire lot. On the other hand, a larger sample, while considerably reducing

---

[1] This problem was included by H. Steinhaus in his paper *Wycena statystyczna jako metoda odbioru towarów produkcji masowej (Statistical Evaluation as a Method for Accepting Mass Produced Goods)*, Studia i prace statystyczne (Statistical Studies and Papers), 1950, No. 2. The example discussed here has been borrowed from this paper.

the possibility of any appreciable variation between the value Z and the value W, would involve additional costs for testing a larger number of electric bulbs.

An optimum sample size must be established, i.e. an optimum n must be determined. Let us point out that in our example we assumed beforehand that we shall use decision function (3). This function allots a determined value of the decision variable Z to every possible sample. We have not examined whether or not this function is optimum in order to concentrate on the matter of choosing an optimum sample size.

The expression $|Z-W|$ which denotes the absolute value of the difference between the amount which the consignee pays to the supplier and the actual value of the lot is a measure of the loss which we want to minimize. Of course, the minimum value of this difference equals 0, when the entire lot is tested, i.e. when $'n = N$. However, as we emphasized, tests will involve certain costs K expressed by the formula

$$K(n) = C + n \cdot k \tag{4}$$

in which C is a constant, k is the cost of testing one bulb, and n is the number of bulbs in the sample. Of course, the cost K will increase as the size of the sample increases.

In view of this, we try to choose such a number n that the sum of costs and losses involved in the test due to an inaccurate evaluation of the lot is a minimum. We denote this sum as S:

$$S = |Z - W| + K(n). \tag{5}$$

Since Z is a random variable according to formula (3) as it can take on a different value for a sample of the same size, depending on the value of $\bar{x}_n$ in this sample, the sum S is also a random variable. As in all such cases, we try to choose such an n that the expected value S, that is, $E(S)$ is the lowest possible. Then, of course, we have

$$E(S) = E[|Z - W| + K(n)] = E|Z - W| + K(n). \tag{6}$$

In calculating n which minimizes the above expression, we can meet with various situations:

1. The distribution of variable x is known. This case is trivial since knowing the distribution of variable x, the value of the lot is definitely determined. In this case there is no need at all to take a sample.
2. The distribution of variable x is known, e.g. it is normal, but the mean value of this distribution is unknown. In such a situation, the expression $E|Z-W|$ depends precisely on this average value. Assuming that this average value is a random variable of a known distribution, we thereby also have a fixed distribution of $E|Z-W|$ which in this case is a random variable. Thus, it is possible to calculate

the mathematical expectation of the variable $E|Z-W|$ i.e. $E[E|Z-W|]$ and n must be so determined that the expression $E[E|Z-W| + K(n)]$ becomes a minimum.

If the distribution of the average is not known, an optimum n can be determined by means of the minmax rule. This means that n should be chosen [to produce;

$$\underset{n}{\text{Min}}\{\underset{a}{\text{Max}}[E|Z-W| + K(n)]\}$$

wherein a denotes the unknown average value of variable x.

3. Finally, it can happen that we do not know anything about the distribution of variable x except that it may assume a value at least equalling some fixed number b_1 and at most a value equalling number b_2. In this case, the minmax rule can also be used to determine the optimum size of the sample.

In solving the above example, we shall only consider case 3.

To determine the optimum value of n by the minmax rule it is necessary first to determine the maximum of expression (6). Of course, this maximum depends on n; hence it is a function of n. Next, we select n so that this function is minimized.

Let us note that $E|Z-W|$ appearing in expression (6), can be written somewhat differently. From equation (3) it follows that

$$\bar{x}_n = \frac{Z}{N}. \tag{7}$$

If we divide both sides of equation (1) by N, we obtain:

$$\frac{W}{N} = \frac{1}{N}\sum_{i=1}^{N} x_i. \tag{8}$$

Thus, $\dfrac{W}{N}$ is simply the real average value of the bulb. We denote this average by the symbol M:

$$M = \frac{W}{N}. \tag{9}$$

Using equations (7) and (9), we can replace Z in the expression $E|Z-W|$ by the term $\bar{x}_n N$ and W by MN. We then have

$$E|Z-W| = E|\bar{x}_n N - MN| = N \cdot E|\bar{x}_n - M|. \tag{10}$$

But the expression under the absolute value sign can be transformed in the following manner:

$$\bar{x}_n - M = \frac{\sum_{i=1}^{n} x_i}{n} - M = \frac{1}{n}\left[\sum_{i=1}^{n} x_i - nM\right] = \frac{1}{n}\sum_{i=1}^{n}(x_i - M).$$

By this transformation, formula (10) now takes the form

$$E|Z-W| = \frac{N}{n}E\left|\sum_{i=1}^{n}(x_i-M)\right|$$

or the equivalent form

$$E|Z-W| = \frac{N}{\sqrt{n}}E\left|\sum_{i=1}^{n}\frac{(x_i-M)}{\sqrt{n}}\right|. \tag{11}$$

The question arises as to the highest value expression $E\left|\sum_{i=1}^{n}\frac{(x_i-M)}{\sqrt{n}}\right|$ can assume for a fixed n.

The answer to this question is made more difficult as we do not know the distribution of the random variable x. If, however, we assume that $n \to \infty$, the distribution of the variable $\sum_{i=1}^{n}\frac{(x_i-M)}{\sqrt{n}}$ would, in accordance with the central theorem of the probability calculus, tend to a normal distribution with an average value of 0 and a standard deviation σ, where σ is the standard deviation of the variable (x_i-M). It is known from the probability calculus that the mathematical expectation of the absolute value of a random variable of a normal distribution with an average value 0

and standard deviation σ is $\sqrt{\frac{2}{\pi}}$.

It can be shown that the maximum value of the average deviation can amount to $\pm\frac{b_2-b_1}{2}$.

Thus, the maximum value of expression (11) (for high values of n) can be assumed to be

$$\text{Max } E|Z-W| = \frac{N}{\sqrt{n}}\cdot\frac{b_2-b_1}{2}\cdot\sqrt{\frac{2}{\pi}} \cong \frac{0\cdot4.N.(b_2-b_1)}{\sqrt{n}}.$$

Turning back to equation (6), we can, therefore, write

$$\text{Max } E(S) = \frac{0\cdot4.N.(b_2-b_1)}{\sqrt{n}}+C+nk. \tag{12}$$

Now the value of n can be so chosen that expression (12) attains its minimum. For this it is enough to differentiate Max $E(S)$ and to set the derivative thus obtained equal to zero in order to determine optimum n. By differentiating (12) and setting the derivative equal zero, we obtain:

$$-0\cdot2N(b_2-b_1)n^{-\frac{3}{2}}+k=0.$$

Therefore,

$$n = \left[\frac{N(b_2 - b_1)}{5k} \right]^{\frac{2}{3}}. \tag{13}$$

Since, in deriving formula (13) for the optimum sample size, we assumed that $n \to \infty$, this formula can only be applied when the values for N, b_2, b_1, and k are such that the n obtained is sufficiently large. In practice, it is enough if $n > 25$. To derive an appropriate formula for an optimum sample size, without the assumption that $n \to \infty$, would be considerably more complicated in this case.

Against the background of the above example, we have shown the problem of determining an optimum sample size.

Hitherto, both in Section 32 and in the preceding ones, we assumed that the size of the sample is set beforehand in the sense that we establish the magnitude of n before proceeding to tests. This number can be established at an optimum, for instance, as in our example above or even more arbitrarily.

To each possible sample of this established size an appropriate value of the decision variable was allotted by means of the decision function.

In general, the problem of determining an optimum sample size is considerably more complicated than would appear from our example. For, when elements for a sample can be collected at certain intervals of time, it may be more advantageous not to establish the sample size in advance. The sample size is made to depend on the results of previous observations.

This method of sampling is called *the sequential method*. After each new sampling of an additional element for the sample, we have two possibilities: either to stop the test and determine the value of the decision variable according to observations already made, or not to make any decision, postponing it until after the next element of the sample is tested. The following reasoning is at the basis of the sequential sampling method. At every stage in the sampling, it is possible to indicate a value of the decision variable for which the expected loss is the lowest possible. If, however, this minimum expected loss is still relatively large, it may often be due to the fact that the sample hitherto supplied relatively little information about the unknown parameter upon which the decision depends. In such a situation, it may be profitable to bear the additional cost of testing further elements. In this way we generally obtain more information about the unknown parameter and this may contribute to lowering appreciably the expected loss involved in an optimum decision.

Of course, it is to be expected that at a certain moment in the course of a sequential analysis we may stop the test and make one of the possible final decisions. We do this when further sampling entails a larger increase in the costs of tests than the likely decrease of the expected loss.

We shall not go into the details of sequential analysis but would refer the reader to the special studies in this field of statistics.

33. Uses of statistical models

Formally speaking, almost every model (with the exception of strategic models) dealt with in operations research is a statistical model. All our knowledge about parameters of a model comes from observations or experiments. None the less, it is quite a complex matter to solve the majority of statistical models. In view of this, wherever possible, we try to replace the statistical model by a simpler one.

Thus, if the difference in the results of observations on the value of a parameter is sufficiently small, we regard that parameter as a constant and we treat the model as a deterministic one. In other cases, the results of observations on the value of a parameter may differ quite considerably but we have at our disposal so many observations that the distribution of probabilities with which the parameter takes on the various values can be assumed to be known. We are then dealing with a probabilistic model.

In some other cases, for which our information about the parameter has to be based on a relatively small number of observations on the parameter, we must treat the model as a statistical one, and use specific statistical methods to determine its solution.

Only strategic models are non-statistical models by their nature in the sense that there is assumed to be no possibility of collecting additional information about the parameter of the model before a decision is taken.

The solution of statistical models can be hindered considerably when the person making the decision does not have a completely free hand in choosing the sampling method, in fixing the number of observations, etc. This is particularly the case when statistical methods are applied to economic problems. Often when making a decision, we must rely on existing material concerning observations of some parameters. Thus, for example, if we think it necessary to change the price of a certain consumer commodity, then in order to make such a change correctly, it is necessary to know, among other things, the elasticity of the demand for this item. This means the elasticity of income, of prices, cross elasticities, etc. However, here sampling cannot be carried out in the same manner as when a lot is sampled in order to establish its quality.

The only information about these elasticities of demand are past records concerning the volume of purchases at profits, prices, etc., prevailing then.

This situation makes statistical methods applied to socio-economic problems differ quite significantly from methods used in technology, biology, etc., where there is much greater freedom in the selection of the type and size of sample. As a result of these various sampling procedures, the methods of solving statistical models — according to the field with which they are concerned — usually differ so much that they lead to completely separate divisions of applied statistics, such as statistical control of production quality, demand analysis, agricultural experimentation, etc.

It would be difficult to study here these special problems more closely and for this reason, in discussing statistical models, we have only given the most general information of the basis on which the solution of every statistical model must be built.

34. Bibliographical notes

A very good introduction to the methods of solving statistical models is given in the second part of R. Schlaifer's book [14]. We mentioned this work earlier in the discussion on the solution of probabilistic models, since a portion of this book deals with this problem. It is written in a style very easy to understand and does not require any extensive mathematical training.

Next, mention should be made of a book by H. Chernoff and L. Moses [3]. This is also a very good exposition of up-to-date methods of solving statistical models. However, it requires a somewhat greater effort on the part of the reader than does Schlaifer's.

A. Wald is the creator of modern statistical methods. His basic work in this field [17] is not easy reading. We can recommend it only to those who have more than just a good mathematical training. An exposition of modern statistical methods, with reference to the connection between these methods and the theory of games, is contained in a book by D. Blackwell and M. Girshick [1]. This book is also mainly for mathematicians.

The reader may find the more traditional methods of mathematical statistics, which are not directly designed for the needs of operations research, in a book by M. Fisz [8] or by H. Cramér [5].

The sequential method of sampling is dealt with in a special work by A. Wald [16].

The reader can become acquainted with statistical methods as applied to statistical quality control from the books by J. Oderfeld [12] and J. Obalski [11].

Information on the application of statistical methods to some economic problems is to be found in a collective study edited by T. Koopmans [10].

Many papers are devoted to the use of specific statistical methods in studies of demand. In the first place, mention should be made of the papers by H. Wold [18] and R. Stone (15). A study particularly easy to understand in this field, and perhaps the nearest to operations research in its scope, is the book by R. Brown [2]. Attention should also be drawn to an interesting book by I. Pisarev [13] devoted to research on demand.

Where there is great freedom as to the method of sampling, e.g. in technology, agriculture, etc., there are also special problems involved. These problems are also the subjects of many books of which mention should be made first of those by R. A. Fisher [7], O. Davies [6], W. Cochran and G. Cox [4] and O. Kempthorne [9].

BIBLIOGRAPHY

[1] Blackwell, D. and Girshick, M., *Theory of Games and Statistical Decisions*, New York, 1954, J. Wiley.

[2] Brown, R., *Statistical Forecasting for Inventory Control*, New York, 1959, McGraw-Hill.

[3] Chernoff, H. and Moses, L., *Elementary Decision Theory*, New York, 1959, J. Wiley.

[4] Cochran, W. and Cox, G., *Experimental Design*, New York, 1957, J. Wiley (2nd ed.).

[5] Cramér, H., *Mathematical Methods of Statistics*, Princeton, 1946.

[6] Davies, O., *Design and Analysis of Industrial Experiments*, London, 1954, Oliver and Boyd.

[7] Fisher, R.A., *The Design of Experiments*, London, 1949, Oliver and Boyd.

[8] Fisz, M., *Rachunek prawdopodobieństwa i statystyka matematyczna (Probability Calculus and Mathematical Statistics)*, Warsaw, 1958, PWN. English translation published by J. Wiley, 1963.

[9] Kempthorne, O., *The Design and Analysis of Experiments*, New York, 1952, J. Wiley.

[10] Koopmans, T. (ed), *Statistical Inference in Dynamic Economic Models*, New York, 1950, J. Wiley.

[11] Obalski, J., *Statystyczna kontrola jakości podczas produkcji (Statistical Quality Control During Production)*, Warsaw, 1955, PWT.

[12] Oderfeld, J., *Zarys statystycznej kontroli jakości (Outline of Statistical Quality Control)*, Warsaw, 1954, PWN.

[13] Pisarev, I., *Metodologicheskiye voprosy izucheniya urovnya zherzni trudyashchikhsya (Methodological Questions of Determining the Living Standard of Workers)*, Moscow, 1959.

[14] Schlaifer, R., *Probability and Statistics for Business Decisions*, New York, 1959, McGraw-Hill.

[15] Stone, R., *The Measurement of Consumers' Expenditure and Behaviour in the United Kingdom*, Cambridge, 1954, Cambridge Univ. Press.

[16] Wald, A., *Sequential Analysis*, New York, 1947, J. Wiley.

[17] Wald, A., *Statistical Decision Functions*, New York, 1950, J. Wiley.

[18] Wold, H., *Demand Analysis*, New York, 1952, J. Wiley.

CHAPTER 7

Dynamic Programming

35. The basis of dynamic programming

In our preceding analyses, we have discussed the principal methods used in solving models encountered in operations research. These methods, as known, vary according to the character of the parameters appearing in the model.

Dynamic programming is a method which enables to determine optimum decisions (hence, to solve models) independently of the character of the parameters provided, however, that the model has some fixed structure. As a result of this, frequently, when making a decision we must remember both its immediate consequences and that the realization of these decisions can be the starting point for further similar decisions. In other words, we must remember that in making analogous decisions in the future, we may be in a better or worse position, depending on decisions taken earlier.

Example 1. Imagine that within a certain definite period of time — e.g. period (a, T), in which a is the initial point and T the end point — the distribution of the demand for goods supplied by a wholesale house is known. This demand, at any interval of time (t_1, t_2) within the period (a, T) is determined by formula

$$Z = \int_{t_1}^{t_2} z(t)\,dt. \tag{1}$$

This situation is illustrated in Fig. 1.35.

In order to simplify the graph we used a constant value for function $z(t)$. In subsequent calculations relating to this example we shall assume that

$$z(t) = 2. \tag{2}$$

The demand for the given goods in the period from t_1 to t_2 is represented by the area of this function, hence, by the integral as determined in formula (1). This is the hatched area in Figure 1.35.

A wholesale house is to determine four intervals of time (within the period a, T) at which it will order goods from the factory in such quantities that the whole demand can be satisfied. In determining the intervals of time at which orders are to be placed, the wholesaler will be guided by the costs involved in completing these orders. Let us assume that the warehouse charges per unit of goods in a unit of time amount to 1,000 zlotys[1]. Moreover, the wholesaler has certain fixed costs which are connected with the order but are independent of the volume of the order and can generally vary in time. Let these constant costs, dependent on the instant the order is placed, be determined by function $s(t)$. In order to simplify our problem, we take a particularly simplified form of this function in our example

$$s(t) = 1.\tag{3}$$

Proceeding to the solution, let us note that, regardless of the intervals of time at which the four orders are placed, the wholesaler must purchase the amount of goods dictated by demand in the period (a, T). Thus, in the search for four instants at which the sum of costs entailed in satisfying the demand will be the lowest, we can ignore the purchase costs and take into account only the warehouse charges and the costs of placing the order.

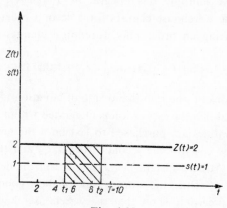

Fig. 1.35

Moreover, let us note that, assuming the wholesaler does not have stocks from earlier periods, the opening order must be placed at the instant a[2]. We still have to fix three further intervals of time for placing orders. Let us denote them by x_1, x_2 and x_3, respectively. For the time being, let us assume that besides the time a in which the order must be placed, the wholesaler is considering the possibility of only one more period (and not three). Hence, the aim is to determine such a time x_1 that the sum of warehouse charges and the costs of placing orders is the lowest possible.

If x_1 were determined somehow, the placing of an order at time x_1 would affect the warehouse charges and ordering costs. For one order, at time a, these costs, which we denote by K_1, would amount to

---

[1] This includes all costs associated with storage, hence the cost of freezing capital.

[2] To simplify the problem, we assume that the orders are filled immediately.

$$K_1 = s(a) + 1{,}000 \int_a^T (t-a) z(t) \, dt \qquad\qquad (4)$$

in which $s(a)$ stands for the fixed costs of the order at time a. The other component, expressed in the form of an integral, consists of the warehouse charges.

The time of storing the goods sold at time t is $t - a$, i.e. the time from the instant the purchase is made, in our case a, to the instant of sale, t. At every instant t, the demand is determined by $z(t) \, \Delta t$ where Δt is a sufficiently small interval of time. The warehouse charges are proportional to the product of the quantity of goods and the storage time. Thus, $z(t) \, \Delta t$ should be multiplied by $t - a$. The products $(t-a) \, z(t) \, \Delta t$ should be summed up for all the possible values of variable t. Since we assumed that t is a continuous variable, this expression should be integrated instead of being summed up. Since it costs us 1,000 zlotys to store a unit of goods for a unit of time, we multiply this integral by 1,000.

In turn, we calculate warehouse charges for a second order at instant x_1. Then, the total costs of placing an order plus warehouse charges amount to:

$$K_2 = s(a) + 1{,}000 \int_a^{x_1} (t-a) z(t) \, dt + s(x_1) + 1{,}000 \int_{x_1}^T (t-x_1) z(t) \, dt. \qquad (5)$$

The first two expressions on the right-hand side of equation (5) are understandable. It should only be added that the expression is integrated within the limits of a and x_1, since at instant a quantities are purchased to last until the next order, i.e. until x_1. To these costs add the costs of the second order $s(x_1)$ and the warehouse charges of the lot purchased. At each instant $t > x_1$ we satisfy the demand with the goods purchased at moment x_1. Thus, the storage time of these goods is $t - x_1$. Considerations similar to the preceding show that the warehouse charges of the goods from the time of purchase at instant x_1 are expressed by the integral appearing as the last component of the sum in equation (5).

It is easy now to determine the amount the wholesaler saves in costs by placing his orders at two instants, i.e. a and x_1, instead of at one instant a.[1]) These savings, which we denote by N_1, will depend on x_1 and can be presented as the difference between K_1 and K_2.

$$N_1(x_1) = K_1 - K_2 = s(a) + 1{,}000 \int_a^{x_1} (t-a) z(t) \, dt + 1{,}000 \int_{x_1}^T (t-a) z(t) \, dt$$

$$- s(a) - 1{,}000 \int_a^{x_1} (t-a) z(t) \, dt - s(x_1) - 1{,}000 \int_{x_1}^T (t-x_1) z(t) \, dt.$$

We split the integral between a to T, appearing in formula (4), into the sum of two integrals within the limits from a to x_1, to from x_1 to T, respectively. After simplifying, we have

---

[1]) Of course, these savings can sometimes be negative.

$$N_1(x_1) = 1{,}000 \int\limits_{x_1}^{T} (t-a)\, z(t)\, dt - 1{,}000 \int\limits_{x_1}^{T} (t-x_1)\, z(t)\, dt - s(x_1) \tag{6}$$

$$= 1{,}000 \int\limits_{x_1}^{T} t\, z(t)\, dt - 1{,}000\, a \int\limits_{x_1}^{T} z(t)\, dt$$

$$- 1{,}000 \int\limits_{x_1}^{T} t\, z(t)\, dt + 1{,}000\, x_1 \int\limits_{x_1}^{T} z(t)\, dt - s(x_1)$$

$$= 1{,}000\,(x_1-a) \int\limits_{x_1}^{T} z(t)\, dt - s(x_1)$$

Since the wholesaler can set the values of x_1 at will as long as it lies within the given period of time (a, T), he can choose x_1 so as to achieve maximum "savings" on costs incurred in placing a new order at the instant x_1. Let us denote the maximum value of function $N_1(x_1)$ by f_1. Quantity f_1, as a maximum of a function of a single variable, is a constant. It will be more convenient for us, however, to treat this expression as a function of some parameter. Let this parameter be the instant at which the first order is placed. In our case, this is a. Therefore, we can write:

$$f_1(a) = \operatorname*{Max}_{a<x_1<T} \left[1{,}000\,(x_1-a) \int\limits_{x_1}^{T} z(t)\, dt - s(x_1) \right]. \tag{7}$$

Next, we consider the situation in which, besides the necessary order at the instant a, the wholesaler decides to place two further orders at instants x_1 and x_2, where $x_2 > x_1$, i.e. x_2 is more distant from the initial point than x_1.

We assume for the present that x_1 has been chosen is some way, but for the time being we are not concerned whether it was chosen optimally or not. If x_1 has already been chosen, the wholesaler can of course only select instant x_2 for the new order in the best way. Obviously, condition $x_1 < x_2 < T$ must be met. Formally speaking, the problem is reduced to solving a similar problem to the previous. The problem is to choose at some interval of time (x_1, T) the optimum time for a new order.

It can be said, therefore, that by placing a new order at instant x_2 within the time interval (x_1, T) it is possible to obtain a maximum saving in costs amounting to:

$$f_1(x_1) = \operatorname*{Max}_{x_1<x_2<T} \left[1{,}000\,(x_2-x_1) \int\limits_{x_2}^{T} z(t)\, dt - s(x_2) \right]. \tag{8}$$

This is simply function f_1 determined by formula (7) except that instead of x_1 we now have x_2, and x_1 takes now the place of a.

The situation can now be defined as follows: an order placed at instant x_1 gives a saving in costs (as compared with the case of a single order at the instant a) equal to the sum $N_1(x_1)$ determined by formula (6). Placing an order at the next instant x_2 within the interval of time (x_1, T) may increase the savings by $f_1(x_1)$ at most. Therefore, the total savings which are given by two orders placed at times x_1 and x_2 can be expressed as

$$N_2(x_1) = N_1(x_1) + f_1(x_1) = 1{,}000\,(x_1 - a) \int_{x_1}^{T} z(t)\,dt - s(x_1) + f_1(x_1).$$

Of course, it is best to select x_1 so that the total savings are the highest possible. Denoting these maximum savings by f_2, we have:

$$f_2(a) = \operatorname*{Max}_{a < x_1 < T} N_2(x_1) = \operatorname*{Max}_{a < x_1 < T} \left[1{,}000\,(x_1 - a) \int_{x_1}^{T} z(t)\,dt - s(x_1) + f_1(x_1) \right]. \tag{9}$$

Expression f_2 is a constant; for considerations similar to the earlier ones it is more convenient to write it as a function of parameter a, i.e. of the time at which the initial order was given.

Fi nally, let us consider the last case when, in addition to the order placed at moment a, the wholesaler wants to make a decision on three further most appropriate times for placing orders x_1, x_2 and x_3.

As before, let us assume for the moment that the time at which the first order x_1 is placed has already been established and only x_2 and x_3 have to be determined. In other words, we are to fix two orders within the interval (x_1, T). The maximum saving in costs which can be attained by the placing two orders within this interval of time is merely the value of function f_2 at point x_1. Therefore, we have

$$f_2(x_1) = \operatorname*{Max}_{x_1 < x_2 < T} \left[1{,}000\,(x_2 - x_1) \int_{x_2}^{T} z(t)\,dt - s(x_2) + f_1(x_2) \right].$$

$f_2(x_1)$ is the maximum saving in costs obtained by introducing two further instants for placing orders within the interval (x_1, T). Hence, the total savings effected by introducing three orders at times x_1, x_2 and x_3 amount to

$$N_3(x_1) = N_1(x_1) + f_2(x_1) = 1{,}000\,(x_1 - a) \int_{x_1}^{T} z(t)\,dt - s(x_1) + f_2(x_1).$$

The time x_1 for placing an order is now so chosen that the savings $N_3(x_1)$ are the highest possible. These maximum savings, denoted by f_3, can be presented in the form

$$f_3(a) = \operatorname*{Max}_{a < x_1 < T} N_3(x_1) = \operatorname*{Max}_{a < x_1 < T} \left[1{,}000\,(x_1 - a) \int_{x_1}^{T} z(t)\,dt - s(x_1) + f_2(x_1) \right]. \tag{10}$$

On this basis we come to general formulae. Considering the problem of an optimum choice of intervals of time for orders within the interval (a, T), we obtain:

$$f_1(a) = \operatorname*{Max}_{a < x_1 < T} \left[1{,}000\,(x_1 - a) \int_{x_1}^{T} z(t)\,dt - s(x_1) \right] \tag{11}$$

$$f_i(a) = \underset{a < x_1 < T}{\text{Max}} \left[1{,}000\,(x_1 - a)\int_{x_1}^{T} z(t)\,dt - s(x_1) + f_{i-1}(x_1)\right]. \qquad (12)$$

$$\text{for } i = 1, 3 \ldots$$

Formulae (11) and (12) constitute the general solution of our problem.

If we want to determine the optimum values for x_1^*, x_2^* and x_3^*, we proceed as follows:

(1) we compute functions $f_1(a)$, $f_2(a)$ and $f_3(a)$,

(2) in calculating the above functions, we determine the values of x_1 for which the expressions under the Max sign in formulae (11) and (12) have a maximum for $i = 1, 2, 3$. These are the times for the earliest placing of an order in the case of one order, two orders and three orders.[1] These values are, of course, the function of parameter a and they can be denoted as $\bar{x}_1(a)$, $\bar{x}_2(a)$, $\bar{x}_3(a)$, respectively,

(3) the optimum instant for the earliest order will be $\bar{x}_3(a)$, that is

$$x_1^* = \bar{x}_3(a).$$

If we now substitute x_1^* for $\bar{x}_2(a)$, we obtain

$$x_2^* = \bar{x}_2(x_1^*).$$

This is so because $\bar{x}_2(a)$ determines the optimum instant for the earliest order, if two orders are to be placed in the interval between a and T.

Similarly, we have

$$x_3^* = \bar{x}_3(x_2^*).$$

We now calculate the sequence of functions $f_1(a), f_2(a), f_3(a)$, the sequence of functions $\bar{x}_1(a)$, $\bar{x}_2(a)$ and $\bar{x}_3(a)$ and the solutions x_1^*, x_2^* and x_3^*.

First, we copy the expression under the maximum sign in formula (11):

$$1{,}000\,(x_1 - a)\int_{x_1}^{10} 2\,dt - 1 = 1{,}000\,(x_1 - a)(20 - 2x_1) - 1.$$

Here, we made use of formulae (2) and (3) which define further functions $z(t)$ and $s(t)$ in our example and we took $T = 10$. After simplifying, the above expression will take the form:

$$20{,}000x_1 - 2{,}000x_1^2 - 20{,}000a + 2{,}000ax_1 - 1. \qquad (13)$$

After differentiating and setting the derivative of the above expression equal to zero, we obtain:

$$20{,}000 - 4{,}000x_1 + 2{,}000a = 0$$

---

[1] Besides the order placed at the initial time a.

thus,

$$x_1 = \frac{10+a}{2}.$$

Therefore, with our connotations, we have

$$\bar{x}_1(a) = \frac{10+a}{2}. \tag{14}$$

Expression (13) comes after the Max sign in formula (11). Therefore, if we substitute the value $\bar{x}_1(a)$ for x_1 in (13), we obtain

$$\begin{aligned} f_1(a) &= 10{,}000(10+a) - 500(10+a)^2 - 20{,}000a + 1{,}000\,a(10+a) - 1 \\ &= 50{,}000 - 10{,}000\,a + 500\,a^2 - 1. \end{aligned} \tag{15}$$

Next, we compute $\bar{x}_2(a)$ and $f_2(a)$. Function $f_2(a)$ is determined by formula (12). It assumes the form

$$f_2(a) = \operatorname*{Max}_{a<x_1<10} [20{,}000\,x_1 - 2{,}000\,x_1^2 - 20{,}000\,a + 2{,}000\,ax_1 - 1 \tag{16}$$
$$+ 50{,}000 - 10{,}000\,x_1 + 500\,x_1^2 - 1].$$

In order to find the maximum of the expression after the Max sign, the expression must be differentiated and its derivative equated to zero for the purpose of finding the appropriate x_1. The derivative equated to zero is:

$$20{,}000 - 4{,}000\,x_1 + 2{,}000\,a - 10{,}000 + 1{,}000\,x_1 = 0.$$

From this we find $x_1 = \dfrac{10+2a}{3}$

Thus, with our connotations we have

$$\bar{x}_2(a) = \frac{10+2a}{3}. \tag{17}$$

Substituting the value of $\bar{x}_2(a)$ for x_1 in the expression after the Max sign of formula (16), we obtain

$$f_2(a) = \frac{20{,}000}{3}\cdot(10+2a) - \frac{2{,}000}{9}\cdot(10+2a)^2 - 20{,}000a$$
$$+ \frac{2{,}000}{3}\cdot(10a+2a^2) - 1 + 50{,}000 - 10{,}000\cdot\frac{10+2a}{3} \tag{18}$$
$$+ \frac{500}{9}\cdot(10+2a)^2 - 1 = \frac{10{,}000}{3}\cdot(10+2a) - \frac{500}{3}\cdot(10+2a)^2$$
$$+ \frac{2{,}000}{3}\cdot(10a+2a^2) - 20{,}000a + 50{,}000 - 2.$$

Finally, we find functions $f_3(a)$ and $\bar{x}_3(a)$.

In accordance with formula (12) we have

$$f_3(a) = \underset{a < x_1 < 10}{\text{Max}} \left[1{,}000\,(x_1 - a) \int_{x_1}^{10} 2\,dt - 1 + f_2(x_1) \right].$$

Using (13) and formula (18), we obtain:

$$f_3(a) = \underset{a < x_1 < 10}{\text{Max}} \left[20{,}000 x_1 - 2{,}000 x_1^2 - 20{,}000 a + 2{,}000\, a x_1 - 1 \right.$$

$$+ \frac{10{,}000}{3} \cdot (10 + 2x_1) - \frac{500}{3} \cdot (10 + 2x_1)^2 + \frac{2{,}000}{3} \cdot (10 x_1 + 2x_1^2)$$

$$\left. - 20{,}000 x_1 + 50{,}000 - 2 \right].$$

Differentiating the expression after the Max sign and equating the resultant derivative to zero, we obtain:

$$20{,}000 - 4{,}000 x_1 + 2{,}000 a + \frac{20{,}000}{3} - \frac{2{,}000}{3} \cdot (10 + 2x_1) + \frac{20{,}000}{3}$$

$$+ \frac{8{,}000}{3} x_1 - 20{,}000 = 0.$$

And from this,

$$x_1 = \frac{10 + 3a}{4}$$

or

$$\bar{x}_3(a) = \frac{10 + 3a}{4}. \tag{19}$$

If we were considering the problem of fixing optimum times for placing orders x_1^*, x_2^*, x_3^* within the interval $(0, 10)$, the calculations so far carried out would enable to arrive at a solution.

We assumed that the order must be placed at the instant $a = 0$ at all events. Therefore, if the aim is to determine three further instants for placing orders, then the earliest of these x_1, must be fixed according to formula (19), i.e.

$$x_1^* = \bar{x}_3(a) = \frac{10 + 3a}{4} = \frac{10 + 3.0}{4} = 2 \cdot 5.$$

Having established the time for placing an order at point x_1^*, we still have to determine two further times for orders within the interval $(x_1^*, 10)$. The earlier of these two is determined by formula (17). Namely, we have

$$x_2^* = \bar{x}_2(x_1^*) = \frac{10 + 2.2 \cdot 5}{3} = 5.$$

Finally, since time x_2^* is fixed, it remains to determine a time for an order within $(x_2^*, 10)$. According to formula (14) we have

$$x_3^* = \bar{x}_1(x_2^*) = \frac{10+5}{2} = 7 \cdot 5.$$

Thus, the three most advantageous times for placing orders (besides the opening order) within the interval $(0,10)$ are: $x_1^* = 2 \cdot 5$, $x_2^* = 5$, $x_3^* = 7 \cdot 5$. The result obtained here agrees with the answer given by intuition since we assumed that the demand is evenly distributed over the entire interval and the costs involved in placing orders are independent of the time at which an order is placed. Of course, generally, it would be difficult to foresee what the optimum ordering time intervals should be.

This simple example gives some idea of dynamic programming. It consists, namely, in replacing the problem of finding a maximum or minimum value of a function of many variables (e.g. n) by the solution of another equivalent problem. This equivalent problem consists in determining n times the maxima or minima of certain functions, each of these functions being already a function of a single variable.

Thus, in our example, it was easy to formulate the problem as one of finding the maximum or minimum of a function of three variables x_1, x_2, x_3. For, it is easy to observe that the total costs[1] involved in orders (fixed costs and warehouse charges) at times x_1, x_2 and x_3, on the assumption that in addition an order was placed at the initial time, are

$$K = s(a) + 1{,}000 \int_a^{x_1} (t-a)\, z(t)\, dt + s(x_1) + 1{,}000 \int_{x_1}^{x_2} (t-x_1)\, z(t)\, dt$$
$$+ s(x_2) + 1{,}000 \int_{x_2}^{x_3} (t-x_2)\, z(t)\, dt + s(x_3) + 1{,}000 \int_{x_3}^{T} (t-x_3)\, z(t)\, dt.$$

Function K is a function of three variables x_1, x_2 and x_3, which, according to the assumption, must fulfill the natural condition:

$$a < x_1 < x_2 < x_3 < T.$$

To determine the optimum x_1, x_2 and x_3, it is necessary to choose values so that function K has a minimum. To determine the minimum or maximum of a function of many variables entails considerable computational difficulties. Dynamic programming reduces these difficulties appreciably. It is generally much simpler

---

[1] Disregarding the price of the goods purchased.

to determine the maximum or minimum of a function of a single variable many times than to find the maximum or minimum of a function of many variables once.

Of course, the dynamic programming method can only be used, under certain definite conditions, to solve problems involving the determination of the maximum or minimum for a function of many variables. The problem is namely that decision variables are sometimes arranged naturally in a certain sequence. Usually this arrangement of decision variables appears in dynamic problems, i.e. in problems accounting for the time factor. In such cases, the decision variables are very often linked to certain definite time intervals and, because of this, are easily arranged in some sequence. This was the case in our example where we arranged the variables so that by x_1 we denoted the earliest time at which an order was placed, by x_2 a later time and by x_3 an instant later than x_2.

However, it is worth while adding here that sometimes such natural arrangements of variables appear not only in problems of a dynamic character.[1]

In addition to the purely computational aspects dynamic programming has the added quality that it generally permits a more thorough study of the structure of an optimum solution.

Functions of the type of (11) and (12) — $f_i(a)$ — are actually the maximum values of criterion-functions (depending on the criterion, they could also be minimum values). Every such function has a corresponding function $\overline{x}_1(a)$. In problems with n decision variables, by successively determining the functions $f_1(a)$, $f_2(a),...$, we finally succeed in computing $f_n(a)$ and $\overline{x}_n(a)$ which is the optimum value of the first of the decision variables. It is apparent that this solution is given in a functional form, as a function of some parameter a. This function shows how the value of the first decision variable varies with the variation of parameter a. The optimum value of the next variable is $\overline{x}_{n-1}(a)$, the value of the first variable being substituted for a, i.e. $\overline{x}_n(a)=x_1^*$. Since $\overline{x}_{n-1}(a)$ is given as a function, even though the value of the first variable x_1 may not have been determined optimally (e.g. if instead of x_1^*, x_1' is adopted), it is easy to select the optimum value of variable x_2 which, in this case, is $\overline{x}_{n-1}(x_1')$.

Finally, to conclude this section, one further comment. If there are many variables, dynamic programming, as is easily surmised, becomes very laborious.

Let us assume that the formulae obtained for f_i are of the form

$$f_1(a) = \operatorname*{Max}_{a<x<b} k(x, a)$$

$$f_i(a) = \operatorname*{Max}_{a<x<b} \left[k(x,a)+f_{i-1}(x) \right] \quad \text{for} \quad i = 2,\ 3,.... \tag{20}$$

---

[1] See W. Sadowski, *A Few Remarks on the Assortment Problem*, Management Science, Vol. 6, No. 1, 1959.

Now, under certain conditions, the sequence of functions $f_i(a)$ converges to a limit which we denote by $f(a)$. Under these conditions, instead of the sequence of relations (20) we have only one relation:

$$f(a) = \underset{a<x<b}{\text{Max}} \left[k(x,a)+f(x)\right]. \tag{21}$$

In a problem with a large number of variables, therefore, if $f_i(a)$ is convergent to a certain limit, then instead of investigating the sequence of relations (20), we can consider equation (21) only. The value of x thus found, for which $k(x,a) + f(x)$ reaches its maximum, is the value which the first of the variables assumes.

Of course, the solution for x is obtained here as a function of $x(a)$. It replaces functions $\overline{x}_1(a)$, $\overline{x}_2(a)$,... which we obtain in the case of a small number of decision variables. The other values of the decision variables are obtained only from function $x(a)$. It should be added, however, that relation (21) causes considerable difficulty, as the functional form of f is not defined in it. Thus, this is a functional equation in which function f must be chosen so as to satisfy relation (21). In general, this is not a simple matter.

36. The application of dynamic programming to the determination of the size of stocks

There are many uses for dynamic programming in the solution of various types of models. From a formal point of view, every dynamic problem (regardless of whether or not it is a deterministic, probabilistic, strategic or statistical model) can be formulated in the language of dynamic programming.

In this section we give only one example which we shall state in the language of dynamic programming. This example concerns the problem of an optimum size of stock.[1] This problem, however, is given here in a more general outline than in all the previous examples.

Example 1. A factory draws up its production plan for a period of 12 months. At the end of each month the factory must supply the same quantity of goods which it manufactures; however, this quantity is not determined uniquely. The factory knows only the probability of the demand being at a given level.

Let $g(y)$ stand for the function of the intensity of demand y. Therefore, if this function takes the shape given in Fig. 1.36, the probability that the demand will be larger than y_1, for instance, will be expressed by the integral

$$\int_{y_1}^{\infty} g(y)\,dy.$$

---

[1] This example is formulated in terms similar to those in the book by R. Bellman, *Dynamic Programming*, Princeton 1957, Princeton Univ. Press.

The geometrical interpretation of this integral is, of course, the hatched area under the graph of function $g(y)$.

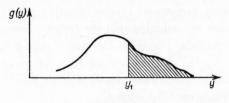

Fig. 1.36

Let us denote the monthly production costs by $k(x)$, in which x designates the output.

When the demand in a certain month is larger than the sum of stocks from previous months plus the output of the last month, the factory can meet this excess demand, but at higher costs given by function $u(v)$, in which v is the excess demand. The problem consists in establishing such a production plan that the cost of satisfying the demand for the goods concerned, will be a minimum. Let us denote the monthly outputs by $x_1, x_2,...,x_{12}$. We must fix them so that the expected delivery costs will be a minimum. We speak of expected costs here because the costs are not linked directly to our decision concerning monthly production plans. These costs depend on demand. If the demand proves larger than the amount of available goods, it is necessary to make good the quantity in short supply at quite high costs. Otherwise, a surplus of goods will be stocked.

The problem which we have to solve is basically a problem involving twelve variables. We can therefore build a model in which these twelve variables appear, and the expected costs being functions of these variables can be minimized, in this way determining the optimum values for $x_1, x_2,...,x_{12}$. However, this problem would be difficult to solve and for this reason we have recourse to dynamic programming procedures.

Hence, we have the following connotations:

$g(v)$ is the probability density of the monthly demand,

$k(x)$ are the monthly production costs dependent on the volume of output x,

$u(v)$ is the cost of meeting the surplus demand v.

The enterprise may have available at any moment a stock z. Now, it will be convenient for us to take for our decision variables not the values of outputs in the various months $(x_1, x_2, ... x_n)$ but the magnitudes X_i determined as follows:

$$x_i = X_i - z_{i-1}$$

or

$$X_i = x_i + z_{i-1}. \tag{1}$$

Therefore, X_i is the quantity of goods available at the end of each month (output plus stock from the previous month). It is found to be easier to operate with this variable than with variable x_i. It is noteworthy that X_i, as emerges from its definition, can assume only non-negative values (output plus stock).

We begin our analyses by assuming that the factory, having some definite stock on hand from earlier periods, has only one month before it and must decide on the volume of output x_1 for the next month only, or make a decision about X_1, which comes to the same thing. This means, it must decide to which level of X_1 stocks should be supplemented by output.

If we plan an output of x_1, that is, $X_1 - z$, we have production costs of $k(X_1 - z)$. Moreover, if it should appear that this output and the stock do not meet demand y, additional costs of $u(y - X_1)$ must be borne. Expected costs of this type will amount to

$$\int_{X_1}^{\infty} u(y - X_1) g(y) \, dy.$$

Thus, the total expected costs for an output of $X_1 - z$, with an initial stock of z, amount to

$$K_1(z, X_1) = k(X_1 - z) + \int_{X_1}^{\infty} u(y - X_1) g(y) \, dy. \tag{2}$$

Of course, X_1 (i.e. stock z plus production in the given month) should be so established that the expected costs $K_1(z, X_1)$ are as low as possible. Let us denote these minimum expected costs by $f_1(z)$. They are a function of the initial stock:

$$f_1(z) = \operatorname*{Min}_{X_1 \geqslant z} K_1(z, X_1) = \operatorname*{Min}_{X_1 \geqslant z} \left[k(X_1 - z) + \int_{X_1}^{\infty} u(y - X_1) g(y) \, dy \right]. \tag{3}$$

Note that by definition, variable X_1 must not be smaller than z, that is, not smaller than the stock from the previous month. The optimum magnitude of X_1, denoted by $\overline{X}_1$, depends, of course, on the volume of stock from the previous month. We express this by the term $\overline{X}_1(z)$.

Next, let us assume that the factory has to plan ahead for two instead of one month. Assume, also that the output for the first month has already been defined and, hence, the value of X_1 has been established (on the assumption that the initial stock z is known).

If we want to make a decision as to the value of X in the following month — we denote this value by X_2 — we must consider that there can be two different initial situations:

a) no stock was left over from the previous month; this is the case when the demand y in the previous month was equal to or larger than X_1,

b) some stock was left over from the previous month; this occurs when demand y in the previous month was smaller than X_1. The surplus stock is then $X_1 - y$.

In the first case, the determination of the optimum X_2 consists in selecting X_2 in such a manner, the initial stock being zero, that the costs in the next month will be the lowest possible. These minimum costs are determined by equation (3), provided that $z = 0$, and X_2 takes the place of X_1. We then have:

$$f_1(0) = \operatorname*{Min}_{X_2 \geqslant 0} K_1(0, X_2). \tag{4}$$

We are involved in such costs if demand y in the previous month was equal to or larger than X_1. Thus, the expected magnitude of costs in this case amounts to:

$$\int_{X_1}^{\infty} f_1(0) \cdot g(y)\, dy = f_1(0) \int_{X_1}^{\infty} g(y)\, dy. \tag{5}$$

A different case may arise, however, when a stock of $X_1 - y$ is left over from the first month. In this case, having an initial stock of $X_1 - y$, the problem of finding the optimum X_2 amounts to establishing X_2 so as to have the lowest possible costs in the second month. They are determined by equation (3) for $z = X_1 - y$. Thus, we have

$$f_1(X_1 - y) = \operatorname*{Min}_{X_2 \geqslant X_1 - y} K_1(X_1 - y, X_2). \tag{6}$$

Costs as given by (6) are incurred if demand y in the previous month was lower than X_1.

This, of course, is a random event. In view of this, the expected costs in this case will amount to:

$$\int_{0}^{X_1} f_1(X_1 - y) g(y)\, dy. \tag{7}$$

Thus, the total minimum costs corresponding to the production and demand plans in the second month are

$$K_2(X_1) = f_1(0) \int_{X_1}^{\infty} g(y)\, dy + \int_{0}^{X_1} f_1(X_1 - y) g(y)\, dy.$$

Disregarding now the assumption that X_1 was fixed *a priori*, the minimum sum of expected costs in two months can be presented as follows:

$$f_2(z) = \operatorname*{Min}_{X_1 \geqslant z} \left[K_1(z, X_1) + K_2(X_1) \right] = \operatorname*{Min}_{X_1 \geqslant z} \left[k(X_1 - z) \right. \tag{8}$$

$$+ \int_{X_1}^{\infty} u(y - X_1) g(y)\, dy + f_1(0) \int_{X_1}^{\infty} g(y)\, dy + \int_{0}^{X_1} f_1(X_1 - y) \cdot g(y)\, dy \Big].$$

The value of X_1 which minimizes the function under the Min symbol is denoted by $\overline{X}_2(z)$. This is the sum of stocks and output in the first month, on the assumption that a bi-monthly plan is being drawn up.

Reasoning along the lines followed in solving the problem in the previous section, we easily arrive at the general formula

$$f_i(z) = \underset{X_1 \geqslant z}{\text{Min}} \left[k(X_1 - z) + \int_{X_1}^{\infty} u(y - X_1) g(y) dy + f_{i-1}(0) \int_{X_1}^{\infty} g(y) dy \right.$$

$$\left. + \int_{0}^{X_1} f_{i-1}(X_1 - y) g(y) dy \right] \quad \text{for} \quad i = 2, 3, \ldots. \tag{9}$$

To each i corresponds an appropriate value of $\overline{X}_i(z)$.

If we had specific functions $g(y)$, $k(x)$ and $u(v)$, then in order to calculate production plans for twelve successive months it would be necessary to proceed as follows. We denote the optimum output in the twelve consecutive months by x_1^* x_2^*, ... x_{12}^* and by X_1^*, X_2^*, ..., X_{12}^* the optimum values of variables X_i defined by the equation

$$X_i = x_i + z_{i-1}.$$

Knowing the initial stock z from the previous period, we can compute a sequence of functions: $f_1(z)$ according to formula (3) and $f_2(z), f_3(z), \ldots, f_{12}(z)$ according to formula (9). At the same time we calculate functions $\overline{X}_1(z), \overline{X}_2(z), \ldots, \overline{X}_{12}(z)$.

The planning period comprising 12 months, $\overline{X}_{12}(z)$ is the optimum magnitude of the sum of stocks and output in the first month. Since the initial stock z is known, for instance, z_p, we have

$$\overline{X}_{12}(z_p) = X_1^*.$$

This means that the optimum output in the first month is

$$x_1^* = X_1^* - z_p.$$

At the end of the first month, when demand is already known, the volume of stocks remaining from the first month will also be known. Let us denote this by z_1.

Hence, we have a situation in which the problem is to fix an optimal X for a period of 11 months ahead.

In view of this, the optimum sum of stocks and output for the second month X_2 is

$$X_2^* = \overline{X}_{11}(z_1).$$

And, therefore, the optimum output in the second month will be

$$x_2^* = X_2^* - z_1, \text{ etc.}$$

In concluding the discussion of this example, let us note that with a larger number of periods it is worth while introducing a discount factor. We are concerned with the comparability of monetary outlays in various periods of time. For instance, let the discount factor be D for some period. This means that a zloty spent in some future period has now the value of D.

It is easy to perceive that the introduction of the discount factor D will lead to a change in formula (3). It will now take the form

$$f_1(z) = \operatorname*{Min}_{X_1 \geqslant z} \left[k(X_1 - z) + D \int_{X_1}^{\infty} u(y - X_1) g(y) \, dy \right]. \tag{10}$$

The change here is that when demand in the first period proves larger than the sum of stocks plus output X_1, it is only then, at the boundary between the first and second periods, that we incur certain costs. Their expected value must be multiplied by the discount factor D in order to obtain costs comparable to the current production costs of $k(X_1 - z)$.

The derivation of formula (8) will also undergo some change, resulting in a change in the formula itself. This means that the costs $K_2(X_1)$, being the costs of the second month, must be multiplied by the factor D. As a result, we obtain

$$f_2(z) = \operatorname*{Min}_{X_1 \geqslant z} \left[k(X_1 - z) + D \int_{X_1}^{\infty} u(y - X_1) g(y) \, dy + D f_1(0) \int_{X_1}^{\infty} g(y) \, dy \right.$$
$$\left. + D \int_0^{X_1} f_1(X_1 - y) g(y) \, dy \right].$$

The general form of the formula for $i = 2, 3, \dots$ will be

$$f_i(z) = \operatorname*{Min}_{X_1 \geqslant z} \left[k(X_1 - z) + D \int_{X_1}^{\infty} u(y - X_1) g(y) \, dy + D f_1(0) \int_{X_1}^{\infty} g(y) \, dy \right.$$
$$\left. + D \int_0^{X_1} f_1(X_1 - y) g(y) \, dy \right].$$

Attention should also be drawn to the fact that the method of dynamic programming casts much light on the structure of an optimum solution. For instance, as regards stocks of, say, a commercial firm, a certain policy is often pursued with the conviction that it is optimum. One of the more common types of inventory policies consists in determining two magnitudes: a minimum volume of stock *m* and a maximum volume *M*. Whenever the stocks drop to the level *m*, they are built up again to the level *M*. Even disregarding the problem of an accurate selection of values for *m* and *M*, there still arises the question as to whether this type of policy can be regarded as optimal at all.

A closer analysis of this problem by the methods of dynamic programming shows that the answer to this question is not final. Sometimes this type of policy is optimum; at other times, however, it is not. At this point, however, we shall not enter into these problems.

Let us add that the aforementioned example can be generalized along various lines. In particular, a certain time can be assumed to elapse between the moment the decision is made and its realization (e.g. an order for goods and their delivery), or that this period is a random variable with a definite probability.

37. The problem of "bottle-necks"

In Sections 35 and 36 we became acquainted with the fundamentals of dynamic programming on the basis of the simplest examples. We devoted relatively little space to dynamic programming, not because we think it an unimportant method of solving programmes, but because we did not see any possibility of giving a wider exposition of this method without having recourse to the more complex mathematical procedures.

A more complete exposition of dynamic programming would give a good idea of the great role it can play in finding solutions to diverse problems. In the present section we only want to draw attention to one quite essential problem to which dynamic programming can be applied, namely, the problem of "bottle-necks". We shall show this problem and the possibility of using dynamic programming on a simplified example taken from R. Bellman.[1]

Imagine that we are dealing with three interdependent industries: the motorcar, steel and engineering industries.[2] We make the following assumptions:

(1) steel and machinery are needed (i.e. products of the steel and engineering industries) to increase production capacity of each of the three industries mentioned,

(2) steel and production capacity of the motorcar industry are required to turn out cars,

(3) to produce steel, the steel industry requires a production capacity,

(4) to produce machinery the engineering industry requires steel and a production capacity,

---

[1] Dynamic Programming: Princeton, 1957, Chapters VI and VII.

[2] In order to simplify the example we assume that all equipment required in the steel and motorcar industries is manufactured in the industry, referred to here as the engineering industry.

(5) the output of each industry is determined by its production capacity and the amount of raw materials[1] so that it is directly proportional to the smallest figure representing production capacity and the amount of raw materials.

Assumption (5) requires some explanation. Before proceeding to give an explanation, it will be more convenient to introduce appropriate connotations first.

They are:

$x_1(t)$ is the car output from a given time to time t,

$x_2(t)$ is the production capacity of the motorcar industry at time t,

$x_3(t)$ is the stock of steel at time t,

$x_4(t)$ is the production capacity of the steel industry at time t,

$x_5(t)$ is the stock of machines at time t,

$x_6(t)$ is the production capacity of the engineering industry at time t.

We assume that we are considering T periods of time starting from the moment 0; hence, we can take $t = 0, 1, 2, 3,..., T$.

Knowing the production capacities of the various industries and the state of the stocks of steel and machines at the instant $t = 0$, our task is to plan an increase in the production capacities and output of the industries so that $x_1(T)$, that is, the volume of car output from the instant $t = 0$ to the instant $t = T$, is the largest possible.

We introduce the following connotations:

$z_i(t)$ is the amount of steel used at the time t to increase $x_i(t)$ (where $i = 1, 2, ... , 6$),

and $w_i(t)$ is the number of machines used at the time t to increase $x_i(t)$ (where $i = 1, 2, ... , 6$).

From assumptions (2) to (5) it follows that

$w_1(t) = 0$ since machines are not needed in the production of cars (assumption 2),

$w_3(t) = 0$ since machines are not needed in the production of steel (assumption 3),

$w_5(t) = 0$ since machines are not needed in the production of machines (assumption 4),

$z_3(t) = 0$ since only the production capacity of the steel industry is required for the production of steel (assumption 3).

Let us now resume our interpretation of assumption 5. If we consider the motorcar industry, for instance, the number of cars manufactured in a certain period (e.g. from the time t to $t+1$) will depend on the steel available to the industry at the outset of this period, that is $x_3(t)$.

---

[1] By "raw materials" we mean here steel and machines.

The proportionality assumption indicates that if the amount of steel were un-limited, the car output in the given period would depend only on the production capacity of the industry (this would be the bottle-neck in car production) and would amount to, for instance, $\gamma_1 x_2(t)$. On the other hand, if the production capacity of the motorcar industry were unlimited, this industry's output would be determined by the amount of steel and would amount to, for instance, $\alpha_1 z_1(t)$. In the latter case, the amount of steel would be the bottle-neck in the motorcar industry.

The linear programming method could be employed[1] to solve the problem of planning the output of the various industries and the increase in their productive capacities at various periods in such a way as to obtain a maximum $x_1(T)$.

Unfortunately, when the number of industries is somewhat larger the number of variables we have to consider increases so much that the calculations involved in solving the problem become extremely complicated. It is apparent that the above problem can be solved by the method of dynamic programming. Dynamic programm-ing has an advantage over linear programming in this case:

1) relations of a non-linear type can be considered,

2) not only can a numerical solution of the problem be obtained (as in linear pro-gramming), but it is also possible to penetrate into the character of the relation-ship between the values of the initial parameters, such as $x_1(0)$, $x_2(0)$, ..., $x_6(0)$, and the optimum solution; a knowledge of this relationship allows us to penetrate deeper into the essence of the problem,

3) the number of necessary calculations can be reduced considerably as compared with a solution arrived at by linear programming.

These comments only state the problem but do not give a detailed account of the method of solving it by means of dynamic programming. It should be reiterated here that even the formulation of this problem in the language of dynamic programm-ing, let alone the solution, requires complicated mathematical operations. In view of this, we have only stated the problem here.

38. Bibliographical notes

Dynamic programming is the newest method of solving models which appear in operations research. This method was created in the nineteen-fifties. The lit-erature in this field, therefore, is still rather modest. Many short papers, it is true, have been published in various journals, but no book written in an accessible manner has yet appeared in this field. The only monograph devoted to dynamic programming is the book by the creator of this method, R. Bellman [1]. However, the reader should be warned that this is a difficult book requiring a good mathematical back-

---

[1] Since we assumed that the relationships which appear here are linear.

ground, especially in the classical branches of mathematics. We therefore draw the reader's attention to the fact that there are some textbooks on operations research which present more accessible expositions of the principal notions underlying this theory. In particular, mention should be made of the books by A. Vazsonyi [3] and by M. Sasieni, A. Yaspan and L. Friedman [2].

BIBLIOGRAPHY

[1] Bellman, R., *Dynamic Programming,* Princeton, 1957, Princeton Univ. Press.
[2] Sasieni, M., Yaspan, A., and Friedman, L. *Operations Research,* New York, 1959, J. Wiley.
[3] Vazsonyi, A., *Scientific Programming in Business and Industry,* New York, 1958, J. Wiley.

CHAPTER 8

Conclusion

39. Application of operations research in Poland

In concluding this survey of the principal methods used in operations research, I should like to stress that inevitably this survey is rather superficial. The purpose of this book was to introduce the problems of operations research to the reader. A closer knowledge of the various methods and their uses, requires special study. The aim of this book was merely to state the problems of operations research. It seemed that this purpose could be best accomplished if we limited the use of mathematical tools to a minimum in the exposition. On the other hand, I illustrated the ideas with examples, nearly all of which were not practical examples taken from life. I did this deliberately, for in most cases practical examples are much more complicated than those considered here. A discussion of practical examples would take up much space and, moreover, would distract the reader from the essential features of the various methods discussed.

Another reason why I did not cite practical examples is that a considerable proportion of the published examples in operations research concerns the capitalist economy. These examples are of a certain methodological significance but solutions which are good for a capitalist enterprise must differ in many respects from the solutions adopted for a socialist one. For these reasons it was thought that simplified examples would be adequate to obtain an insight into the methods of operations research.

Hitherto practical applications of operations research in Poland have been very modest.

Some efforts in this direction have already been made. It seems useful to mention them here. First of all, I shall discuss several uses of linear programming[1].

One of the first attempts to introduce linear programming in Poland was made in the coated caramels department of the July 22nd Confectionery Works in Warsaw. The idea was to determine an optimum production plan for the various confectioneries made in this department. In drawing up this plan, the following circumstances were taken into account:

a) some of the raw materials used (cocoa beans, peanuts and almonds) were available in limited quantities;

---

[1] This is based on the article "O zastosowaniu programowania liniowego" (On the Application of Linear Programming) by W. Tomaszewski in *Ekonomista (The Economist)*, No. 5, 1958.

b) the total output (in physical units) of the whole coated caramels department was to be at least 1,500 tons. This was a condition arising from the plan allocated to the enterprise;

c) an analysis of the market demand for individual kinds of caramels indicated that at least some of the products should be manufactured in some definite quantities;

d) the output of some sorts of caramels could not exceed certain quantities as a result of limited production capacity. Of course, formally speaking, there were such conditions for all the types, none the less, the production capacity for some types was so large that in practice this kind of restraint could be disregarded.

Table 1.39 gives all the above conditions.

In this problem accumulation (i.e. the sum of turnover tax and profit) was accepted as the criterion for the selection of the optimum production plan. The set of values of decision variables X_1, X_2, ... X_{11} for which total accumulation is the highest will be accepted as optimum.

The conditions arising from limited quantities of raw materials being available are as follow:

$$236X_1+366X_2+194X_3+194X_4+226X_5+226X_6+198X_7+363X_8 \tag{1}$$
$$+321X_9+701X_{10}+349X_{11} \leqslant 378,250$$

$$31X_1+32X_2+381X_5+34X_9 \leqslant 45,000 \tag{2}$$

$$7X_1+10X_5+12 \cdot 5X_{11} \leqslant 3,500. \tag{3}$$

Condition (1) refers to cocoa beans, condition (2) to peanuts and condition (3) to almonds. All the coefficients here are given in kilograms according to the data in Table 1.39.

The next condition is the result of the plan assigned to the firm: the total production of coated caramels could not be less than 1,500 tons. This can be written as

$$X_1+X_2+X_3+X_4+X_5+X_6+X_7+X_8+X_9+X_{10}+X_{11} \geqslant 1,500. \tag{4}$$

Further conditions resulting from market analysis defined the minimum outputs of some kinds of caramels:

$$X_1 \geqslant 700 \tag{5}$$
$$X_6+X_7 \geqslant 260 \tag{6}$$
$$X_8 \geqslant 50 \tag{7}$$
$$X_9 \geqslant 20 \tag{8}$$
$$X_{10} \geqslant 30 \tag{9}$$
$$X_{11} \geqslant 100. \tag{10}$$

18

TABLE 1/39

Product		Consumption of restricted materials, kg per ton of product			Requirements due to limited production capacities and market analysis, output in tons		Accumulation, zlotys per ton of product
		cocoa beans	peanuts	almonds	no less than	no greater than	
Chocolate sweets	X_1	236	31	7	700	—	18,300
Cinema sweets	X_2	366	32	—	—	—	26,800
Pralines, 3 kg boxes	X_3	194	—	—	—	60	15,300
Pralines, 0·25 and 0·5 kg boxes	X_4	194	—	—	—	200	19,100
Chinese dragées	X_5	226	381	10	—	50	23,500
Liquor beans and chocolate pastilles	X_6	226	—	—	} 260	350	11,600
Chocolate-coated raisins	X_7	198	—	—		51	5,100
Amateur's sweets	X_8	363	—	—	50	100	20,300
Grilled croquettes and waffles	X_9	321	34	—	20	50	17,900
Cocoa truffles	X_{10}	701	—	—	30	50	32,800
Coffee and orange sweets	X_{11}	349	—	12·5	100	—	24,800
Material limits, tons		378 25	45	3·5	—	—	—

The last group of conditions arose from the limited production capacities for certain types:

$$X_3 \leqslant 60 \qquad (11)$$
$$X_4 \leqslant 200 \qquad (12)$$
$$X_5 \leqslant 50 \qquad (13)$$
$$X_6 \leqslant 350 \qquad (14)$$
$$X_7 \leqslant 51 \qquad (15)$$
$$X_8 \leqslant 100 \qquad (16)$$
$$X_9 \leqslant 50 \qquad (17)$$
$$X_{10} \leqslant 50. \qquad (18)$$

From the values for X_1, X_2, ... X_{11} fulfilling conditions (1) to (18), we must choose the set of values for which the total accumulation A is a maximum, i.e.

$$A = 18,300X_1 + 26,800X_2 + 15,300X_3 + 19,100X_4 + 23,500X_5$$
$$+ 11,600X_6 + 5,100X_7 + 20,300X_8 + 17,900X_9 + 32,800X_{10} + 24,800X_{11} \text{ (max.)} \quad (19)$$

The linear programme above, apart from its importance, does not differ in any way from the programmes we examined in Chapter III. Its solution does not present any major difficulty. Before proceeding to the computations, we must convert the set of inequalities (1) to (18) to a set of equations, introducing slack variables in relations of the "$\leqslant$" type and slack and artificial variables in relations of the "$\geqslant$" type. Using the simplex method, we arrive at the following solution[1]:

$$X_1 = 700 \qquad X_7 = 0$$
$$X_2 = 32 \cdot 8 \qquad X_8 = 50$$
$$X_3 = 60 \qquad X_9 = 20$$
$$X_4 = 200 \qquad X_{10} = 30$$
$$X_5 = 50 \qquad X_{11} = 100.$$
$$X_6 = 260$$

It follows from the solution that the maximum accumulation obtainable satisfying conditions (1) to (18) is

$$A = 27,460,400 \text{ zlotys}$$

Note that for 1957, the period to which this example refers, the firm planned an accumulation of about six million less, i.e. about 21,500,000 zlotys. This means that the application of linear programming methods made it possible to determine the scale of the production plan so as to ensure a total accumulation about 27 per cent higher than originally contemplated.

It should be added that to achieve such a substantial improvement in the results by using linear programming methods is rather rare. Experience abroad shows that the improvements in results achieved by the introduction of linear programming methods fluctuate within the limits of 7 to 10 per cent.

So, for instance, in the same paper by W. Tomaszewski another much simpler example of the application of linear programming was quoted. There, the improvement in the results was not so significant. This example referred to production at the Warsaw Brewery. A study was made of the production of malt, pale ale and brown beer. The bottle-neck was the relatively low production capacity of the basic production department, the brewing chambers. We take the production capacity of the brewing chamber to be $1000^0/_{00}$ and in Table 2.39 we have the per mille capacities of the brewing chamber for the manufacture of 1 hectolitre of beer of the appropriate type. The other columns of this table give the conditions for the production of the individual types of beer as laid down in the plan of the brewery and as dictated by market analysis.

---

[1] We cite this solution from the article by Tomaszewski mentioned above.

TABLE 2/39

Beer	Outlay in ⁰/₀₀ production capacity per hl	Conditions stemming from plan and market analysis, output in hl	
		not less than	not more than
Beer X_1	1/300	192,250	—
Stout X_2	1/396	—	32,450
Ale X_3	1/216	33,300	—

In order to establish the optimum output of the individual types of beer we have to choose X_1, X_2 and X_3 so that, by fulfilling the conditions below, the total production (in physical units) is the highest. In this problem, the total output was accepted as criterion for the optimality of the plan.

The condition attached to the limited production capacity of the brewing chamber is as follows:

$$\frac{1}{300} X_1 + \frac{1}{396} X_2 + \frac{1}{216} X_3 \leqslant 1,000 \tag{20}$$

The conditions arising from the plan allotted for pale ale and brown beer are

$$X_1 \geqslant 192,250 \tag{21}$$

$$X_3 \geqslant 33,300. \tag{22}$$

Finally, the condition dictated by marked analysis is:

$$X_2 \leqslant 32,450. \tag{23}$$

The variables X_1, X_2 and X_3 should be assigned such values that the total output is a maximum (satisfying conditions (20) to (23)), i.e.

$$P = X_1 + X_2 + X_3 \text{ (max.)}$$

wherein P stands for the total output.

The solution obtained by the simplex method gave the following results

$$X_1 = 229,168$$

$$X_2 = 32,450$$

$$X_3 = 33,300$$

which, consequently, gave a total output $P = 294,948$ hectolitres. This output was only 20,000 hectolitres higher than originally planned. This constituted an improvement of 7 per cent in comparison to the plan determined otherwise than by linear programming.

Having quoted these two examples from the field of linear programming, I should like to mention other applications of operations research. I have in mind the application of operations research in the electrical engineering industry. These applications concern the determination of an optimum lot-size and an optimum volume of stock for parts seldom required.

As far as the first problem is concerned, in two factories operated by the Associated Machinery and Electrical Equipment Industry, namely, in the A-8 Factories at Bielsko-Biała and the A-Z Factories in Łódź, the question of optimum lot-sizes was studied.[1]

The practice in the factories was to produce nearly all the parts required for the assembly of individual finished products in lots at three-monthly intervals. For instance, if 100 products of a certain type were assembled in one month, the parts required for their assembly were manufactured in lots of 300. It is easy to see that this solution was not the best. The cost of starting up a series of individual parts could vary, storage costs (including costs of freezing capital) also vary, [etc. W. Radzikowski, the author of the paper cited, proposed that these factories use the formula for optimum lot-size, mentioned in Section 6. This formula was appropriately adapted (it refers mainly to a practical way of calculating warehouse charges) and, as a result of its application, it was found that most of the parts produced in these factories should be manufactured in lots of 0.85 to 2.1 times the monthly demand, depending on the type of component.

In one of the factories referred to, viz. the A-8 Factories in Bielsko, a study was also made to determine an optimum stock-size of parts[2] seldom required.

This problem was similar to that discussed in Example 2.19. In the particular case of the A-8 Factories this problem was as follows.

A certain number of products manufactured by the A-8 Factories are specially fitted. This is to say, the product, assembled from several hundred parts, has several "special" parts. The difficulty is that it is impossible to determine exactly how many such special parts would be required in the future. This may depend on the demand for some equipment for an installation. As a rule, this demand appears rather late when there is no time to manufacture the special equipment. In view of this, the factory must maintain a certain inventory of various special parts which

[1] Cf. W. Radzikowski, *Badania operacyjne w praktyce (Operations Research in Practice),* Ekonomika i Organizacja Pracy (Economics and Organization of Labour) 1959, No. 9.

[2] Cf. W. Radzikowski, *Metody określania optymalnego zapasu części rzadko potrzebnych (Methods of Determining an Optimum Volume of Stock for Parts Seldom Required),* Organizacja Samorząd Zarządzanie (Self-government Organization), 1959, No. 12.

may be needed so that the lack of one part shall not cause delay in production and deliveries.

In the cited article by W. Radzikowski, a rational way of determining the optimum volume of stock for this type of spare parts was given on the basis of probabilistic methods, mentioned in Section 19. These methods were adapted to the specific requirements and working conditions of the A-8 Factories.

As may be seen from the examples quoted, they refer to comparatively simple problems which many factories face, however, every day. The benefits derived from the use of operations research in an enterprise, multiplied by the number of enterprises in the country, represents enormous savings. It seems that the methods of operations research are a powerful instrument for the detection of reserves. Of course, it is neither a universal nor the only instrument, but it does seem that it is not to be scorned.

It is noteworthy that the more complicated the problem to which we want to apply the methods of operations research, the more useful these methods are. Whenever the problem is simple, the solution obtained by experience or intuition will certainly approximate the optimum solution.

In a capitalist economy a single enterprise is, as a rule, the sphere for the application of operations research to economic problems. Socialist enterprises can also benefit from the application of these methods, if appropriately adapted. But the sphere of application of operations research in a socialist economy is much wider, covering the whole economy which is organised in a planned fashion. The methods of operations research can be one of the means of such control. Linear programming methods can play here a particular role.

A great deal of work must still be done in order to develop the most appropriate methods for the determination of optimum solutions for these problems, solved in a more or less satisfactory manner in everyday planning practice. It should also be remembered that the application of operations research methods entails the use of high-speed (electronic) computers. Such computers are especially necessary in applications of operations research on a national scale or even in large enterprises. In particular, the solution of linear programmes involves a large number of computations. However, it should not be thought that it is impossible to solve linear programmes without such computers. For instance, it is not particularly difficult to solve a programme of twenty or thirty variables using ordinary calculating machines.

40. Notes on the criterion-function

Every model dealt with in operations research, includes a function of decision variables and the value of this function constitutes a criterion. The solution of the models consists in finding such values of the decision variables which, fulfilling the conditions of the model, guarantee the largest (or smallest) possible value for the criterion-function.

In connection with the practical applications of operations research there always arises the problem of choosing, or simply of constructing, an appropriate criterion-function. This matter is not always as straightforward as would seem from our reasoning. I should like to draw here attention to some of the most typical difficulties which crop up in connection with the choice and construction of an appropriate criterion for the assessment of the results of any decision.

Strictly speaking, such criterion should be nothing else but a "preference function" of the person making the decision[1]. This function attaches a certain factor to each possible value of the decision variable. A higher value of the factor denotes a more advantageous situation than does a lower value. In order that a preference function may be suitable as a criterion in the evaluation of a decision to be chosen it must satisfy certain conditions. The principal condition is conformity, or in other words, the transitiveness of the preferences.

If we denote by A a set of decision variable values which has a lower factor than a different set B, the factor for C being higher than that for B, we say that the condition of transitiveness is satisfied if, of the two possible alternatives A and C, we acknowledge C to be more advantageous than A.

The conditions which the preference function must fulfill in probabilistic models are much more complicated since in this case the results of the activity are not definitively linked to one decision.[2]

In practice it is extremely difficult and it can even be said to be practically impossible, to establish a preference function when one person makes the decision. And this is the main difficulty which I mentioned at the beginning.

The easiest way to overcome this difficulty is to use as a criterion another function having approximately the same properties as the preference function. Such a function may be profit in certain conditions or costs in others. On a national scale, national income could be such a function, etc. These, however, are all substitute criteria and for this reason they are not always a satisfactory tool which would enable to make a choice of the best decision. Thus, in practice, we quite often have a situation when it is difficult to decide which of the possible criteria should be used. Frequently, the person making the decision wants to assess the consequences of a decision, using not only one, but several, criteria.

---

[1] Cf. O. Lange, *Ekonomia polityczna (Political Economy)*, Vol. I, Chap. VI, Warsaw, 1959, PWN.

[2] Cf. D. Luce and H. Raiffa, *Games and Decisions*, New York, 1957, J. Wiley.

For instance, let these criteria be the functions

$$F_1(X_1, X_2, ..., X_n)$$
$$F_2(X_1, X_2, ..., X_n)$$
$$f_1(X_1, X_2, ..., X_n)$$

in which $X_1, X_2, ... , X_n$ are decision variables.

With three criteria F_1, F_2 and f_1 of which, for instance, the first two must be maximized and the third minimized, the problem of finding the optimum decision is actually insoluble. For, as a rule, values of decision variables which maximize one function, for instance F_1, do not maximize the second function F_2, and do not minimize function f_1. In order to solve this problem, these criteria must be arranged according to priority. In other words, the person making the decision must determine which criterion is the most important, which is less important and which is the least significant. We shall illustrate how such priorities can be assigned on a simple example involving two criteria.

For instance, let the primary criterion be the function $F_1(X_1, ... X_n)$ and the additional criterion-function be $F_2(X_1 ... X_n)$. This means that we first choose values for decision variables $X_1, X_2, ... , X_n$ for which the function $F_1(X_1, ... , X_n)$ reaches a maximum. Of course, this is a conditional maximum since the decision variables must satisfy the conditions resulting from the relationships contained in the model.

If this maximum of function F_1 does not exceed some set value F_1^*, we regard the solution as final. If, however, function F_1 reaches its maximum at a point for which the value of this function is greater than F_1^*, then we do not take it to be final but modify it by taking in turn the next criterion $F_2(X_1, X_2, ... , X_n)$. We then look for such values of decision variables $X_1, X_2, ... , X_n$ that function $F_2(X_1, ... , X_n)$ reaches a maximum for the conditions of the variables arising from the model and for the condition

$$F_1(X_1, X_2, ..., X_n) \geqslant F_1^*.$$

The result obtained is final. Of course, if we had yet a third criterion, for instance, $F_3(X_1, ... , X_n)$, the story would be repeated. That is, if the maximum of function F_2 is not smaller than the number F_2^* established beforehand, we would then apply the third criterion. Otherwise, we would have to rely on the solution already obtained.

The proposed way out of the situation in which we have more than one criterion presents certain difficulties. It involves establishing a very simple preference function in relation to the criteria. The problem is, namely, to establish some areas of preference in the criterion space. This is illustrated by Fig. 1.40 for the case of two criteria. Thus, area II is taken to be more advantageous than area I.

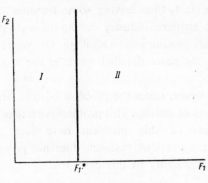

Fig. 1.40

However, it seems that it is much easier to construct this type of preference function in relation to criteria than to construct such a function in relation to decision variables.

41. The problem of activity goals

In our analyses so far, we have always assumed that the targets of activity are clearly defined. For instance, the target of an activity may be to produce certain goods, or to meet the demands of a consignee for a certain quantity of goods, etc. Wherever the targets are determined unequivocally, the appropriate model can be solved by the methods discussed in preceding chapters. There are situations, however, in which these targets cannot be exactly defined, and what is more, such a definition is frequently not even desirable. An example will explain the problem in this instance.

Let us assume that the problem which we have set ourselves is to develop an industry to produce passenger aircraft. It should be borne in mind that if from the outset we directly defined in full detail the type of airplanes, it is certain that they would be outdated by the time they went into production. This is due to the fact that a certain period of time must elapse from the moment the decision is made to build an airplane factory until the production of airplanes is started. During this period, the construction of airplanes could be subject to changes as a result of technical improvements and other factors.

What, then, is the situation and what can be done?

If we defined exactly the type of airplane we are to manufacture at the start, we could determine an optimum decision ensuring the best use of resources for the production of airplanes of the type stipulated. As we said before, the danger then is that such an airplane will already be outdated at the moment of production. In order to avoid this, it is possible not to give too detailed specifications concerning the airplane at the start, thus leaving some freedom to amend the plan for the construction of the airplane industry during the realization of the plan according to changes in aircraft production technology. Of course, the nearer the completion of investments, the more detailed must be the specification as production is to start.

Such a procedure, however, raises the problem of determining optimum decisions without any precise target of activity. This problem is extremely complex and difficult. Systematic investigations of this problem have just been begun. It should however be noted that operations research does not provide any solutions which could be accepted as satisfactory in this case.

42. Organizational problems

The purpose of this section is to draw the reader's attention to one further difficulty involved in the practical applications of operations research. As in any other field, in decision-making, there is a certain "division of labour". This means that within an organization, e.g. an enterprise, corporation or even a whole national economy, certain decisions of a fundamental character are made at the top; some decisions are made at intermediate levels and, finally, local decisions are made at the lowest levels of the organizational ladder. The existence of such a "division of labour" in decision-making is explained by the fact that the more precise the decision and the more it concerns only relatively small fragments of the whole organization, the more detailed is the information required for making such a decision. And, the fullest information in this field have the bodies at the lowest levels.

On the other hand, decisions of a basic character must take into account the whole organization which they concern. The appropriate information is in the hands of those at the top of the organization and only they are in a position to make the correct decisions.

In connection with this decentralization of decision-making, whatever its extent, there arise interesting problems from the point of view of operations research. One of these problems, probably the most important, is the degree of decentralization involved.

Decentralization has good and bad consequences; thus, certainly neither complete centralization nor complete decentralization is the best way out.

One aspect of decentralization is that it is known in advance that the decisions made at lower levels cannot be optimum from the viewpoint of the whole organization. This matter is connected with the choice of the criterion for the assessment of the extent to which the decision is optimum. In this system there are specific priorities as to criteria. For instance, there are primary criteria used at top level. The lower levels cannot use these criteria. It is difficult to imagine an enterprise taking the national income as a criterion, for the simple reason that it would be difficult for the enterprise to establish a relationship between its decision variables and the national income. In view of this, the lower levels use different criteria from those used at higher levels. The criteria at lower levels, it is true, are imposed by the top but it is immensely difficult, or downright impossible, to construct a system of criteria fully compatible with the primary criterion. By compatibility of lower level criteria with primary criteria we mean a state of affairs in which the decentralized decisions based on this system of criteria lead to the same results as the centralized decisions on the basis of the primary criterion.

An excellent field for research on this problem is the construction of a system of lower-level criteria most compatible with the primary criterion.

However, in deciding to go ahead with decentralization in spite of the drawbacks we mentioned, we also bear in mind the good sides. From the viewpoint of operations research the advantage of decentralization is that the decisions are based on relatively accurate information about the parameters affecting the decision. Thanks to decentralization the whole system becomes more elastic, permitting relatively speedy reaction to "local" changes. Moreover, it is also worth stressing that in a partially decentralized system the information service is much less expensive than in a fully centralized system. With complete centralization, even the most trivial information must be immediately transmitted to the central level which is the only decision-making centre.

Problems linked with the "organization" of decision-making are of great significance. Unfortunately, research in this field is only beginning.

Name Index

Subject Index

291